S0-BMS-276

analog-digital
CONVERSION HANDBOOK

by
The Engineering Staff of
Analog Devices, Inc.

Edited by
Daniel H. Sheingold

Published by
Analog Devices, Inc.
Norwood, Massachusetts 02062 U.S.A.

Copyright © 1976 by Analog Devices, Inc.
Copyright © 1972 by Analog Devices, Inc.

Printed in the United States of America

Second Edition, June, 1976

All rights reserved. This book, or parts thereof, must not
be reproduced in any form without permission of the
copyright owner.

Information furnished by Analog Devices, Inc., is believed
to be accurate and reliable. However, no responsibility is
assumed by Analog Devices, Inc., for its use.

Analog Devices, Inc., makes no representation that the
interconnection of its circuits as described herein will not
infringe on existing or future patent rights, nor do the
descriptions contained herein imply the granting of licenses
to make, use, or sell equipment constructed in accordance therewith.

Specifications are subject to change without notice.

Library of Congress Catalog Card No. 76-13334
ISBN: 0916550-02-8

Additional copies may be ordered from Analog Devices, Inc.,
P. O. Box 796, Norwood, Mass 02062.

PREFACE

This book, a milestone rather than a culmination, is the direct outgrowth of a series of conversations with Ray Stata and Jim Pastoriza, starting at the beginning of 1969. At that time (and increasingly since then), it was felt that the growing availability of data-processing facilities at low cost — especially minicomputers — would bring the analog-digital interface, in the form of modular A/D and D/A converters and accessories, out of the specialty houses and into the realm of the working design engineer.

Although there are books in print on digital, analog, and hybrid computing, on circuit design, and on digital communication theory and sampled-data systems, there were — and still are — virtually no books that could serve as a guide to the engineer on the practical aspects of understanding, specifying, and applying the commercially-available modular elements of conversion systems in these pursuits.

Lest any reader either expect or question our altruism in publishing this book, let us first of all say that this book will seek to tell you merely "Everything You Always Wanted to Know About Data-Conversion System Design Using Modules*" rather than "*Everything* About Data-Conversion Systems," which would be an impossible (and at any rate, unrewarding) task.

Our viewpoint and credentials are those of a major producer of conversion-system integrated circuits and modules for the open market, and a growing supplier of high-performance monolithic-IC parts for in-house design and manufacture. We strive neither to hide nor to unduly emphasize our commercial motives, and the reader may find that the resulting honesty will impart a down-to-earth sense of practicality and realism.

On the other hand, we have restricted our temptations to crass commercialism to the extent of using model numbers and product specifications in the text for their flesh-and-blood illustrative effect. Our catalogs, data sheets, and other propaganda — and those of our competitors — are separately available in sufficient panoply, partisan quality, and timeliness, to make any effort to

*And Had Already Asked

outshine them in the present volume less than desirable (even if possible).

It is our hope that this volume will help the purely-digital or purely-analog hardware designer obtain appropriate practical knowledge of the complementary field, and that it will serve as a useful text and reference source for all designers of interface equipment. We will welcome the comments and suggestions of our readers for the benefit of future editions and readers.

June 1, 1972   *D. H. Sheingold*
Norwood, Mass.

ACKNOWLEDGEMENTS

This book has been written by the engineering staff at Analog Devices. Individual contributors to Part I, *Converters at Work,* include Ivar Wold, Barry Hilton, Mike Lindheimer, and Stanley Froud; to Part II, *Converters,* Dick Ferrero, Rick Spofford, Bob Craven, Cy Brown, Frank McCormack, Wayne Marshall, and Lew Counts; to Part III, *Accessories,* Walter Borlase, C. Peter Zicko, Dr. Berry Phillips and Al Sanchez; to Part IV, *Guide for the Troubled,* Marty Gross, Dwight Wahr, Jim Maxwell, and other members of our Sales Engineering staff.

In addition, this volume could not have been possible without the dedicated work of our Publications group, under Mrs. Marie Etchells; the cooperation of members of our top management team; the stimulation and understanding of Lawrence T. Sullivan, our Vice President, Marketing; and, finally, the original impetus and continuing encouragement (as well as budget authorization) provided by our President, Ray Stata.

Last — but surely not least — we thank our customers, past, present, and (yes) future, for their many stimulating questions, which revealed the need for such a book, and for the invaluable opportunity to gain mutual application experience, through an open and continuing dialogue. Since it might be inappropriate to mention that their custom, in the final analysis, has paid for this volume, we shall refrain from doing so.

CONTENTS IN BRIEF

Preface and Acknowledgements   i

Contents: In Brief   iii
           In Detail   iv

Introduction   ix

PART I: CONVERTERS AT WORK

Chapter 1	Data-System Components	I-1
Chapter 2	Data Acquisition	I-13
Chapter 3	Data Distribution	I-41
Chapter 4	Analog Functions with Digital Components	I-53
Chapter 5	Applications of Converter Systems	I-77
	A. Automatic Testing	I-78
	B. Communications and Signal Analysis	I-84
	C. Displays	I-93
	D. Commerce, Industry, and Elsewhere	I-104

PART II: CONVERTERS

Chapter 1	Understanding Converters	II-1
Chapter 2	Designing Converters	II-55
Chapter 3	Testing Converters	II-89
Chapter 4	Specifying Converters	II-129
Chapter 5	Applying Converters Successfully	II-155

PART III: OTHER SYSTEM COMPONENTS

Chapter 1	Operational Amplifiers	III-1
Chapter 2	Instrumentation Amplifiers	III-31
Chapter 3	Multiplexers and Multiplexing	III-43
Chapter 4	Sample-Holds	III-73

PART IV: GUIDE FOR THE TROUBLED   IV-1

Bibliography   xi

Index   xvii

CONTENTS IN DETAIL

Preface and Acknowledgements   i

Contents: In Brief   iii
          In Detail   iv

Introduction   ix

PART I: CONVERTERS AT WORK

    Chapter 1. Data-System Components   I-1

Sensors; Amplifiers; Common-Mode Problems; Isolation; Function Modules; Multiplexers; Digital Multiplexing; Sample-Hold Circuits; A/D Converters; D/A Converters; Registers; Up-Down Counters; Filters; Comparators; Power Supplies; Digital Panel Meters (and DVM's); Digital Displays; One More Important Element

    Chapter 2. Data Acquisition   I-13

Then and Now; Environment and Complexity; Key Factors; Single-Channel Conversion Subsystems; Direct Conversion; Sample-Hold and Conversion; Signal Conditioning; Multi-Channel Conversion; Multiplexing the Outputs of Single-Channel Converters; Multiplexing the Outputs of Sample-Holds; Multiplexing the Inputs of Sample-Holds; Multiplexing Low-Level Data; More than One Tier of Multiplexers; Signal Conditioning; Ratiometric Conversion; Wide Dynamic Ranges; Noise Reduction

    Chapter 3. Data Distribution   I-41

Factors Affecting Distribution-System Design; Digital vs. Analog Distribution; Converter-per-Channel Distribution; Simultaneous Updating; Analog Distribution; Acquisition vs. Distribution; Filtering/Smoothing; The Cost Factor; Minimizing Calibration Errors by Servoing; Isolation

    Chapter 4. Analog Functions with Digital Components   I-53

Sources; Scale Factors and Modulations; Functional Relationships; Trigonometric Applications; Waveforms; Functions of Time; Digital Servo Devices

Chapter 5. Applications of Converter Systems   I-77

A. Automatic Testing   I-78

Uses for Automatic Testing; Ingredients of Test
Systems; Converters in Test Systems;

B. Communications and Signal Analysis   I-84

Shift-Register Delay Line; Read Out into Memory;
Read Out as an Analog Signal; Recirculate; Perform Signal
Averaging by Addition; Time Compression by Sampling;
Real-Time Correlation; Incremental Delay Line as a Filter;
Recursive Filtering

C. Cathode-Ray-Tube Displays   I-93

Basic System; Uses of D/A Converters in Displays;
Raster Displays; Dot-Matrix Displays; Graphic Displays;
Delay-Line Integrator; Vectors and Segments; Differential
Linearity and Linearity; Speed and Dynamics

D. Commerce, Industry, and Elsewhere   I-104

Automatic Scale Zeroing; Low-Noise Communi-
cations; Music-Distribution Systems; Power-Rectifier
Monitoring; List of Areas Where A/D and D/A Conversion
May Help

PART II: CONVERTERS

Chapter 1. Understanding Converters   II-1

Analog Quantities; Digital Quantities; The Binary Code;
Basic Conversion Relationships; Other Codes; Binary-Coded
Decimal (BCD); Overranging; 2-4-2-1 BCD; Gray Code;
Analog Polarity; Bipolar Codes; Code Conversion; Other
Codes; Arbitrary Biasing and Scaling; DAC's as Multipliers
and ADC's as Dividers; Ground Rule; Power Supplies;
Digital Logic Levels; Control Logic – The Status Output;
The Strobe; Analog Signals; D/A Converter Circuits; Resis-
tance Ladders; Switching; References; Bipolar Conversion;
Registers on DAC's; A/D Converter Circuits; Successive-
Approximations; Integration; Counter Types; Parallel Types

Chapter 2. Designing Converters   II-55

Converter Design; Review of D/A Techniques; The Importance of Logic Buffering; Monolithic Components; Component Tolerance; Interquad Divider; Reference Loop; Trimming High-Accuracy Converters; Temperature-Variation Effects; Current vs. Voltage Output; Error Budgets; Layout Considerations; Successive-Approximation A/D Converters; The Logic Sequencer; Comparators: The Most Critical Element; Other Considerations in A/D Converter Design

Chapter 3. Testing Converters   II-89

Linearity; D/A Converters; A/D Converters; Gain Calibration; Zero and Gain Calibration; Unipolar DAC; Bipolar DAC Using Offset-Binary or 2's Complement; Temperature Effects; Differential Nonlinearity; Monotonicity; DAC Testing; Dynamic Programming; Bit-Scan Mode; Count Mode; Differential-Linearity Tester; Digital Dither Generator; Settling-Time Measurement; Zero and Full Scale; Comparator Thermal Effects; Alternate Method for Zero and Full-Scale Measurement; Major Carry; ADC Testing; Dynamic Crossplot; Anomalous Errors; Single-Shot Conversion Errors; Semi-Automatic Testing

Chapter 4. Specifying Converters   II-129

Two Basic Factors; Defining the Objectives – Application Checklists; Considerations for D/A Converters; Considerations for A/D Converters; Considerations for Analog Multiplexers and Sample-Holds; Definitions of Specifications; System-Component Selection Process; Typical Converter Classifications; An Example of the Selection and Verification Process; First Approximation; Error Analysis

Chapter 5. Applying Converters Successfully   II-155

Making the Proper System Choices; Data-Acquisition Systems; Three Classes of Converter Specifications; Approaches to Relaxing the Specifications; Logarithmic Compression; Filtering; Sample-Hold; Contributions to Error; Installation and Grounding; Reducing Common-Mode Errors

PART III: OTHER SYSTEM COMPONENTS

Chapter 1. Operational Amplifiers   III-1

Understanding Operational Amplifiers; The Ideal Op Amp; Non-Inverting Amplifier; Inverting Amplifier; Gain, Errors, and Stability; Difference Amplifier; Inside-Out Follower; Static Errors of Op Amps; Choosing an Op Amp; Classification of Amplifiers; Definitions of Specifications; Selection Principles; Selection Process

Chapter 2. Instrumentation Amplifiers   III-31

Design; Applications; Specifications; An Example; Isolation Amplifiers

Chapter 3. Multiplexers and Multiplexing   III-43

Functional Requirements; Analog Elements; Digital Elements; Basic Analog Multiplexer Configurations; High-Level Multiplexers; Low-Level Multiplexing; Errors in High-Level Multiplexers; Static Errors; Dynamic Errors; Errors in Low-Level Multiplexers; The Multiplexer System in High-Noise-Level Environments

Chapter 4. Sample-Holds   III-73

Uses of Sample-Holds; Characteristics of Real Sample-Holds; Typical Designs; Applications

PART IV: GUIDE FOR THE TROUBLED   IV-1

Frequently-Asked Questions; Frequently-Encountered Problems; Frequently-Given Advice; What to Do If All Else Fails

APPENDIX: Bibliography   xi

INDEX   xvii

INTRODUCTION: How to Use This Book

The users of this book, whether students or experienced design engineers, have a wide variety of backgrounds, interests, and needs. Although it is not expected to totally satisfy any reader, all who seek enlightenment, ideas, or guidance on matters having to do with modular and I.C. conversion devices should find something of value.

Whatever his interest, the reader will find this brief Introduction of assistance in making the best use of the book. Its self-explanatory structure is laid bare in the "Contents in Detail," which every reader should explore thoroughly before proceeding further. If he approaches with specific questions, the key to the answers might be found via "Frequently Asked Questions," in Part IV.

One can read through this book sequentially, but it is not necessary to do so; browsing is encouraged. Each unit is essentially self-contained. Though this involves some redundancy, it also enables a topic to be approached from several points of view. The Index should be useful in exploring any topic in depth.

The Bibliography is a brief and eclectic assortment of sources of information on various topics covered within the book. Each item is chosen, either because of its specific practical value or timely interest, or because it in turn has a reference section that will "fan out" and give the reader large coverage from a small base.

Design engineers should use this Handbook in conjunction with the most-recent edition of the comprehensive *Analog Devices Product Guide*. In addition to its up-to-date contents and much data (with prices) on specific products, it also contains a wealth of technical information, not all of which is duplicated in these pages.

Readers are invited to communicate to us their comments and suggestions for future editions of this Handbook, as to content, *errata*, omissions believed significant, and new applications ideas.

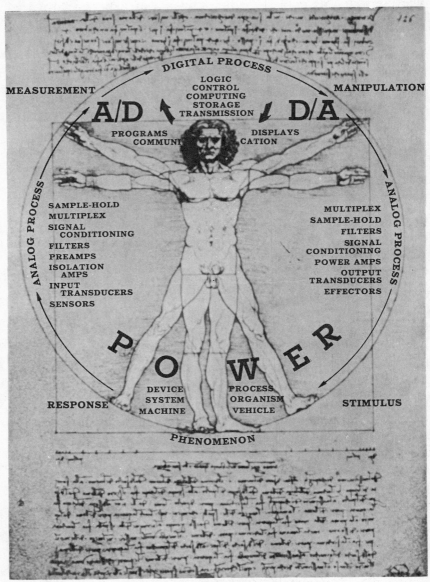

(D. H. Sheingold, with apologies to Leonardo da Vinci: Rule of Proportions, Academy of Fine Arts, Venice)

Figure 1. Functions in a Data System

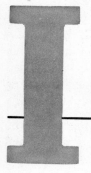

Data-System Components

This book is basically about A/D and D/A converters: understanding them, applying them, testing them, choosing them, and using them in systems.

When used in systems, they are often accompanied by an impressive panoply of other devices, both analog and digital, to measure input signals and perform intermediate processing with varying degrees of sophistication.

This chapter provides what might be termed a brief biographical "thumbnail" sketch of the main role players. Their general characteristics and aptitudes are summarized, and their roles in further conversion activity are hinted at within the short discussions devoted to each device.

In this book, the reader will quickly find that by far the greater weight of discussion is given to the properties and uses of *analog* circuits and their characteristics in the performance of system functions. The reasons for this lie primarily in the extreme fine-structure and the many degrees of freedom associated with analog circuits. They must labor in the real world, where noise immunity is a function of resolution and signal level, speed is a function of signal level, accuracy is a function of component tolerance and signal level, and the challenges to the designer's knowledge and ingenuity are many and unrelenting. On the other hand, their basic promise, in favorable environments, is functional simplicity, speed, and overall low cost.

With digital techniques, on the other hand, the principal challenges are to combinational ingenuity, equipment architecture, decreasing the cost and complexity of interconnections, and – in common with analog techniques – anticipating where Murphy's Law will strike next, and debugging where anticipation has failed. Digital circuits have high noise immunity, no drift, high speed (individually) and low cost (individually), and the rules for using them are few and simple.

With the exception of pre-amplification, a great many of the functions described here in analog form could be performed digitally, after the conversion. That they are not often is (so far) the result of favorable tradeoffs in cost, speed, and complexity. However, reductions in cost of digital integrated circuits and the increase of chip complexity are gradually making feasible the development of devices that are intended to perform analog functions, but contain digital components. Examples of these include analog function generation with read-only memories (ROM's) and generation of high-resolution arbitrary analog delay with shift registers.

Figure 1 illustrates the relationships of the principal components of a data system in a "global" perspective. Those to be introduced in this chapter include the following:

Sensors
Operational Amplifiers
Instrumentation Amplifiers
Isolation Amplifiers
Function Modules
Multiplexers
Sample-Hold Circuits
Analog-to-Digital Converters
Digital-to-Analog Converters
Up-Down Counters
Filters
Power Supplies
Comparators
DPM's
Digital Displays

Rarely will a system use all of the above components; on the other hand, the more-complex systems will often use appreciable quantities of one or another of them.

SENSORS

One might imagine that the systems designer has very little say in the choice of sensor, that he accepts whatever data signals exist without protest and gets on with the interface system design without further ado. However, if the systems engineer can have a say in the selection of the original transducer, he can go a long way towards easing his own conversion-design task.

For example, in monitoring or controlling mechanical shafts, the designer may be confronted with signals obtained by three radically-different position-sensing approaches: digital shaft encoders, synchros, and potentiometers, plus variations on all three.

Likewise, temperature measurements may be accomplished with thermocouple and thermistor, while mechanical force may be measured directly by load cells and strain gauges, or obtained indirectly by integrating the output from accelerometers, or even by counting interference fringes in an optical system.

Although it is not our role to recommend any particular type of signal transducer for a particular application, we thoroughly endorse the idea of getting the systems-design engineer into the act before the signal sources are settled upon, instead of later, when it is found that the designer is painted into a corner by the few options allowed.

AMPLIFIERS

If the transducer signals must simply be scaled up from millivolt levels to an A/D converter's typical ±10-volt full-scale input, an operational amplifier with appropriate closed-loop gain may be the first choice. Possibly, if the system involves many sources, each transducer can be provided with its own local amplifier so that the low-level signals are amplified before being "shipped" to the data center. Besides scaling, operational amplifiers are used for a host of linear and nonlinear, static and dynamic functions.

COMMON-MODE PROBLEMS

If analog data must be transmitted over long distances (and often, over quite short distances), differences in ground potential between signal site and data center will add spice to the interface systems design problem. In order to separate common-mode interference from the signal to be recorded or processed, devices designed for the purpose (i.e., instrumentation amplifiers) may be introduced. Typically, an instrumentation camplifier is characterized by good common-mode-rejection capability, high input impedance, low drift, adjustable gain, and somewhat greater cost than operational amplifiers. They range in form from the monolithic AD520, to potted modules, and considerably larger rack-mounted modules having manual adjustments.

ISOLATION

In the event of either very-high common-mode voltage level or the need for extremely-low common-mode leakage current, or both (as might be mandatory for many clinical medical-electronics applications), an *isolation amplifier* is required to interpose a break in the common-mode path from the signal source to the data center. Isolation amplifiers involve optical isolation or transformer-coupled carrier isolation techniques, and they typically cost about the same as instrumentation amplifiers. Though most-often used for isolating input data from system level, they may also be used for communicating system outputs to devices at other levels.

FUNCTION MODULES

These are special-purpose analog devices and circuits used for a wide variety of signal conditioning operations on signals that are in analog form. Where their accuracy is adequate, they can simply, and at low cost, relieve a processor of an expensive and time-consuming software and computational burden. This category is large and open-ended, but some of the more popular operations performed are multiplication; taking ratios; raising to powers; taking roots; performing special-purpose nonlinear functions such as linearizing transducers; performing rms measurements; computing vector sums; integration and differentiation; current-to-voltage or voltage-to-current transformations, etc. Some of these operations can be purchased in the form of such readily-available devices as multiplier/dividers, log/antilog amplifiers, etc. Others represent but a sampling of the vast potential inherent in operational-amplifier circuitry, available to the designer at low parts cost, and limited only by his ingenuity.

MULTIPLEXERS

If data from many independent signal sources must be processed by the same computer or communications channel, a multiplexer is usually introduced to couple the input signals into the A-D converter in some sequence. Additional logic keeps track of which data source is coupled to the converter at any instant.

Multiplexers are also used in reverse. For example, when the converter must distribute analog information to many different channels, the multiplexer, fed by a high-speed output D/A converter, continually refreshes the various output channels with computer-generated information.

DIGITAL MULTIPLEXING

Often, a digital distribution system uses no device that specifically goes under the label of "digital multiplexer." Unlike the comparable process of shunting analog information from computer to many output channels via a single D/A converter, or from many sources to a single A/D converter, the digital multiplexing function is often delegated to the devices being multiplexed, as they share a set of common inputs.

For example, if many digital sources must be multiplexed into a central computer or data-transmission channel, they are usually tied to the computer by a common set of parallel "bus" lines.

Commands from the computer then instruct the individual sources which one among them must feed its burden of data into the common bus, thence to the computer. Conversely, if the computer is bent on updating a number of digital output registers (each of which might be connected to a D/A converter), the updating process is accomplished by computer commands that strobe the selected register to accept the data being transmitted over the common output bus lines. Only that register instructed to receive the data can do so; the remaining registers simply ignore the data fed in parallel to their input terminals.

SAMPLE-HOLD CIRCUITS

In many interface systems, the original signal varies quite rapidly, calling for some subtlety in the interface linkage. Because an A/D converter takes a finite time to digitize the input signal, changes in this signal level during the actual conversion process could result in gross errors with some converter types. In any event, the lengthy conversion period would be completed some appreciable time following the conversion command, so that the final digital value would never truly represent the data level prevailing at the instant at which the conversion command was transmitted.

Sample-hold devices are typically introduced into the data link to make a fast "acquisition" of the varying analog signal, and "hold" this signal for the duration of the conversion process. Sample-hold circuits are also used in multi-channel distribution installations, where they enable each channel to receive and "hold" its own signal level for activation of different output processes. Usually, a data-acquisition sample-hold circuit must exhibit ultra-fast data acquisition, with minimal droop for a matter of 1 to 50 microseconds. By contrast, an output data distribution sample-hold circuit can be updated more leisurely, but it is often required to "hold" an analog value for many milliseconds – or even seconds – in the interval between updates.

A/D CONVERTERS

These devices, which may range from tiny $50 modules to bulky $5,000 rack-mounted instruments, convert analog input data – usually voltage – into its equivalent digital form. Key characteristics of A/D converters may include absolute and relative accuracy, linearity, monotonicity, resolution, conversion speed, stability, and – of course – price. Other aspects open to choice include input ranges, digital output codes, and physical size.

Although the industry tends to converge upon the successive-approximations technique for a very large number of applications, because of its inherently excellent compromise between speed and accuracy, other popular alternatives include counter-comparator types, and dual-ramp approaches. The dual-ramp is widely-used in digital voltmeters. In addition, synchro-to-digital and resolver-to-digital converters are used where data from mechanical shafts must be converted into digital form.

D/A CONVERTERS

These devices "reconstitute" the original data after processing, storage, or even simple transmission from one location to another in digital form. The basic converter consists of an arrangement of weighted resistance values (or divider ratios), each controlled by a particular level or "significance" of digital input data, that develops varying output voltages or currents in accordance with the digital input code.

Although converters have fixed references, for most applications, a special class of D/A converters exists, having a capability of handling variable and even ac reference sources. These devices are termed *multiplying DAC's*, because their output value is the product of the number represented by the digital input code, and the analog reference voltage, which may vary from full scale to zero, and in some cases, even to negative values. In some instances, such as for ac measurements and resolver/synchro conversion, the multiplying converter's weighted divider circuitry is based on tapped transformers, instead of precision resistors, since turns ratios have excellent long-term stability and immunity to temperature effects.

REGISTERS

Digital registers are used to hold information in readiness for passing it along to computers, D/A's, and so forth. For example, a multi-channel interface system using an A/D converter for every input channel would store the digitized values in each converter's output register until called on by the computer to feed the stored value into the common input bus. The converse holds true for output multiplexing, where a number of D/A converters provide different voltage levels for the independent output channels. Each D/A is then fed by a storage register, which "holds" the digital input word until the computer feeds in the new, updating digital value.

Shift registers are used, for example, where the data is transmitted serially over a single pair of wires, instead of as parallel bits over many wires. In this case, the shift register accumulates a serial input word in much the same way that a train and its many carriages (bits) enters a station. When all the bits have entered the shift register, the data bits (passengers) may be read out (detrained) in parallel.

UP-DOWN COUNTERS

These devices, analogous to ramp generators, are quite useful for performing a variety of "tricks" with A/D and D/A converters. Specifically, they are used in forming electronic servo loops for automatic error correcting, offset adjusting, long-term sample holds, etc.

In electronic servo applications, the up-down counter accumulates pulses representing the variable being controlled, adjusted, or measured, in much the same way that a servo-motor shaft accumulates rotational angle. The counter is often used in conjunction with a D/A converter: to develop an analog value proportional to the accumulated count. The process is also used in tracking-A/D converters and resolver/synchro-to-digital converters.

FILTERS

Filters are used on the input side of an A/D converter to remove unwanted components of the input signal. Noise and line-frequency pickup are also attenuated in this way, but at the expense of reduced response to fast input-signal amplitude variations. Filters are also used on the analog output from D/A converters, in order to smooth out the "lumps" created by discrete digital values. Often, the electromechanical device being actuated by a D/A converter (e.g., d'Arsonval meters, servo motors, magnet coils, loudspeakers, etc.) acts as a filter in its own right, owing to substantial electrical or mechanical inertia.

COMPARATORS

Conversion systems involve both analog and digital comparators. For example, the A/D conversion process involves balancing the unknown input voltage against some form of internally-produced reference. A comparator responds to the polarity of the inequality between input and reference. More-rarely, comparators are used as fast, high-gain (open-loop) amplifiers. Digital comparators, as their name implies, are used on digitized, rather than analog forms of data. For example, a digital comparator might be used in set-point control to provide considerably better accuracy, resolution, and stability, than is possible with an equivalent analog process.

POWER SUPPLIES

Accuracy of interface systems is steadily rising, to the point where 12-bit resolution is quite routine, and 16-bit operation is frequently involved for the higher repeatability, resolution, linearity, and accuracy. Consequently, the design of the dc power system is no longer a trivial matter, since errors that remain second-order effects at 8-10 bits become menacing first-order effects at the 16-bit level. In many instances, careful separation of analog and digital grounds is required, demanding, in turn, considerable isolation between the various outputs that modern power supplies provide.

We certainly advocate raising the priority of power-supply engineering from the status of an "afterthought" to that of an item that should be eliminated as a concern early in the design process. Too often, the power supply design (or choice) is left until last, where it is presumed to be able to take up all the slack or tolerances that other design stages create. Instead, at least as much initial attention should be devoted to the power supply as selection of converters, amplifiers, sample-holds, multiplexers, and other devices. A related question is whether to use power supplies and/or regulators in large, medium, or small "chunks," for major portions of the system, for individual chassis, or perhaps even for mounting on individual boards. The issues involve space, cost, circuit independence vs. induced noise vs. excessive lead length and wire size, avoidance of ground loops, allowable local dissipation levels, etc.

DIGITAL PANEL METERS (and DVM's)

These devices form a kind of self-contained digital processing system all on their own. They can, of course, be used in conjunction with computer or digital recorder, owing to the BCD output that most DPM's provide.

Basically, the DPM may be regarded as an analog-to-digital converter, complete with case, overrange capability, input protection, visual readout, and remote electrical output, usually in BCD format. Thus, the DPM may be used as an A/D converter, complete with visual displays for initial adjustments, in a multi-channel conversion system. Alternatively, it provides a very unambiguous and error-free component for quality-control systems, where human operators use the DPM with high resolution and repeatability in set-point applications for adjusting temperature, pressure, weight, and other industrial variables.

DIGITAL DISPLAYS

Decimal displays are often required in conversion systems for initial setup procedures. Although normal operation of the system involves data rates considerably too fast for the eye to follow, calibration, checkout, and other manual operations nonetheless require a display to be added, often in conjunction with a counter. Thus, manufacturers offer decimal displays in decade increments, and usually with input data compatible with conventional logic levels and prevailing codes.

ONE MORE IMPORTANT ELEMENT

As Figure 1 indicates, there is one additional element that is always present in a data system but seldom shown on a block diagram: *homo sapiens*. These systems are designed, built, tested, and perfected by humans to serve human purposes; and quite often humans interface with data systems in operation, reading displays and making adjustments: to, and within the system. It is to all these humans that this book is fraternally dedicated.

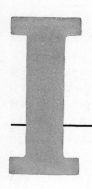

Data Acquisition

Analog data is acquired in digital form for any or all of the following purposes:

Storage
Transmission
Processing
Display

Data may be stored in either raw or processed form; it may be retained for short, medium or long periods. It may be transmitted over long distances (for example, to or from outer space), or short distances (from a lab bench to a minicomputer alongside it). The data may be displayed on a digital panel meter, or as part of a cathode-ray-tube presentation.

Processing can run the gamut from simple comparison to complicated mathematical manipulations. It can be for such purposes as collecting information, converting data to a useful form, using the data for controlling a process, performing repeated calculations to dig out signals buried in noise, generating information for displays, simplifying the jobs of warehouse employees, controlling the color or paint, the thickness of a wrapper, the speed of a subway train.

But it all starts with getting the data in digital form, as rapidly, as accurately, as completely, and as cheaply as necessary.

The basic instrumentality for accomplishing this is the analog/digital converter; it can be a simple shaft digitizer, a DPM with digital outputs, or a sophisticated high-resolution high-speed device. To accommodate the input voltage to the specified conversion relationship, some form of scaling and offsetting may be necessary, performed with an amplifier (/attenuator). To convert analog information from more than one source, either additional converters or a multiplexer may be necessary. To increase the speed with which information may be accurately converted, a sample-hold is desirable. To compress an extra-wide analog signal range, a logarithmic amplifier may be found useful.

The properties of the data-acquisition system depend on both the properties of the analog data itself, and on what is to be done with it.

In this chapter, we shall show some of the configurations that have proven useful and/or popular and discuss some of the considerations involved in the choice of configuration, components, and other elements of the system. Additional information can be found in the chapters on the individual devices.

THEN AND NOW

A decade-and-a-half ago, A/D converters capable of 0.05% performance and 50,000 sample/second conversion rates, cost about $8000, consumed about 500 watts, and had such gargantuan proportions as 2' x 2' x 3'. Today, Analog Devices' Model ADC-12FM requires less than 2 microseconds for a 12-bit 0.0125% conversion, lists singly for well below $1000, and measures 4" x 2" x 0.4".

In the past 15 years, through several "generations" of equipment, data-acquisition hardware has changed radically, thanks primarily to the semiconductor revolution, and prices have come down to the point where digital, rather than analog, "massaging" of information is a matter of routine, rather than exotic necessity.

What have not changed, however, are the fundamental system problems confronting every digital data systems designer. Of course, it helps to have small, quiet, low-cost, cool, low-drain components. But he is still up against the laws of Mother Nature, who often seems to prefer to keep her secrets safely obscured by noise, rfi, ground loops, power-line pickup, and transients coupled into signal lines from machinery. Separating the signals from these obscuring effects, then, becomes a matter for ingenuity and imagination, coupled with a great deal of experience, not merely a matter of purchasing fast, high-resolution A/D converters. (But having them available at realistic cost provides incentives for giving them useful jobs.)

ENVIRONMENT AND COMPLEXITY

Data-acquisition systems can be separated into at least two basic categories: those suited to favorable environments (electrically-quiet laboratories), and those intended for hostile environments (factories, vehicles, military surroundings, and remote installations). The latter group includes industrial process control systems where, for instance, temperature information developed by thermocouples located on tanks, boilers, vats, pipelines, bearings, oil burners, etc., (that often spread over miles of factory real estate) is fed into a central computer that provides real-time process control. Included are digital control of steel mills, automated production processes, numerically-controlled machine tools. Any or all of these applications may be characterized by the vulnerability of data signals to the phenomena mentioned above and the requirement for almost routine isolation and measurement of off-ground voltages. Also included are *electrically*-noisy environments, such as generating stations, where thermocouples measuring bearing temperatures of rotating machinery are exposed to volts of interference caused by megawatt changes in load; and aircraft control systems, radar stations, etc.

On the other hand, for laboratory-instrument applications, and such test systems as those gathering long-term drift information on arrays of zener diodes undergoing constant-temperature life tests in well-shielded ovens, or gas chromatographs, automatic weighing machines, mass spectrometers, and other sophisticated instruments, the system designer's problems are related more to the performing of sensitive measurements (usually under favorable conditions) than to the gross problems of protecting the integrity of analog data.

Systems existing in hostile environments may require devices capable of wide temperature-range operation, excellent shielding, considerable design effort aimed at eliminating common-mode errors and preserving resolution, conversion at early stages, redundant paths for critical measurements, and (perhaps) considerable processing of the digital data to ensure that it is reliable. Measurements in the laboratory, with narrower temperature ranges and less ambient electrical noise, may be easier to make and communicate, but higher accuracies (or resolutions) may require more-sensitive devices, and a still-considerable degree of effort to preserve appropriate signal/noise ratios.

KEY FACTORS

The choice of configuration and circuit building blocks in data acquisition depends on several critical considerations:

1. Resolution and accuracy
2. Number of analog channels to be monitored
3. Sampling rate per channel
4. Throughput rate
5. Signal-conditioning requirements
6. The cost function

Besides the choice of appropriate component performance levels, careful analysis of the above factors is required to obtain the lowest-cost circuit configuration. Typical configurations include:

1. Single-channel possibilities
   Direct conversion
   Preamplification and direct conversion
   Sample-hold and conversion
   Preamplification, sample-hold, and conversion
   Preamplification, signal-conditioning, and any of the above

2. Multi-channel possibilities
   Multiplexing the outputs of single-channel converters

Multiplexing the outputs of sample-holds
Multiplexing the inputs of sample-holds
Multiplexing low-level data
More than 1 tier of multiplexers

Some of the more-interesting signal-conditioning options include

1. Ratiometric conversion
2. Wide-dynamic-range options
   High-resolution conversion
   Range biasing
   Automatic gain switching
   Logarithmic compression
3. Noise-reduction options
   Filtering
   Integrating converters
   Digital processing

Finally, in evaluating tradeoffs, there are at least three types of "budgets" that should be considered: cost budget, system time budget, and error budget.

SINGLE-CHANNEL CONVERSION SUBSYSTEMS

Direct Conversion

Figure 1 represents the simplest digitizing system, a lone A/D converter, performing repetitive conversions at a free-running internally-determined rate. It has power inputs and an analog signal input. Its outputs are a digital code word, including "over-range" indication, (usually in parallel form), polarity information (if necessary), plus a "status" output, to indicate when the output digits are valid.

Perhaps the most well-known converter of this kind is the digital panel meter, which consists of a basic A/D converter and a numerical display. For many applications, the sole purpose of digitizing is to obtain the numerical display, i.e., to use the DPM as a meter, rather than as a system component.

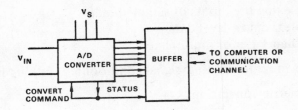

Figure 1. Simplest Data-Acquisition System Configuration

The DPM, however, is not necessarily the best way to digitize a single channel. Its two major shortcomings are: it is slow, and its BCD digital coding must be changed to binary if its output is to be processed by binary equipment. When free-running, its output is strobed into an available interface register when the data is valid, rather than by an interface command.

Converters designed for system applications (including many DPM's, such as the AD2003) can usually receive external commands to convert or hold. For dc and low-frequency signals, the converter is usually a dual-slope type, which has the advantage that it is inherently a low-pass filter, capable of averaging out high-frequency noise, and nulling frequencies harmonically-related to its integrating period. (For this reason, the integrating period is usually made equal to the period of the line frequency, since the major portion of system interference occurs at that frequency and its harmonics.)

If the converter is responding to individually-important samples of the input, the maximum rate of change of the average input for full resolution, and the conversion rate, have the following relationship (binary conversion):

$$\left.\frac{dV}{dt}\right|_{max} = 2^{-n}V_{FS}/T_{CONVERT}$$

For example, if V_{FS} = 10V, n = 11 (1/2048 resolution), and $T_{convert}$ = 0.1s, the maximum rate of change of input is about 1/20 V/s. At faster rates of change, 1 LSB changes cannot be resolved within the sampling period.

If, on the other hand, individual samples are not important, but large numbers of samples are to be dealt with, essentially delineating a stationary process, the only requirement is that the signal be sampled at least twice per cycle of the highest frequency of interest. For this purpose, in the example given above, the maximum signal frequency that can be handled is 5Hz.

So far, the context has been that of the dual-slope integrating A/D converter, which spends about 1/3 of its sampling period performing an integration, and the remainder of the time counting out the average-value-over-the-integrating-period as a digital number, and resetting to initial conditions for the next sample. It should be noted that the dual-slope type will always read out the average value, which results in a valid sample of the input waveform over the integrating "window."

Though it is slow, the integrating A/D converter, such as the ADC-17I, is quite useful for measurements of temperature, battery discharge, and other slowly-varying voltages, especially in the presence of noise.

However, by far the most popular type of converter for system work is the successive-approximations device (described amply in Part 2), since it is capable of high resolution (e.g., 16 bits), high speed (e.g., 1μs for 10-bit conversion), and quite reasonable cost. In the above example, if $T_{convert}$, using a successive-approximation converter, is 10μs, the maximum allowable dV/dt for maintenance of bit-at-a-time resolution becomes 500V/s, an improvement, but far from sensational.

The successive-approximation converter has the weakness that at higher rates of change, it generates substantial linearity errors, because it cannot tolerate change during the weighting process. The converted value lies somewhere between its values at the beginning and the end of conversion; but the time uncertainty approaches the magnitude of the conversion interval. Figure 2 illustrates this point. Finally, even if the signal is slow enough, noise rates-of-change (perhaps introduced by the signal itself) that are excessively-large will cause erroneous readings that cannot be averaged, by either analog or digital means. An external sample-hold can greatly improve matters, as will be shown.

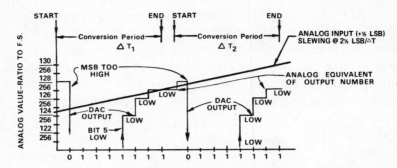

Figure 2. Successive-Approximations Converter Error with Fast-Changing Input (2½LSB Per Conversion Interval). Note that Output Reading of 127/256 FS is the Same for Both Intervals, Though One Starts at 124/256 and the Other Ends at 129/256. Error Increases with Ramp Speed.

Direct conversion, especially near the signal source, is most useful if the data must be transmitted through a noisy environment. This can be seen, even in the case of an 8-bit converter (1/256 resolution) and a high-level 10V signal, if one considers that bits will be lost if the peak-to-peak noise level induced in the analog signal is greater than 40mV (approximately 10V/256); the standard TTL digital noise immunity, on the other hand, is 1.2V (or 2.0 − 0.8V), a gain in signal-to-noise of better than 10:1.

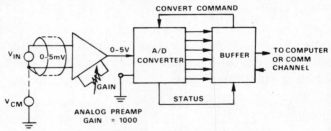

Figure 3. A/D Converter with Preamplifier

Preamplification and Direct Conversion (Figure 3)

Converters designed for OEM system applications are, in most cases* "single-ended" in reference to signal ground, and have normalized analog input ranges of the order of 5 or 10 volts,

---

*Extremely-high-resolution converters, such as the ADC-16Q, have a high-CMR differential front end. DVM's, and some DPM's, also tend to have differential inputs, in consonance with their low full-scale-input levels (e.g., 0.1999V).

single-ended or bipolar. It makes sense to scale signal inputs up or down to the standard converter input level, to make fullest-possible use of the converter's available resolution.

If the signals are of reasonable magnitude (already preamplified or outputs of an analog computer), and already exist within the system, the scaling may be simply accomplished with operational amplifiers in a single-ended or differential configuration. If the signals are from outside the system, or are quite small, or have an appreciable common-mode component, a differential instrumentation amplifier may be profitably used, with characteristics depending on the gain required, the signal level, the needed CMR, bandwidth, impedance levels, and cost tradeoffs.

Finally, if the input signals must be galvanically isolated from the system, a light- or transformer-coupled isolation amplifier must be used to break all conductive signal paths. This kind of isolation is essential in some medical-instrument applications. It is also useful where large common-mode spikes are encountered, for industrial applications requiring *intrinsic safety,* and for all applications in which the signal source is at a high off-ground potential.

Sample-Hold and Conversion (Figure 4)

A successive-approximations converter can be made to operate at considerably-greater accuracies at high speeds, overcoming the weaknesses mentioned above, by introducing a sample-hold at its input. Between conversions, the sample-hold acquires the input signal, and, just before conversion takes place, it is placed in *hold,* where it remains throughout the conversion. It can be seen that, if the S/H responds instantaneously and accurately, the converter can convert changes (from the preceding sample) of any magnitude accurately, at speeds up to the conversion rate. In practical sample-holds, however, there will be acquisition time, tracking delay, and aperture time; typical values of these quantities are $2\mu s$ to 0.01%, a fraction of a μs, and 25ns, with 2-3ns uncertainty. If the aperture time and tracking delay compensate one another, or are unimportant as long as they are consistent, the principal source of time error is the aperture *uncertainty*. The relation between aperture uncertainty and maximum rate of change for maintaining resolution in an n-bit system is

$$dV/dt \Big|_{max} = 2^{-n} V_{FS}/t_{apu}$$

for the example given, (f_{sample} = 100kHz, V_{FS} = 10V, t_{apu} = 3ns)

$$dV/dt \Big|_{max} = 5mV/3ns = 1.67V/\mu s$$

This number is also limited by the *slew rate* specification of the sample-hold.

Figure 4b shows, in contrast with Figure 2, that the successive-approximations converter, with a constant input applied by the S/H, will deliver an accurate digital representation of the beginning input at the end of each conversion interval. Any errors that are functions of time will be due to errors of the sample-hold, including the acquisition errors above, plus droop during the conversion interval, and any linearity, offset, and transient errors. Noise present on the signal, though sampled and converted, may be susceptible to digital averaging by the processor.

Since sample-holds usually operate at unity gain, with errors referred to full-scale (which should be the same as the converter's full scale range), scaling or preamplification should occur before the signal is applied to the sample-hold.

Sample-hold devices can be used with other types of converters, to establish precise timing of the signals being sampled, independently of the time required by a given device to complete a conversion. Their utility is especially evident if the conversion time is variable, as in counter types.

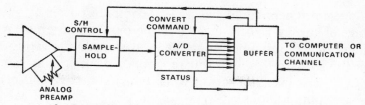

4a. Sample-Hold in Single-Channel Data Acquisition

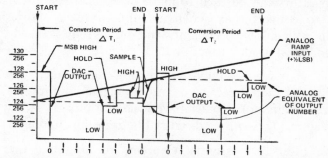

4b. Successive-Approximations Converter Example of Figure 2, Preceded by Sample-Hold. Digital Output is Within ½LSB of Analog Input at Start of Conversion, 124/256, and 127/256.

Signal Conditioning (Figure 5)

This is a blanket term that includes a wide variety of possibilities. Scaling of input gains to match the input signal to the converter's full-scale range is a simple, obvious example. One might also include DC offset to bias odd ranges, such as 2.5 to 7 volts, to levels more compatible with standard converters. Preamplification, as discussed earlier, is a typical example. Linearizing of data from thermocouples and bridges can be performed by analog techniques, using either piece-wise-linear approximations (generated by biased diodes) or smooth series-approximations using low-cost I.C. multipliers; it could also be done digitally, after conversion, using a ROM to store the inverse function.

Analog differentiation could be used to measure the rate at which the input varies; integration could be used to obtain total dosage from a rate of flow. Either could be used to produce a 90° phase shift; an op amp could be used to provide an arbitrary phase shift. Sums and differences can be used to reduce the number of data inputs (analog data *reduction*).

Analog multipliers could be used to compute power by squaring voltage or current signals, or by multiplying them together. Analog dividers of various types could be used to compute ratios or the logarithms of ratios, or square roots. Devices that compute $Y(Z/X)^m$ can take ratios over wide dynamic ranges, and perform ideal-gas computations.

Comparators can be used to make decisions based on analog levels (e.g., to convert only when an input exceeds a threshold or is within a "window.") Op amps and diodes may be used to perform simple "ideal diode" functions.

And – what seems almost like getting "something for nothing" – logarithmic modules can be used for range compression to permit the conversion of signals having resolutions of 10^6 with 12-bit converters. (This will be discussed later in the chapter.)

Active filters are essential elements to minimize the effects of noise, carriers, and unwanted high-frequency components of the input signal. Their growth of use, and the increase of interest in their design are reflected in the large number of magazine articles and the preponderance of filter discussions in such publications as the IEEE *Transactions on Circuit Theory,* plus a growing number of books on the subject.

One could go on and on, but the basic point should have been made: That in system design, all data-processing need not be digital. Analog circuits can perform processing or data reduction effectively, reliably, and economically, and should be considered as alternative ways of reducing numbers of transmission channels, software complexity, noise, and – more often than not – cost.

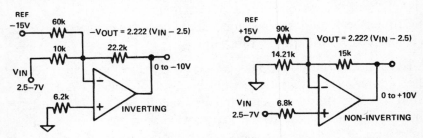

Figure 5a. Op Amps Used for Offset and Scaling

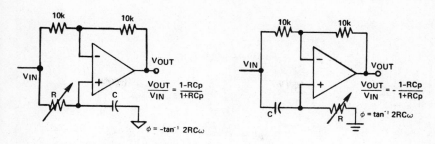

Figure 5b. Op Amp to Generate Arbitrary Phase Shift,
Gain = 1, All-Pass

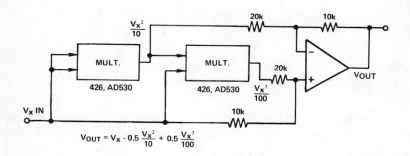

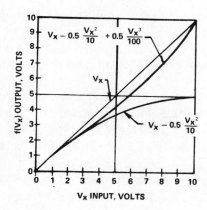

Figure 5c. Using Multipliers for Nonlinear Functional Relationships (Such as Linearization)

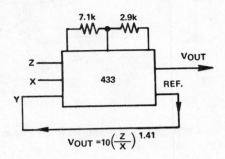

$$V_{OUT} = 10\left(\frac{Z}{X}\right)^{1.41}$$

Figure 5d. Ratio of Two Voltages Raised to Arbitrary Non-Integral Power

MULTI-CHANNEL CONVERSION

In multi-channel conversion systems, elements of the acquisition chain may be shared by two or more input sources. This sharing may occur in a number of ways, depending on the desired properties of the multiplexed system. Large systems may combine several different kinds of multiplexing, as well as cascaded tiers of the same kind.

Multiplexing the Outputs of Single-Channel Converters

Although the conventional way to digitize data from many analog channels is to introduce the time-sharing process, whereby the input of a single A/D converter is multiplexed in sequence among the various analog sources, an alternative parallel conversion approach is becoming increasingly practicable. Cost of A/D converters has dropped radically during the past half-decade, and it is now possible to assemble a multi-channel conversion system, with the seeming extravagance of one converter for every analog source, just as economically as the conventional analog multi-plexed system. (Figure 6.)

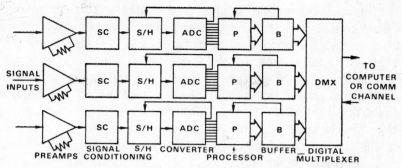

Figure 6a. Basic Multi-Channel Conversion Scheme, Using Digital Multiplexing Before Transmission

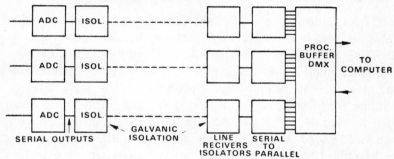

Figure 6b. Multi-Channel Conversion Using Remote A/D Converters

There are a number of important advantages to this parallel conversion approach, which, by the way, is virtually standard practice for resolver/synchro conversions beyond about the 10-bit accuracy level. First of all, quite obviously, slower converters may be used to obtain a given digital throughput rate; alternatively, the converter-per-channel may run at top speed, providing a much greater flow of data into the digital interface. For a constant data rate, however, with more channels (and fewer conversions per channel), the reduced conversion speed, plus the fact that each converter is looking at continuously-changing data, rather than jumping from one level to another, may allow the sample-holds to be eliminated, at a cost saving. Fewer conversions also mean that a slower converter might be used, generally resulting in even further cost saving, especially since some channels may not require a great deal of resolution.

The parallel-conversion approach provides a further advantage when applied to industrial data-acquisition systems, where many strain gages, thermocouples, thermistors, etc., are strung out over a large geographical area. In essence, by digitizing the analog signals right at their source and transmitting serial digital data, rather than the original analog signals, back to the data center, a considerable immunity to line-frequency (50-60-400Hz) pickup and ground-loop interference is achieved. Among other factors, the digital signals can be transformer or optically coupled, for example, to gain complete electrical (hence ground loop) isolation. Also, low-impedance-digital drive and receiving circuits drastically prune vulnerability to noise.

Not least, among the subtle benefits of digitizing sensor signals at their source, is the ability to perform logical operations on the digitized data before it is fed into the computer. In this way, for example, main-frame involvement with data is streamlined and redundancies are minimized. More-specifically, logic circuits can arrange to access data from slowly-varying thermocouple sensors less frequently, while reading-in data from critical sources at enhanced speed. In fact, the versatility of a digital subsystem may be exploited to make its own decision as to when a particular data channel should be fed into the computer: if certain signal sources remain constant or within a narrow range for long periods, then change rapidly later in the process, it is possible to ignore these data until the changes occur. (A local memory stores the stationary values).

In summary, a great deal of flexibility and versatility is gained by transferring the interface process from analog multiplexing to digital multiplexing. Logic decision circuits can exercise judgement on when and what data to feed the computer, and, in general, can give the overall interface a much larger measure of autonomy than is possible with an entirely-analog conversion system. (The computer cannot make decisions about the data submitted by an analog multiplexing system until it has received the data upon which to base its judgements ... this means that the data have been interfaced before the computer can decide that that particular piece of information is redundant. And there is no guarantee that it will be redundant on the next pass.)

Finally, it should be noted that if the data is being transmitted from a lunar vehicle to Earth, the channel is quite crowded, and the sort of *redundancy-reduction data compression* described above is absolutely essential to make sure that the items of data that get through are those having the highest priorities, by virtue of containing intelligence rather than redundant information.*

For each channel of the digitally-multiplexed system, there could be the array described earlier: preamplifier, signal-conditioning, sample/hold, converter. It is also possible that for one or more of the channels, there are a number of sequentially-multiplexed sub-channels, especially if they are carrying similar information.

Multiplexing the Outputs of Sample-Holds

Working back from the interface (with a minimum number of shared elements) towards the more-conventional situation in which the number of shared elements is maximized, we consider the case of a shared A/D converter, with a multiplexer at its input, switching among the outputs of a number of sample-holds (Figure 7). This configuration is found where sample holds are updated rapidly, even simultaneously, then read out in some sequence. It is generally a high-speed system, in which all items of data delineating the state of the system must do so for the same given instant. Multiplexing may be done sequentially, or by random addressing. For this kind of operation, the former is more typical. The sample-holds must have sufficient freedom from droop to avoid accumulating excessive error while awaiting readout, which period may be considerably longer than in the case of the converter-per-channel. Increased throughput rate could be obtained by using additional converters, with fewer multiplex switch points and faster update rate.

Applications that might require this approach include wind-tunnel measurements, seismographic experimentation, or in testing com-

---

*"New approaches to Data-Acquisition System Design," by T. O. Anderson, *Analog Dialogue*, Vol. 5, No. 1, January, 1971.

plex radar or fire-control systems. Often, the event is a one-shot phenomenon, and the information is required at a critical point during the one-shot event ... such as, for example, when a supersonic air blast hits the scale model.

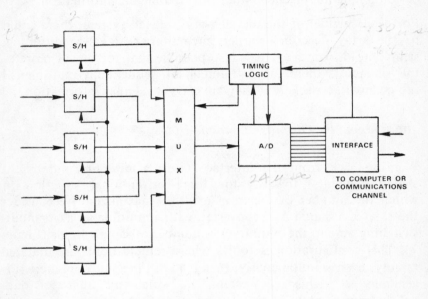

Figure 7.

Multiplexing the Inputs of Sample-Holds

The next step towards increased sharing is to share the sample-hold as well as the A/D converter. Figure 8 shows the typical system embodying this idea. For most-efficient use of time, the multiplexer is seeking the next channel to be converted, while the sample-hold, in *hold*, is having its output converted. When conversion is complete, the *status* line from the converter causes the S/H to return to *sample* and acquire the next channel. Then, after the acquisition time is completed, either immediately, or upon command, the sample-hold is switched to *hold*, a conversion begins, and the multiplex switch moves on.

This system is slower overall than the previous example, and, since the channels may tend to be diverse rather than identical, the multiplexer could equally-well be switching sequentially or in a random-access mode. For some systems, a manual mode, for checkout, may also be desired. In the random-access mode, it is quite possible that some channels (those with more "intelligence", i.e., change/time), will be accessed more frequently).

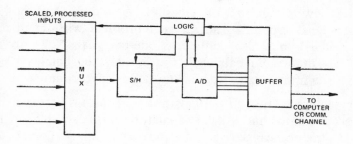

Figure 8. Multi-Channel Analog Multiplexed Interface.

Multiplexing Low-Level Data (Figure 9)

The idea here is that, in addition to sharing the converter and the sample-hold, expensive instrumentation-amplifier capacity must also be conserved. The decreasing cost of instrumentation amplifiers (in fact, of amplifiers of all types), plus the disadvantages of low speed and the engineering effort involved in ensuring the successful transmission and multiplexing of low-level data, are likely to result in decreasing use of this system approach. Some of the considerations are discussed in the chapter on Multiplexing.

Low-level multiplexing is often involved with the use of programmable-gain amplifiers, or the even-more-sophisticated automatic range-switching preamps, which combine the use of converters having modest resolution with range-switching controlled from the interface to obtain additional significant bits. (For example, a 12-bit converter, and 32 steps of adjustable gain, can provide 17-bit resolution, assuming – big *if* – that the resolution is actually present in the signal and that the system is capable of handling it without degradation.)

All the difficulties that are inherent in single-channel low-level circuitry are compounded by the addition of low-level multiplexing of *n* such channels. Not only is guarding necessary, but individual channels should be individually guarded. And, following the principle that the guard should be present right up to the input of the preamplifier, the guard too must be switched (or else driven from the common-mode level as measured separately at the amplifier*). Not only must the problem of pickup be considered, but the new dimension of crosstalk is added. And not only signal-to-signal crosstalk (not a great problem with small differential signals), but also common-mode-to-signal. Not only must input capacitance be balanced, but it must be balanced in the context of a multiplex switch having at least two circuits.

The saving grace (though perhaps not for some) is that systems of this sort are slow, and a large capacitor across each pair of input leads can reduce capacitive unbalance and high-frequency noise, without slowing-down the system excessively.

The usual low-level problems of thermal unbalance at connectors, lead junctions, and switches (and don't forget kovar-to-copper at IC's), must also be dealt with. All such unavoidable thermocouples should have thermal symmetry.

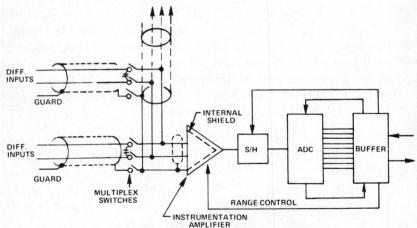

Figure 9. Low-Level Multiplexing

*The extra switch points can be eliminated by passively summing the voltages at the amplifier inputs with two equal resistors, CMV = ½ $(e_1 + e_2)$, and buffering with a simple follower.

More than One Tier of Multiplexers

If there are 64 channels to be multiplexed, the problems of stray capacitance (including capacitive unbalance) are worsened by the parasitic capacitance of the *off* channels on the conducting channel: if there are n channels, the capacitance will be $(n - 1)C_{DGO}$ plus the usual stray wiring capacitance. It is practical to reduce this capacitance by using two tiers of multiplexers. In the above example, with 8 channels per switch, the capacitance is reduced to $14C_{DGO}$ from $63C_{DGO}$.

SIGNAL CONDITIONING

Discussed here are a few topics that keep coming up in connection with data-acquisition systems.

Ratiometric Conversion

Some A/D converters have a *ratiometric,* or "external reference" connection, allowing the output digital number to represent the ratio of the input to an arbitrary (within specified limits) reference input. In effect, the device becomes an analog divider with digital readout.

Devices of this sort are useful in making precision measurements that ignore variation of a device reference. For example, Figure 10 shows how a potentiometer ratio can be measured, independently of variations of the applied voltage, by applying the same voltage to the reference input of the converter.

In a multiplexed system, where measurements may be taken from a number of similar devices, such as strain-gage bridges, the

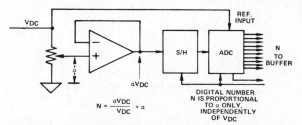

Figure 10. Measuring a Potentiometer Ratio, Independently of the Applied Voltage, a Ratiometric Measurement

common bridge supply may be used as the converter's reference to eliminate normal-mode gain error caused by supply-voltage variation.

Wide Dynamic Ranges

The need for wide-dynamic-range signal conditioning in a single channel may occur in two basic ways: Either it is necessary to resolve a voltage anywhere in the range to a high degree of accuracy, relative to full scale, (for example in the measurement of position in a follow-up system); or it is sufficient to measure a quantity having a wide range of variation to modest accuracy, relative to actual value (for example, to within 1%, over a 10,000:1 range).

For signals in the first category, a high resolution-and-linearity converter (such as the ADC-16Q) is the simplest answer. Another possibility is the use of a moderate-resolution converter (e.g., 12-bit resolution), preceded by an amplifier with switched gain (Figure 11) controlled from the digital interface. In one form of operation, a trial conversion is performed at the lowest gain; if the MSB is 0, the gain is doubled and another conversion is performed; if the MSB is still 0, the gain is doubled again, etc., until either the MSB is turned on or the top end of the range is reached. Each doubling represents an additional bit of resolution.

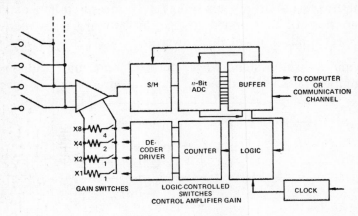

Figure 11. Switched-Gain Amplifier

Yet another possibility, when seeking accurate measurements of small variations about a fixed value of voltage, is to sum a voltage equal to the nominal fixed value (and opposite in polarity) and measure the differences. If the voltage is applied (Figure 12) via a high-resolution DAC, the interface can keep track, digitally, of both the initial value and the difference voltage, using an ADC of quite modest performance. (The tradeoff here is the cost of a high-resolution DAC, such as the DAC-16QM, plus logic and a modest 8-, 10- or 12-bit ADC, vs. a 16-bit ADC.)

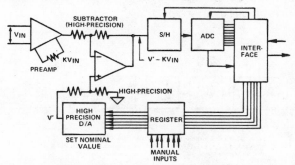

Figure 12. Use of High-Resolution DAC to Measure Small Deviations About a Precisely-Determined Value.

In any of these schemes, it is essential to keep in mind that every element in the front end, wiring, preamplifiers, components, references, must be compatible with the resolution and accuracy sought. This also includes the noise level.

For signals in the second category, the switched-gain amplifier is a satisfactory, but slow-and-expensive approach. An intriguing alternative is to use a logarithmic amplifier for data compression (Figure 13).

The error of a logarithmic amplifier, after calibration, is a *log conformity* error (nonlinearity on a semi-log plot) that is specified in terms of a maximum value at the output, or a maximum ratio to actual input over a specified range. For example, 1% log conformity error means that the error at the output, for 2V/decade* scaling, is 8.6mV, corresponding to an input uncertainty of ±1%. Typical input *voltage* range (i.e., for the Analog

*A *decade* is a 10:1 range of input voltage or current.

Devices 755) is 1mV to 10V. The corresponding output-voltage range is ±4V (i.e., ±2 decades at 2 volts per decade, with respect to a 0.1V reference level.) Since an error of 1% referred to the 1mV minimum input signal is $1/10^6$ of full-scale input, and since the corresponding output error of 8.6mV is $0.0086/8 = 1.075 \times 10^{-3}$ of the output swing, the dynamic range of the signal has been compressed by a factor of 1000, as a result of the logarithmic transformation. This means that a 12-bit converter (with suitable scaling) can be used to digitize the log amplifier output, with a quite-comfortable error margin.

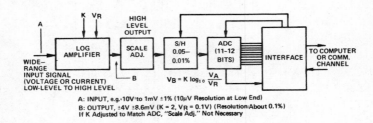

A: INPUT, e.g.·10V'to 1mV ±1% (10μV Resolution at Low End)
B: OUTPUT, ±4V ±8.6mV (K = 2, V_R = 0.1V) (Resolution About 0.1%)
If K Adjusted to Match ADC, "Scale Adj." Not Necessary

Figure 13. Log Amplifier Used for Range Compression in Data-Acquisition System

Though it might appear that the representation of data having an inherent 20 bits of resolution ($10^6 \cong 2^{20}$) by a signal having 12-bit resolution is getting "something for nothing," in violation of *some* Natural Law, the scheme really works. There are, however, some points to consider:

1. Compression is achieved by exponentially distorting the relative value of the Least Significant Bit. Thus, for a 10,000-to-1 signal range, represented by ±4V output, an LSB (of 12 bits, offset binary, suitably scaled) is worth 23mV at 10V input (i.e., 10 $[1 - \log_{10}^{-1} 8/8192]$) and 2.3μV for 1mV input. Therefore, while the approach is quite useful for compressing data requiring essentially constant *fractional* error (e.g., 1%) anywhere in a wide range, it is not at all suited to applications requiring high resolution (e.g., 0.01% FS) *at any point* in the range.

2. Since the digital number is a logarithmic representation of the analog input signal, it must be dealt with as such in the digital process. If the number is to be used in computation, it should be

antilogged, using a ROM and/or software, unless of course the computation is facilitated by the availability of a logarithmic relationship. If the data is simply to be stored or transmitted, and eventually returned to analog form unchanged, it does not require any further digital transformation, just an analog antilog operation following the output D/A conversion (unless logarithmic analog data is acceptable).

3. Since a logarithmic function is inherently unipolar (the logarithm is real only for positive values of the argument − positive signals require a 755N, negative signals a 755P), it is far from ideal for signals that are inherently zero-centered. While it may be useful to bias some types of input signals into a single polarity, functions that demand symmetrical treatment may be badly distorted by the wide variation, in both resolution and speed, between zero and full-scale input. Such functions would profit by a type of compression that is symmetrical about zero. An example of an easily-obtained form is a $\sinh^{-1}$ function (Figure 14), which involves two complementary antilog transconductors (752P and 752N) in the feedback path of an op amp. The resulting function is logarithmic for larger values of input, but it passes through zero, essentially linearly (but slowly).

Noise Reduction

Like diseases, noise is never eliminated, just prevented, cured, or endured, depending on its seriousness and the costs/difficulty of treating it.

Noise in data-acquisition systems takes three basic forms, *transmitted noise,* inherent in the original signal, *inherent noise,* generated within the devices used in data acquisition (preamps, converters, etc.) and *induced noise,* "picked up" from the outside world, power supplies, logic, or other analog channels, by magnetic, electrostatic, or galvanic coupling.

Noise is either *random* or *coherent* (i.e., correlated to some noise-inducing phenomenon within or outside of the system). Random noise is usually generated within components, such as resistors, semiconductor junctions, or transformer cores, while

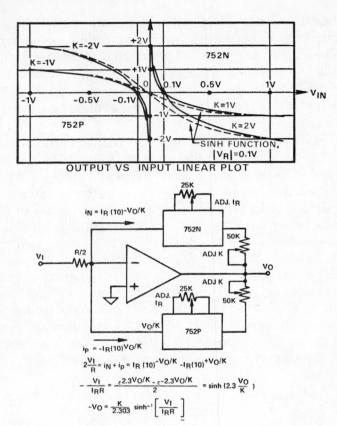

Figure 14. Bipolar Signal Compression Using Complementary
Logarithmic Transconductors to Synthesize $\sinh^{-1}$ Function.

coherent noise is either locally-generated by processes, such as modulation/demodulation (e.g., chopper-stabilization), or coupled-in. Coherent noise often takes the form of "spikes," although it may be of any shape, including — collectively from many sources — pseudorandom.

Noise is characterized in terms of either *root-mean-square (rms)* or *peak-to-peak* measurements, within a stated bandwidth.* Random noise from a given source, within a given bandwidth, will give consistent *rms* measurements. For a typical gaussian amplitude

*For a useful discussion of the properties of noise, see "Noise and Operational Amplifier Circuits," in *Analog Dialogue*, Vol. 3, No. 1.

distribution, and a sufficient number of measurements, one may expect a consistent relationship between the probabilities of obtaining peaks of given size in relation to the rms, as shown in the table in Figure 15.

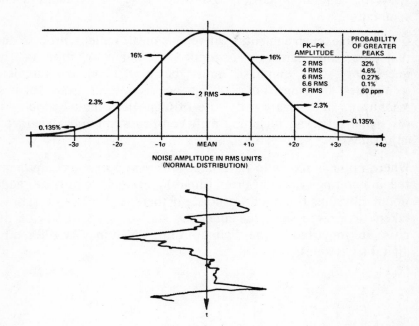

PK--PK AMPLITUDE	PROBABILITY OF GREATER PEAKS
2 RMS	32%
4 RMS	4.6%
6 RMS	0.27%
6.6 RMS	0.1%
P RMS	60 ppm

Figure 15. RMS vs. Peak-to-Peak Amplitudes for Gaussian Noise

RMS values of noise from uncorrelated sources (e.g., from different devices, or from different portions of the frequency spectrum of the same device) add as the square-root of the sum-of-the-squares. However, if noise is dominated by picked-up spikes, root-sum-of-squares is of small comfort.

As we have indicated at the beginning of the chapter, there are two basic forms of system-design problem: those involving essentially ordinary signal levels in unfavorable environments, and those involving extremely high-resolution measurements in favorable environments.

For unfavorable environments, where the major source of noise is *induced noise,* the designer must rely on early preamplification and conversion, isolation, shielding and guarding, signal compression and filtering, and — where possible — an information rate (via fast sampling or parallel paths) that has enough redundancy to allow the digital processor to retrieve data via correlation and summation.

In favorable environments, where the measurement process and the processing hardware introduce the major portion of the uncertainty, the emphasis must be placed on measurement techniques, filtering, choice of data-acquisition hardware for best resolution, and — again — the use of high-speed digital processing for signal retrieval, including drift compensation and scale-factor adjustment.

Where noise is likely to have large spikes as a major component, the integrating-type converter (dual-slope) usually provides additional filtering. For random noise, if there are sufficient samples taken of a given signal channel, the statistical properties of the noise are imparted to the digital output, which may be filtered by digital techniques.

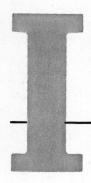

Data Distribution

Chapter 3

After analog data have been converted to digital form and have been duly stored, transmitted, or processed, the results of this handling, as well as some newly-created digital numbers, may be required once again in the "real world" of phenomena. In analog or digital form, they may be used to drive meters or motors, display information, stimulate devices under test, generate heat or light, modulate waveforms, sound the alarm, or – in short – they are converted from abstract numbers to the manipulation of energy.

The multiplexed digital output words are made available in serial order at an output register, for distribution to their destinations. Though an increasing number of real-world functions, such as numerical displays, stepping motors, printers, and the like, are effected by digital numbers (perhaps with "decoding," but without the interposition of electronic analog variables), there is still a widespread – and growing – use of electronic D/A converters in distribution systems. This chapter treats of those systems that use D/A converters.

FACTORS AFFECTING DISTRIBUTION-SYSTEM DESIGN

The configuration, choice of components and their specifications, the system timing, and location of multiplexing, depend, as with data acquisition, on

1. Number of channels
2. Settling time per channel

3. Update rate
4. Output resolution
5. Output linearity and accuracy
6. The nature of the loads
7. The cost function

There are a number of areas for decision by the system designer:

Digital signal readout: Serial paths or parallel paths? Serial words or parallel words?

Signal storage between updates: in digital or analog form? Registers or sample-holds? Single-rank or dual-rank? Sample-holds or inertia?

Multiplexing: Digital or analog? If digital, parallel or serial? If analog, with sample/holds or multiplex switching?

Update: Simultaneous, sequential, or random?

Conversion: At computer or at load? Single converter with analog multiplexing, or many converters with digital multiplexing?

Analog output: Voltage or current? Discrete values or smoothed? Permissible level of switching transients? Isolated or galvanically-connected circuitry?

Techniques to reduce costs: Combining sample-hold and multiplexing. Inertial filtering. Using low-precision DAC's in "slave" circuit for standardized calibration.

DIGITAL vs. ANALOG DISTRIBUTION

The systems designer has a choice between feeding data to analog actuating and indicating devices via either a D/A converter (with storage register) for each channel (Figure 1), or a single D/A converter, with a sample-hold circuit for each channel (Figure 2).

Once updated, a D/A converter-with-input-register will store an analog value indefinitely, or at least, for so long as the power is connected. By contrast, a sample-hold circuit, since it holds the analog data on a capacitor, is susceptible to a definite "droop" (positive or negative) in the analog output as the charge on the capacitor changes due to leakage across the switch, from the amplifier's summing point, or from the supplies (or perhaps even due to the capacitor's own leakage resistance or dielectric absorption). Thus, even though the data may not change at all, as is ideally the case for an aircraft simulator's altimeter in "straight & level" flight, it is necessary to update sample-hold circuits periodically to correct for output droop. On the other hand, so long as the data remains unchanged, a distribution system based on D/A converters (with registers) need not be periodically refreshed.

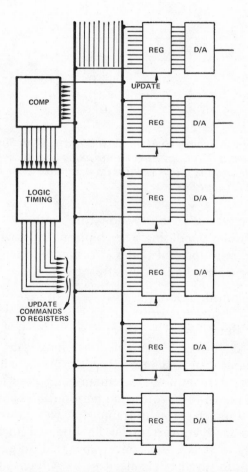

Figure 1. D/A Converter for Each Channel;
Parallel-Word Distribution

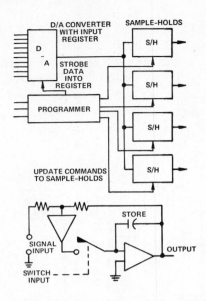

Figure 2. Sample-Hold for Each Channel, With Single Fast, Accurate D/A Converter. Multiplexing Occurs by Sampling Each Channel Individually as its Associated Data Appears on the Input Bus.

The D/A converter's ability to store without error lays the foundation for an "updating by exception" rule, whereby the data channels are only updated if the *information* changes. Otherwise, the computer leaves the D/A unrefreshed.

A further consideration in the use of D/A converters vs. sample-hold circuits lies in the matter of allowing for acquisition and settling time. The data sheet for a typical data-distribution sample-hold circuit at reasonable cost may call for acquisition periods ranging from $2\mu s$ to $20\mu s$ or more. Thus, it is often necessary for the computer to remain connected to each channel for the duration of this acquisition period (unless buffered), which may use up appreciable main-frame time. By contrast, the storage register of a D/A converter can be updated in a fraction of a microsecond, so it is quite conceivable that an entire 10-channel data-distribution system, using one D/A per channel, can be updated in the time required to refresh a single sample-hold circuit.

Offsetting some of the flexibility of the D/A-per-channel data-method is the cost of interconnecting the D/A's to the data source. Parallel data at the 10-bit level requires at least 12 conductors (10 data lines, ground, and command line) from the computer to the D/A converter, which, for fast transmission rates, requires costly multiple twisted pairs. If the D/A's are widely-distributed, as, for example, in a steel rolling mill, installation cost for the cable may easily be the largest single economic factor, far outweighing the cost of the D/A converters. Cable and installation costs can be reduced somewhat by introducing serial, instead of parallel data transmission. However, the penalty now lies in more-involved logic and added updating time (which may not be a problem at all), since each 10-bit channel requires at least 10 times as long to update.

CONVERTER-PER-CHANNEL DISTRIBUTION

Figure 1 illustrates the main ingredients of the distribution approach based on one D/A converter for every channel. Computer data is fed on a parallel bus to all D/A-converter input registers, while an update command is addressed individually to each register. Whenever the computer strobes a new data word into the data bus, it emits a command signal that causes one of the storage registers to accept this new word. A succession of parallel digital words and update commands then completes the data-refreshing cycle. The converters may be randomly addressed (and with varying numbers of data points per channel) or a computer may program sequential addresses, if the data is programmed to arrive in the same order.

Simultaneous Updating

In some instances — for example, in semiconductor test equipment — it is advantageous to update all analog channels simultaneously, thereby minimizing settling time in both the converter's output amplifiers and the IC device undergoing test. A data-distribution arrangement that eliminates delays caused by sequential refreshing of each D/A converter is shown in Figure 3.

This arrangement interposes an extra digital buffer between the computer's data-receiving register and the D/A converter's input register. The system updates the buffer registers serially while a previously-programmed semiconductor test takes place; then, as soon as a new set of analog voltage and current values are required, a command signal feeds the new set of digital words from the buffer registers to the input registers. While the device is being tested at these new voltage and current excitation levels, the buffer registers are again loaded sequentially for the following test.

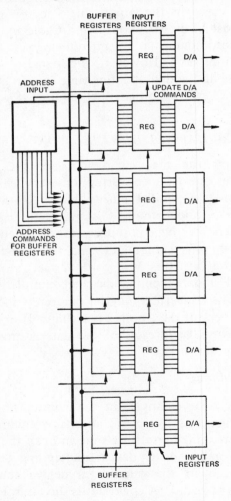

Figure 3. Simultaneous D/A Updating

Serial data transmission, to remote DAC's (with or without galvanic isolation) is conducted in much the same way, using two wires for the data, plus an extra conductor for command signals. However, the buffer register in this case is a shift register, accepting the data serially, but passing it on to the converter in parallel.

ANALOG DISTRIBUTION

Two approaches to sample-hold-circuit updating are shown in Figures 2 and 4. In Figure 2, analog data is "shipped" over a common cable to all the sample-hold circuits. However, each sample-hold device, normally in *hold*, remains oblivious to the input data until a command signal connects it momentarily to the data bus (*sample*). On receipt of its update pulse, the sample-hold circuit acquires whatever analog information appears on the data line and holds this value until subsequently commanded to acquire a new signal level.

An alternative arrangement, using a modular (de)multiplexer for distribution of analog data among individual channels, is shown in Figure 4. Here, the sample-hold circuits respond to whatever signals are presented at their input terminals, and then hold this signal level when the analog input is disconnected. The multiplexer switches serve double duty, both in multiplexing and for charging the *hold* capacitor. Though more subject to leakage and crosstalk than the circuit of Figure 2, this is a simple and low-cost arrangement.

A data-distribution arrangement that eliminates sample-hold circuitry is presented in Figure 5. Here, the purpose is to utilize the inherent storage capacity of the device being activated. For example, it is possible to distribute data among several d'Arsonval indicators in a utility substation simply by exploiting the natural inertia of the meter movement. So long as the data can be refreshed with sufficient rapidity, the meter's average response is simply dependent on the "duty cycle" (dwell time at each switch point to refresh period). Thermal ovens can be controlled by pulsing in this way, as can instrument servos and other devices with built-in inertia of one kind or another. For such applications, the converter should have sufficient peak output current-handling capacity and the switches low-enough resistance (perhaps even electromechanical relays) to avoid introducing errors.

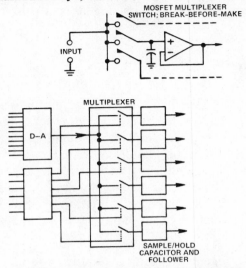

Figure 4. *Multiplexing and Sample-Hold Using Multiplex Switches*

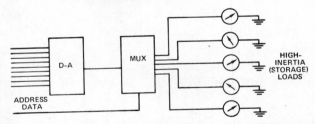

Figure 5. *Using Output-Transducer Inertia for Averaging and Data Storage, Eliminating Per-Channel Storage (Registers or Capacitors/Op Amps)*

ACQUISITION vs. DISTRIBUTION

As a rule, data *acquisition* poses more challenging problems than data *distribution*, but some of the problems assume different shapes. Since data distribution can take place at macroscopic power levels (volts and milliamperes), noise is not a great problem (except for *induced* noise in hostile environments). To the contrary, DAC outputs are sometimes boosted, as in programmable power supplies; in such cases, it is useful for the DAC's output amplifier system to have remote sensing to avoid errors due to voltage drops in the wiring. This may also be the case for high-resolution DAC's (such as DAC-16QG) at modest power levels.

Sample-holds used in data acquisition must have short aperture time (or at least small aperture uncertainty) because they must either deal with the "instantaneous" value of a signal, or sample it rapidly at equal time intervals. Their *hold* time need be no longer than is necessary for the ADC to digitize the signal. In short, the emphasis in sample-hold circuits for data acquisition lies on rapid acquisition, followed by rapid conversion. By contrast, sample-hold configurations used for data distribution usually permit relaxed update timing, but the analog values may have to be preserved for long periods without "droop." Thus, sample-holds for data distribution must have long *hold* times, and short acquisition-and-settling times. Where high resolution (12 bits or better) and large ratios of *hold* to *settling time* are necessary, multiple D/A distribution, with storage in registers becomes preferable.

FILTERING/SMOOTHING

In data acquisition, the purpose of filtering is to remove (or at least reduce) analog transmitted, inherent, or induced input noise. In distribution, filtering is used to reduce "noise" caused by quantization (finite increments of digital resolution causing discontinuous analog outputs – the obverse side of quantization uncertainty in A/D conversion), and to deal with coupled-in switching transients and "glitches" (which are large spikes caused by intermediate codes introduced by asymmetrical switching times at such transitions as $011 \ldots 11 \to 100 \ldots 00$).

Discontinuities are often tolerable, especially in DC-value testing, where they occur at the application of test conditions, and readings are not taken until the system has settled. On the other hand, if the converter is producing an analog ramp in discrete steps, the discontinuities may have to be smoothed, and certainly any feedthrough transients and/or "glitches" must be minimized. Linear filtering of glitches is impractical, because they have far from uniform magnitudes and they do not occur at uniform intervals; hence, filtering leads to badly-distorted waveforms. Glitches are minimized at the DAC by very fast switching with the best-possible matching of rise and fall times (to minimize the energy in the pulse), and then plucked out by "deglitcher" circuitry, which *holds* the output fixed during switching, then releases it for normal settling. The DAC-10DF is an example of a DAC specifically designed for this purpose.

For reconstructing very coarse sampled data, sophisticated interpolation techniques are used to overcome the limitations of simple filtering. An example is integration of the difference between two adjacent values so that the "points" are connected by straight lines, and the discontinuities become more-easily-filtered changes in slope rather than steps.

THE COST FACTOR

As of this writing, costs of both low-resolution DAC's and sample-holds are decreasing rapidly, but monolithic DAC's promise the lowest ultimate cost. For very-low-resolution systems (10 bits or less), multiple DAC's, even with the added costs of registers, may be cheaper than sample-holds (and give generally-better performance, as we have noted). From 10 to 12 bits, sample-holds appear to hold the cost edge. Above 12 bits, it is difficult to obtain sample-holds with adequate resolution and speed because of the problem of obtaining capacitors with decent dielectric absorption characteristics. So, for high resolution, converters-with-registers, though expensive, must win by default.

MINIMIZING CALIBRATION ERRORS BY SERVOING

Where many low-cost DAC's are used, it is possible to produce outputs that have absolute accuracy limited only by their resolution. This is done by slaving their outputs to that of a high-resolution, accurately-calibrated, temperature-stabilized master DAC (Figure 6).

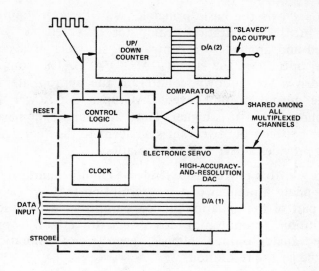

Figure 6a. Controlled-Output DAC

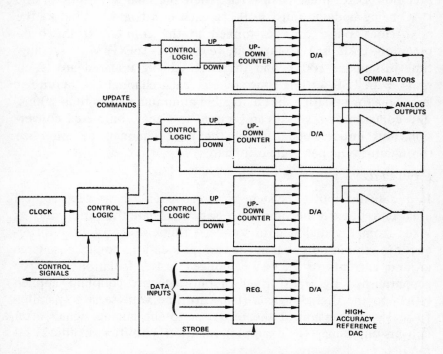

Figure 6b. Low-Cost High-Accuracy Distribution

I–51

Figure 6a shows the basic principle, with "master" and "slave" DAC's. In this illustration, computer data fed to D/A(1) is converted and applied to a comparator in which it is compared with the output of the slaved DAC, D/A(2). The comparator's output drives an up/down counter in the appropriate sense to drive the output of the slaved DAC up if it is lower than the master and down if it is higher. Thus, at balance, the slaved DAC will hunt between the two values adjacent to the "correct" value. Filtering provides a degree of interpolation.

In Figure 6b, this process is extended to multi-channel multiplexing, to update a number of lower-resolution DAC's. Use of feedback as part of the updating process permits an array of low-cost, low-resolution (monotonic) converters to establish precisely-controlled analog output voltages, regardless of calibration drift, but limited by the resolution.

The principal disadvantage of this scheme is its slowness, since the precision DAC must first settle, then the analog output of the DAC being updated must settle to each new trial value before the next clock pulse can be applied to the counter. If the high-precision DAC is a 16-bit unit, (e.g., DAC-16QG) with settling-time just under $100\mu s$, and the DAC's being updated are 12-bit units, with LSB-settling times of $2\mu s$, each channel can require at least 8ms for updating, but a possible minimum of less than $200\mu s$. The comparator reversal can be used to signal completed conversion and initiate updating of the next channel, to minimize throughput time per cycle of update.

ISOLATION

If a data-distribution system is spread over a large geographical area, it frequently becomes necessary to isolate the various analog loads from the digital data source. Otherwise, substantial differences in ground potential at the various locations could cause large ground currents or excessive induced noise. Isolation could be accomplished by transformer or photoelectric coupling, applied either to the digital signals (two-wire line with serial-to-parallel-to-analog conversion at the load), or to the analog signals after conversion, using (for example) isolation amplifiers in the 272-4 family.

I

Analog-Digital Functions

Chapter 4

ANALOG FUNCTIONS WITH DIGITAL COMPONENTS

The "analog" world has numerous circuit tricks that occur time and again, employing op amps, multiplier/dividers, filters, phase shifters, function generators, etc. The term "analog" commonly has two meanings, *both of which* are intended here: "analog" in the sense of dealing with measurable quantities rather than abstract *digital* numbers, and "analog" in the sense of *continuous* (derivatives existing nearly everywhere), rather than *discontinuous* (quantized).

There have been a few excellent books on the applications of operational amplifiers, fewer on the applications of op amps and analog function modules, and virtually none on the use of digital components (converters, counters, shift registers, etc.) in the service of analog relationships.

There are many excellent auguries favoring an intimate, long, and happy marriage between the two families. Analog devices are cheap, plentiful, and capable of a great deal of functional versatility; digital devices are cheap, plentiful, and capable of a great deal of functional versatility. The reasons there has been little apparent intercourse between them are twofold: Interface devices, such as A/D and D/A converters have heretofore been too expensive to be wasted as components (remember the days of $227 op amps and $50 transistors?), and practitioners who volubly embrace the tricks of both trades are either extremely rare or remain well-hidden.

This chapter is in no sense intended as an encyclopedia (in either breadth or depth) of such connubial (i.e., "hybrid") circuits; that volume is yet to be written. Rather, the few representative items included here are intended to be suggestive of what is possible, and to stimulate the reader to bring his creative faculties to bear on new ways of looking at problems that he may have conceived of as being strictly "analog" or "digital." For those already laboring in the vineyard, there will be no revelations, but perhaps there is something a little new or different to make a scan worthwhile. The circuits are presented in the form of independent modular panels that stand alone ("bite-size morsels," to aid digestion). The selected examples are:

SOURCES
   Digitally-Controlled Voltage Source
   Manual Digital Inputs
      Thumbwheel BCD switch
      Toggle-switch register
   Digitally-Controlled Current Sources
      "Current-output" DAC
      Current gain: floating load
      Current gain: buffered load
      Current to grounded load

SCALE FACTORS AND MODULATIONS
   Digitally-Controlled Direct Gains
   Digitally-Controlled Inverse Gains
   High-Precision Analog Multiplication
   . . . or Division

FUNCTIONAL RELATIONSHIPS
   Analog Functions with Memory Devices
   Arbitrarily-Programmable Functional Relationships
   Sinusoidal Input-Output Relationships

TRIGONOMETRIC APPLICATIONS
   Digital Phase Shifter
   Digital/Resolver Converter (Resolver Simulator)
   Resolver (Digital) Control Transformer

WAVEFORMS
Sawtooth
Triangular-Wave
Sinusoidal

FUNCTIONS OF TIME
Precision Analog Delay Line
Tapped Delay Line
Serial Delay Line
Analog-to-Frequency Converter

DIGITAL SERVO DEVICES
Tracking Sample-Hold (A/D Converter)
Digital Pulse Stretcher
Digital Peak-Follower (with Hysteresis)
Automatic Zeroing Circuit

DIGITALLY-CONTROLLED VOLTAGE SOURCE
(or Precision Power Supply)

A well-calibrated D/A converter is probably the simplest available source of arbitrary precision voltages. Turn on the power, set the digital input, and expect (and receive) the voltage you asked for. With a 10-bit converter, resolution is 0.1%; with a 12-bit converter, 0.024%; and with a 16-bit converter, 0.0015% (15ppm).

Let it be driven by a computer, and you have a ready supply of voltage for fast or slow automatic testing. Set it manually (with a "toggle-switch register," or with BCD thumbwheel switches), and it's a convenient "volt-box," or a handy reference source. Or set it permanently by hard-wiring its logic inputs. No resistors or pots necessary!

If its output op amp doesn't have adequate output current, follow it with an inside-the-loop current booster. Feedback to the built-in amplifier-feedback-resistor will make the output virtually independent of the booster's dc characteristics. It can be followed with an op amp having higher-voltage output and precisely-set fixed gain, if high voltage is needed. Doing this outside the DAC's loop protects the converter's circuitry (including the low-voltage digital components) from accidental exposure to fault voltages.

Because the setting is done digitally with (e.g.) TTL logic levels, the voltage can be set from a distant location, or in the presence of a fair amount of electrical noise, relying on the inherently-high noise immunity of digital signals (at the cost of additional wire for the parallel circuits). If noise pickup is not a major factor, it is interesting to note that the switches can be closed "passively," i.e., to the power-supply return for "0", left open for "1".

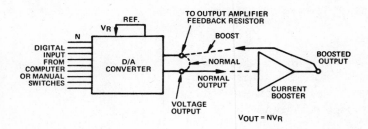

MANUAL DIGITAL INPUTS

All that is needed to obtain a given output voltage from a D/A converter is to close the appropriate switches. Human beings usually prefer base-10 numbers or BCD coding, despite the fact that it throws away inherent binary resolution at the rate of 2-bits-out-of-12 (12BCD = 1/1000, 10BIN = 1/1024).

Thumbwheel-switch Encoder

A thumbwheel-switch encoder is the simplest way for the operator, especially if he is mathematically unsophisticated, since the base-10 number can be set directly, and all the appropriate switches are automatically closed. A D/A converter with BCD coding should be used. The switch points that are "0" (positive true) are connected to ground; those that are "1" are either left open or connected to $+V_s$ (but be sure to use a break-before-make switch). The wiring for one decade of thumbwheel switchery is shown ("1" open). If the converter has *complementary BCD* coding, the complementary switch connections should be used.

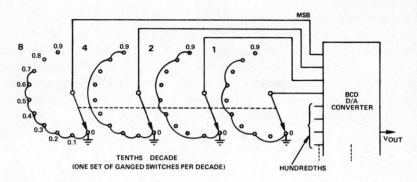

TENTHS   DECADE
(ONE SET OF GANGED SWITCHES PER DECADE)

HUNDREDTHS

Toggle-Switch Register

The toggle-switch register is physically more elementary, and it may be used with either binary or BCD-coded DAC's. It does require some calculations, though, especially for binary settings. As an aid to calculation, two tables are given, one for BCD (the same code is used for each digit), and one for binary equivalents of representative decimal fractions of full scale. Interpolation is performed by adding or subtracting an appropriate set of terms (binary rules) to form the desired sum. Note that multiplication or division by 2 simply moves a number one place to the left or right; by 4, two places left or right, etc.

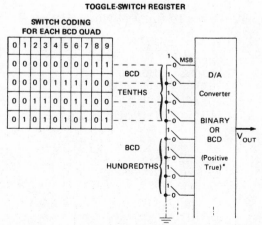

TOGGLE-SWITCH REGISTER

SWITCH CODING
FOR EACH BCD QUAD

0	1	2	3	4	5	6	7	8	9
0	0	0	0	0	0	0	0	1	1
0	0	0	0	1	1	1	1	0	0
0	0	1	1	0	0	1	1	0	0
0	1	0	1	0	1	0	1	0	1

*If converter operates with complementary logic, perform computations the same way, but use complementary switch settings.

For unipolar binary coding, the digits to the right of the "decimal" point form the code, MSB leftmost. For bipolar 2's complement, divide the magnitude by two for the positive number, then complement all digits and add 1 LSB for the negative number. For offset binary, complement the 2's-complement MSB. (See Chapter 1, Part 2, for a more-complete discussion of coding and conversion relationships in bipolar DAC's.)

BINARY EQUIVALENTS OF DECIMAL FRACTIONS

┌─MSB

0.8	0.1100	1100	1100	1101	0
0.5	0.1000	0000	0000	0000	0
0.4	0.0110	0110	0110	0110	1
0.25	0.0100	0000	0000	0000	0
0.2	0.0011	0011	0011	0011	0
0.125	0.0010	0000	0000	0000	0
0.1	0.0001	1001	1001	1001	1
0.08	0.0001	0100	0111	1010	1
0.0625	0.0001	0000	0000	0000	0
0.04	0.0000	1010	0011	1101	0
0.02	0.0000	0101	0001	1110	1
0.01	0.0000	0010	1000	1111	0
0.008	0.0000	0010	0000	1100	1
0.004	0.0000	0001	0000	0110	0
0.002	0.0000	0000	1000	0011	0
0.001	0.0000	0000	0100	0001	1
0.0008	0.0000	0000	0011	0100	1
0.0004	0.0000	0000	0001	1010	0
0.0002	0.0000	0000	0000	1101	0
0.0001	0.0000	0000	0000	0110	1

Converting Base-10 Number to Binary Switch Setting – 2 Examples (12-Bit Conversion)

1. +0.9FS   (Note: 0.9 = 0.5 + 0.4)

0.5	0.1000	0000	0000
+0.4	+0.0110	0110	0110
0.9	0.1110	0110	0110

   Code: 1110   0110   0110, Straight Binary

2. −0.6FS, 2's Complement (Note: 0.6 = 0.4 + 0.2)

0.4	0.0110	0110	0110
0.2	+0.0011	0011	0011
0.6	0.1001	1001	1001

Code:	1001	1001	1001, Straight Binary
× ½	0100	1100	1100 Scale Expansion
Compl.	1011	0011	0011 One's Complement
+1 LSB	1011	0011	0100, Two's Complement

DIGITALLY-CONTROLLED CURRENT SOURCES

Many analog current sources have been developed with the variations that provide such diverse advantages as low cost, simplicity, ability to ground the load, etc. In conventional all-analog circuits, the original controlling input is derived typically from a precision potentiometer, zener diode, or other reference. However, availability of versatile D/A converters now permits convenient digital control of current values, making, for example, programmable current supplies an inexpensive reality. As with voltage sources, the adjustments may be performed by either a computer or a human operator. These are a representative few among the many ways of accomplishing current drive.

"Current-Output" DAC

This would appear to be the simplest form of digital-to-current output source. However, it is unsatisfactory, because it generally has appreciable internal admittance "looking back," and this admittance (and the load) must be included in computations of the share of current reaching the load. For this reason, the principal application of the current-output DAC is to drive inverting-operational-amplifier input terminals, which are normally at zero potential and thus impose negligible loading error.

The output resistance of these DAC's is introduced by the resistive dividers used for attenuation of less-significant-bit currents (as is explained in Chapter 2, Part II). It is feasible, for applications in which a restricted number of discrete values of current (say 16) are required, to construct highly-precise fast current-output converters with high internal resistance, using the AD551 quad current switches (*ibid.*).

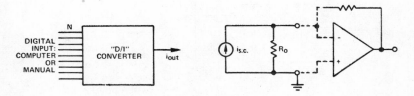

Current Gain — Floating Load

In this application, a load that has both terminals available is connected between the amplifier output terminal and the return lead of the feedback resistor. The attenuation introduced by R_M, if used, produces current gain. If the amplifier's output current is inadequate, a booster may be used, inside the loop (BF). For large currents, a separate booster supply should be used, with only the R_M pickoff point connected to the converter's analog ground.

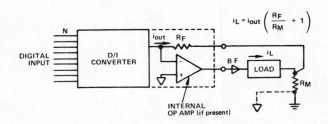

Current Gain — Buffered Load

For applications in which the amplifier's output range imposes serious restrictions on the kind of load that might be driven, a transistor with the load in its collector (or drain, in the case of FET's) allows a wide range of voltage swing across the load. Examples of loads that might be driven in this manner are CRT deflection coils, motor windings, chart-recorder pen drives, etc.

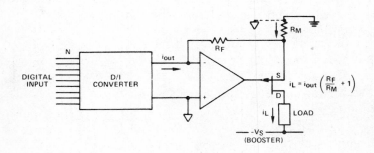

Current to Grounded Load

There are a number of ways of driving current to a grounded load, all of which employ both positive and negative feedback to measure and control the current. One example, using a voltage source and two operational amplifiers, is shown here. Amplifier A1 measures the difference voltage across R_M (direct from the top and inverted from the bottom via A2) and sets it equal to the DAC's V_{out}, thus forcing a current V_{out}/R_M through the load. In the general case, the resistor ratios can be adjusted for scaling, the drive could be from a current source, boosters could be used (at point "BF"), etc. As with all operational amplifier circuits having complicated (or even simple) dynamics, attention should be paid to dynamic stability: feedback capacitors may not be as helpful as capacitance shunting the load.

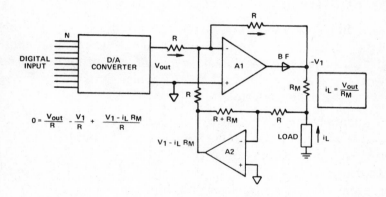

DIGITALLY-CONTROLLED SCALE FACTORS

A D/A converter that accepts variable references (i.e., a *multiplying* DAC) can be thought of as a digitally-controlled potentiometer. As such, it can be used for setting gains, either by a computer or a human operator. Computer-setting might be used, for example, in adaptive control systems; manual setting might be employed where the device being controlled is remote (think of it as a potentiometer with a long shaft).

The multiplying D/A converter can also be thought of as a means of modulating a computer output by an analog signal. For example, if the computer is developing a square wave, the analog signal might be amplitude-modulating it.

The simplest device operates in one quadrant, with either a positive or a negative analog signal and straight binary or BCD coding.

For two-quadrant operation, there are two modes: bipolar analog and bipolar digital. Bipolar analog operation simply requires a bipolar analog input and straight binary or BCD digital coding. It also requires a converter that can accept analog signals of either polarity. Such DAC's as the DAC-12M, that use voltage switching and R-2R ladder networks, are capable of this form of operation; current-source DAC's are usually unipolar, though the devices employing monolithic quad switches will accept a wide signal range without appreciable degradation of linearity.

Bipolar digital operation can involve offset-binary (or 2's complement) coding, with an inverted version of the analog input applied to the offset reference terminal, or to one end of an R-2R ladder network; or sign-magnitude coding (unipolar DAC), with the sign bit switching the output polarity.

Four-quadrant operation involves a combination of circumstances: a DAC that can respond to both bipolar analog and bipolar digital inputs in the correct polarity, with appropriate speed and feedthrough performance. "Feedthrough" is the analog output signal that appears when the digital input is calling for zero gain.

Shown here are four ways (among many) that digital gain control can be used to perform useful functions.

Direct Scale Factor

This circuit provides simple digital scale adjustment, proportional to the digital number. As noted, the digital number can be applied either by a computer signal, or manually.

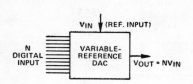

DIGITAL POLARITY	ANALOG POLARITY	
	UNIPOLAR	BIPOLAR
UNIPOLAR	ONE-QUADRANT	2-QUADRANT
BIPOLAR	2-QUADRANT	4-QUADRANT

Inverse Scale Factor

With the DAC in the feedback loop of an operational amplifier, the gain is inversely-proportional to the digital number. As a follower, all gains must be greater than unity, since even full feedback is 1 LSB less than unity gain. As an inverter, the resistor ratio can be chosen for attenuation, so that normalized unity gain can occur at a mid-scale value (if $R_f/R_i = 0.1$, nominal minimum gain is 0.1 (N = F.S.), and unity gain is at N = 0.1). But noise-and-error-gain will be $\cong 1/N$. The rules of feedback call for unipolar (positive) feedback gains only. (Signal may be bipolar).

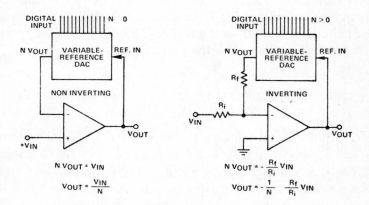

High-Precision Analog Multiplication

Since a 12-bit multiplying DAC develops accuracies to within considerably better than 0.1%, it is possible to make an analog multiplier having excellent accuracy by converting one of the inputs to digital form and using it to control the gain of a multiplying DAC. If the ADC is ratiometric, the output is a function of three variables. (V_R should always be larger than V_1, or else overrange indication will be necessary.)

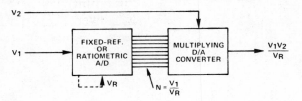

. . . *or Division*

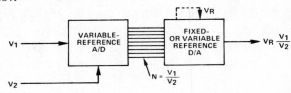

Since an A/D converter digitizes the ratio of the "input" to the "reference", a D/A converter will convert the ratio back to a voltage. Again, if the D/A is a multiplying type, the output is a function of three variables. For both of these applications, the A/D may be connected for free-running operation, and either the A/D or the D/A should have a register to buffer the D/A from the conversion process and store the previous value.

FUNCTIONAL RELATIONSHIPS

The term "functional relationship" implies a black-box operation, linear or nonlinear, $y = f(x)$, f being any single-valued realizable function. It is distinguished from a "function generator," which implies a *time function* (i.e., in a function generator, $y = f(t)$). By applying a linearly-increasing function of time to a device having a given functional relationship, one can create a function generator.

In analog circuitry, functions are traditionally embodied in three ways:

1. Using a natural function (e.g., the inherently logarithmic diode characteristic for log and antilog circuitry, the transconductance relationships of transistors for transconductance multipliers, the ability of a capacitor to store charge for integration).

2. Using diode-resistor networks to form piecewise-linear approximations to a nonlinear function.

3. Using combinations of natural functions to approximate arbitrary relationships, for example, power series using multipliers to generate the x^2, x^3, x^4, etc., terms.

Now that converters and memories are available at low cost, a fourth approach becomes feasible:

4. Using memories (e.g., ROM's, singly or in groups) to store a function digitally, and converting-in and -out with A/D's and D/A's, as shown in the illustration. Typical applications already in growing use are trigonometric transformations and thermocouple compensators.

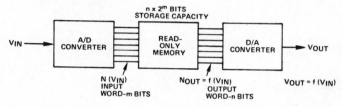

Arbitrarily-Programmable Functional Relationships

Besides standard functions that can be purchased in ROM's, it is also possible to buy programmable read-only memories, that can be programmed by the purchaser to simulate functional relationships.

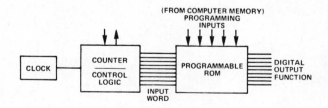

Sinusoidal Input-Output Relationships

An example of the approach is the use of a read-only memory that has the values of $sin\theta$ stored in it for $0° < \theta < 90°$. Two additional digits provide quadrant information, one to complement the input in the even-numbered quadrants, the other to provide the output sign-change for the 3rd and 4th quadrants. The input arrives from an angle-to-digital transducer, the corresponding sinusoidal number values are developed and applied to a D/A converter, and it makes the sine function available as a voltage. If the D/A converter is a multiplying type, computations of the form $R\sin\phi$ are readily performed.

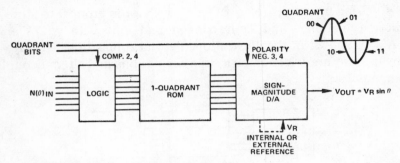

TRIGONOMETRIC APPLICATIONS

Digital Phase Shifter

The Figure shows two multiplying D/A converters used as digitally-controlled attenuators multiplying the reference signals $V\sin\omega t$ and $V\cos\omega t$ by the vector component of θ. The summed output from the two converters is then the vector $V\sin(\omega t + \theta)$, where the phase angle θ is set by the converter's digital inputs.

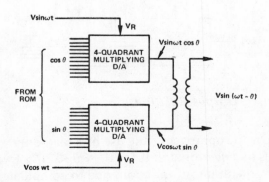

Digital/Resolver Converter (Resolver Simulator)

Similar to the above configuration, but having the common reference input to both multipliers, V *sin ωt*, this configuration obtains the two components V *sinωt sin θ* and V *sinωt cosθ*, which express resolver data for angle θ. The resolver data can be converted into synchro format with a Scott-T transformer, or an equivalent network in which operational amplifiers provide the appropriate voltage ratios. This resolver simulator can be enclosed within a feedback loop to operate as a resolver-to-digital converter.

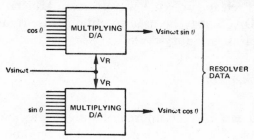

Resolver (Digital) Control Transformer

Using the *actual* resolver line voltages V *sinωt sinθ* and V *sinωt cosθ* as the converter reference inputs, and multiplying by digital equivalents to *cos α* and *sin α*, an output proportional to the angular error, θ − α (for small angular errors) is developed. Operated in this mode, the configuration simulates a resolver control transformer.

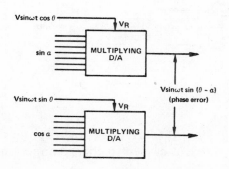

WAVEFORM GENERATION

Linear waveforms are generated digitally by clocks and counters, processed by ROM's to obtain arbitrary shapes, and converted to analog functions of time by DAC's.[1] As long as the original digital function can be created, then an analog output can be made to follow (within its speed limitations). The ease of manipulation and ability to lock timing operations to precise clocks gives the digital approach considerable edge in versatility over many analog alternatives. Deglitching and filtering may be used as (and if) necessary to clean up the waveforms. Arbitrary counts and very-simple DAC's may be used to obtain pulse trains or few-steps staircases of arbitrary duty cycle.

Sawtooth Generator

This sweep generator is composed of a digital clock, a counter, and a DAC. The clock pulses increment the counter, and the sequential counter steps increment the DAC output. After the counter is full, it returns to its empty state and starts counting again. Both amplitude and period of the sweep generator are easily and precisely adjustable. The resolution is determined by the number of counts and choice of D/A converter, ranging from the 16-bit DAC-16QG, with its 65,536 steps, down to 10- or fewer-bit converters with 1,024 steps, and below.

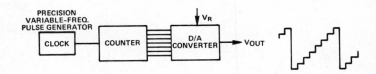

Triangular-Wave Generator

Instead of being allowed to overflow, the counter in this case is an up-down counter that is caused to change direction when it is full,

[1]See also chapter 5, section B.

and again when it is empty. Two approaches to reversing direction are shown. In one, the reversal is generated during the full (and empty) states; in the other, it is generated by the carry (borrow) occurring at the leading edge of the next pulse. The result, at the DAC output, is essentially a triangular-wave of precise amplitude and frequency. With little additional logic, full-scale dwell (or dwell-and-reversal at any level) provides trapezoidal waveforms.

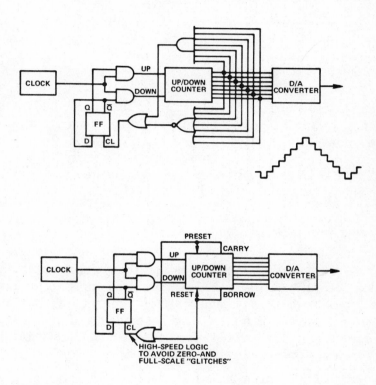

Sine-Wave Generator

If the digital count is fed to a sinusoidal ROM, and its output, accompanied by polarity information, is applied to a sine-magnitude-coded DAC, the output of the DAC will be an n-bit quantized sine wave. Its frequency is determined by the clock, and its amplitude can be controlled externally or by the use of a multiplying DAC.

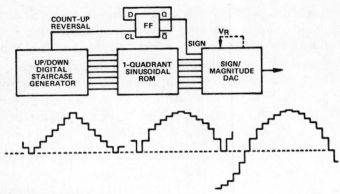

TIME FUNCTIONS

The ability of flip-flops to store information, undegraded by time, and the continually decreasing cost of storage capacity, are strong motivations to seek ways of eliminating capacitor circuits, with their leakage, dielectric hysteresis, and nonlinearity. "Distortionless" time delay, integration, and sample-hold are a few targets for such effort.

Precision Analog Delay Line

There are interesting applications for good analog delay lines: analog correlation, "distortionless" signal compression or expansion (i.e., "riding the gain" without missing a drumbeat), electronic echo-chamber effects, analog modeling of processes that incorporate pure time delay for predictive control, design of filters with arbitrary transfer functions, are a few.[2]

But there hadn't been a decent way of building a practical analog time-delay device that is variable over microseconds to minutes to months, until shift registers became available with many bits at low cost-per-bit.

Active or passive filter-type delay lines were seldom "distortionless," analog "bucket brigades" had excessive leakage errors at low speeds, as well as a resolution-vs.-cost problem (this latter being

²See also chapter 5, section B.

solved by the new MOS high-speed bucket brigades), tape recording wasn't efficacious at high speeds, and the use of mainframe memory was too expensive (and bulky for portable instruments).

In the example shown, the delay is produced by shift registers (e.g., 256-bit) for n parallel digital channels, each channel representing 1 bit of converted analog signal. For 10-bit conversion, and 10 delay lines, signals that can be quantized into 1024 discrete levels can be delayed with a resolution of 1/256 of the delay time (e.g., $1\mu s$ of $256\mu s$, 1/16s of 16s, $1.38°$ per cycle of a sinusoidal ac signal of period equal to the delay time, etc.).

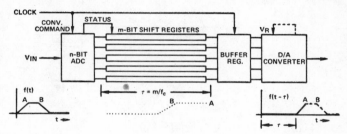

Tapped Delay Line

This device makes a number of points in the history of a waveform available simultaneously. It is simply the delay line with an increased number of discrete "chunks" of delay, and readout via DAC's at each point. Multiplying DAC's allow such interesting functions as $f(t) \cdot f(t-\tau)$ to be computed for a variety of values of τ.

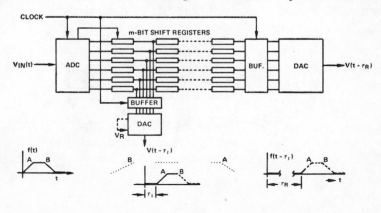

Serial Delay Line

For signals that do not require sampling at top speed, a considerable saving of the cost of delay lines (or increase in the time-resolution of the delay) can be achieved by feeding the converted signal into the line serially, and converting back to parallel information before the D/A conversion. Since the signal is being clocked through the line, a bit-at-a-time, few if any additional bits of shift register capacity are needed.

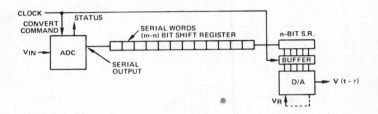

Precision Average-Frequency-to-Voltage Converter

In this application, the output of a frequency-or analog-event-meter (e.g., 16 bits) is applied to the usual BCD readout. In addition, the 8 (or more) least-significant bits are converted to voltage, providing a very sensitive analog measure of small frequency changes. It is feasible to also convert the top 8 bits, and use a low-cost analog divider, such as the AD530, to get a continuous analog readout of the fractional deviation.

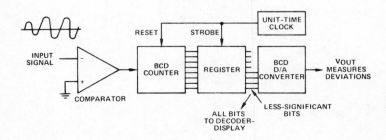

DIGITAL SERVO CIRCUITS

Most A/D converter designs involve feedback. Thus the very means of conversion implies that the combination of analog-digital interaction and the power of feedback can yield quite valuable results. A few examples are sample-hold, peak-detecting, and automatic zero-setting.

Tracking Sample-Hold (A/D Converter)

This circuit, also mentioned in the chapter on sample-holds, is especially useful as a track-and-infinite-hold device. It can acquire the analog signal within a minimum of 1 count and a maximum of 2^n counts, and, upon command, *hold* it indefinitely without degradation, providing both digital and analog readout. Since it uses an up-down counter, it will track the analog signal at a constant rate (2^{-n} FS per count), and "hunt" between the two digital values that straddle the analog value, if it remains constant.

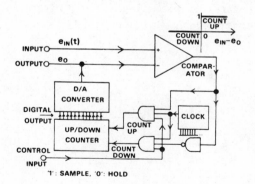

'1' : SAMPLE, '0' : HOLD

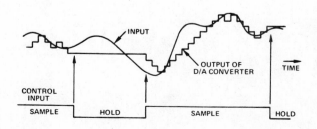

For slowly-varying analog signals, the tracking sample-hold is one of the lowest-cost ways to convert, since it eliminates the need for a sample-hold. However, its conversion time is variable, which introduces timing errors in sampled-data systems, since the most-recently acquired value may represent any value of signal during the interval between interrogations. Also, its response depends to a great extent on the amount and type of noise present.

Digital Pulse Stretcher

For extremely-fast acquisition-very-long hold, this circuit, consisting of a fast sample-hold and a fast successive-approximations A/D converter will provide the best results. Both analog and digital outputs are available. If the internal D/A converter's output can be made available without slowing conversion, the output D/A shown in the Figure is unnecessary. The SHA-2A is kept in *sample* at all times except during conversion. When switched to *hold,* it should have a "head start" of about 100ns for its transients to die down before conversion starts. But aperture time is 10ns with 0.25ns jitter.

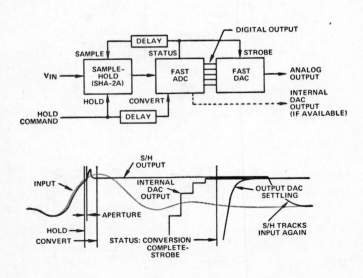

Digital Peak-Follower (with Hysteresis)

Similar to the tracking sample-hold, but using an up-counter (a valley-follower would use a down-counter), this circuit will *hold* the highest value of input that it has been able to track. However, to provide a small measure of immunity to noise, hysteresis makes the circuit insensitive to small changes; in order for the input to be followed, it must be higher than the stored value by a preset amount. A similar circuit can be used for valley following, and two such circuits with an output subtractor will provide peak-to-peak measurement.

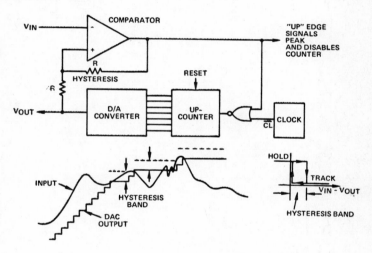

Automatic Set-Point Circuit

If a circuit under test is to be calibrated from time to time (e.g., each time some element, perhaps a device under test, is changed), the resetting and the level to which a test value must be reset, may be adjusted digitally. In the example, an output of the circuit must be set to a value equal to a calibrating value set by DAC-1. The values are compared, and a clock increments a counter, which updates a DAC, setting the input that performs the calibrating adjustment. When the comparator changes sign, calibration is complete, and the sign change indicates a "Ready" condition. The calibration value is retained until a new calibration cycle is initiated by resetting the counter and gating the clock.

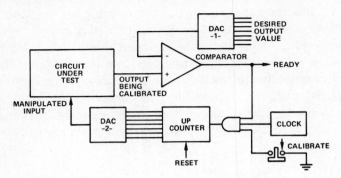

Applications of Converters

Chapter 5

APPLICATIONS OF CONVERTER SYSTEMS

    A.   AUTOMATIC TESTING
    B.   COMMUNICATIONS AND SIGNAL ANALYSIS
    C.   DISPLAYS
    D.   COMMERCE AND INDUSTRY

Chapters 1-4 have introduced the basic hardware elements of systems and equipment that involve converters, shown the basic configurations of data-acquisition and data-distribution systems, and indicated a few examples of the uses of digital and analog elements in intimate combination.

This chapter will illustrate the scope and breadth of systems and equipment that have been conceived of or built involving converters. The examples are drawn from a variety of sources, but they share the ideas, hardware, and circuit structures that have already been touched upon.

The intent is to inform the reader of what has been done, to suggest what can be done, and to arouse thoughts of what *might* be done by adding the conceptual tools described in this volume to the fund of knowledge and experience that he already possesses pertaining to his own field of endeavor.

I-77

A.   AUTOMATIC TESTING

"Automatic testing of electronic devices has been a major factor not only in the overall improvement of product quality and reliability, but also in the dramatic lowering of product costs."[1]

— Harold T. McAleer, General Radio Company

Although a major (and in some ways an obvious) market for electronic testing equipment, makers and users of electronic devices have not been the only beneficiaries of automatic testing. Anyone who has had his blood tested recently, has flown safely in a 747 jet aircraft, or has contemplated purchasing a new Volkswagen, has been exposed to the potential savings (and not only financial) inherent in automatic testing.

The cost savings, both immediate and long term, result from a number of characteristics of automatic testing:

Human resources are conserved. Fewer persons can conduct more (and more-thorough) tests of high complexity with minimal training.

Volume. Large numbers of tests can be performed in a short time: either many tests on complex devices or fewer tests on large numbers of devices.

Reliability and consistency. A well-designed test program will perform identical tests leading to consistent results, with no aberrations due to misreading, fatigue, etc. If failure occurs in mid-test and repairs are made, the entire test cycle can be repeated, numerous times if necessary, with full confidence that the most recent test has "cut no corners."

Multiplexing of adjustments and readouts. An instrument designed for use in automatic testing bears little physical resemblance to conventional instruments, since it need have neither binding posts, knobs, readout, nor even "front panel;" it shares the system's readout devices; connections and adjustments are made by the system.

[1] *IEEE Spectrum,* May, 1971, "A Look at Automatic Testing"

Automatic Calibration. Any necessary calibrations, zero-adjustments, nonlinear-device compensations, or other predicted allowances can be made under system command. Range-changing can also be fully automated.

Measurement statistics. The system can retain in memory the results of all tests, the results of discrepant tests, and/or histograms of specific parameters, and print them out upon request. Yield studies can lead to product improvements, elimination of sources of repeated rejections, and prediction or tracing of future failures.

In short, a well thought-out, designed, and implemented automated test facility can reliably perform large numbers of tests, around the clock, on a "100%" basis, consistently and without tiring, with accuracy and skill, and with feedback to the designer for the next generation of the product. Skilled test personnel can be applied to more-creative pursuits than routine manual testing of the ins-and-outs of complex systems.

Then, as mentioned above, there are the many intangible benefits, that pay off in human values as well as dollars-and-cents: the aircraft engine that didn't fail, the electrical chassis that didn't need field repair, the steel rolling mill that didn't run away, the hospital patient that survived, the vendor whose reputation remained consistently high.

USES FOR AUTOMATIC TESTING

The manufacturer of components, such as integrated circuits, benefits greatly, because testing is a far-from-negligible cost in the integrated circuits business. Besides delivering a higher level of acceptable quality to the customer, he also develops more-accurate knowledge of yields and trends, and can serve needs for specific selection categories. For the producer of high-performance specialty IC's, such as Analog Devices, it is an indispensable tool. Such devices as the laser-trimmed AD506 low-offset FET-input op amps, the AD530/CERT monolithic multiplier/divider (with computer printout of trim voltages), and the $1\mu V/°C$ "superbeta" AD508 op amp (tested after null adjustment), would be so costly as to be infeasible if manual measurements and adjustments were involved. (Instead, the additional cost is a small fraction of the price of the standard unit.)

The user of large numbers of identical components can also benefit: He can weed out discrepant units in incoming inspection; measure, select, and grade units for different applications (rather than paying the manufacturer extra to do the same job); and keep comparative statistics from lot-to-lot and vendor-to-vendor. It may be noted, as a matter of perspective, that an average saving of 10¢ on 100,000 units is $10,000.

The manufacturer of equipment and systems can test subassemblies in-process, or as received from subcontractors; he can also test completed pieces of equipment thoroughly. In both cases, the test system can be programmed for GO/NO at points of discrepancy, and to either reject the device for later evaluation, or branch into a diagnostic mode, to isolate the portion of the circuit (or perhaps even the component or connection) that is faulty. Repaired units can be recycled and subjected to the same battery of tests as the new units.

Highly-complex systems, such as jet aircraft and their various subsystems, can be tested thoroughly on the ground by a small number of persons in a short time, with a high probability of finding any faults, or the discrepancies that might indicate incipient faults. In addition, the on-board test and monitoring system can provide warning to the crew of anomalous subsystem behavior, and, as the electronic portions become increasingly sophisticated, it can perform a degree of diagnostic testing.

INGREDIENTS OF TEST SYSTEMS

For systems that test devices, the test begins with the *unit under test.* It must be handled, maneuvered into place, connected to. Then a *stimulus* is applied, and a *response* must be measured. The response is compared with a set of possible responses, and a *decision* is made (accept, reject, grade-and-sort, perform an adjustment) and communicated (print, store, mark, analyze), and a new instruction is given (next test, next set of connections, next device, wait for manual instruction, etc.). An outline of such a system is shown in the block diagram of Figure 1.

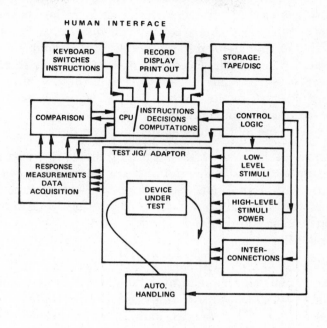

Figure 1. Test System Ingredients in Typical Configuration

Devices have at least two leads (resistors, capacitors), but they may have many more (op amps have at least six, printed-circuit boards may have 20 or more.) The instructions must call for connecting the appropriate stimulus generators and power sources to the appropriate terminals, and the appropriate measuring devices (bridges, amplifiers, etc.) to *their* appropriate terminals, and making all opens, shorts, "grounds," links, etc., as required for the test step. Some of these may be hard-wired in the adaptor; others must be called for by software, or manual setting. Minimal noise pickup, interference, and parasitic effects caused by lead resistance, capacitance, and inductance are absolutely essential.

Converters in Test Systems

It may be fairly evident that much of the engineering and hardware cost of test systems goes into fixtures, switching devices, computers, peripherals, displays, wiring, and cabinetry. However, since the stimuli are digitally-controlled, and the responses must be returned to digital form for processing, it should be evident that converters and their accessories play a key role in ensuring test accuracy, speed, and reliability, yet represent but a small fraction of the cost of the system. For this reason, it may be false economy to use conversion devices that are anything but entirely adequate to do the job, or to seek to cut cost corners.

Typical uses of D/A converters in testing include: programmable power supplies, pulse generators, sweep generators, waveform generators (with appropriate digital inputs). They may be used as offset and gain "potentiometers" in calibration loops, as bridge-balancing voltage sources, and as part of A/D converters, sample-holds, peak-followers, etc.

A/D converters, either with multiplexing or per-channel, return the measurements to digital form, after processing by isolation or differential amplifiers, by op amps as electrometers, by multipliers, ratio devices, log devices, and all the other paraphernalia mentioned in Chapter 2.

An essential decision that must be made is the degree to which analog data reduction will be used, as compared with the performance of similar functions by digital software. Whatever the realities of the system itself, this consideration depends largely upon the background and experience of the designer; we suggest that analog-oriented designers not overlook the possibilities of software for reliable routine computation, and that digital designers consider the decreasing cost of functions that can be performed with analog modules and linear integrated circuits, and the balance between too much and too little data.

Much that could be said about system optimization, in terms of getting the best-possible interference-free measurements of suitable accuracy, has already been mentioned in several places in this book; and test systems are probably the most representative class of design problems requiring active application of these principles.

In component tests, where the lead-runs to the unit-under-test (UUT) are controllable, as is the local environment, the main sources of interference arise from the proximity of input, output, power, and logic leads in the vicinity of the test adaptor. In large-system testing, long leads, including multiconductor cables and connectors; the presence of electrical noise (RFI, power line, and switching-transient spikes); and possibly unfavorable environmental conditions (temperature, humidity, vibration), may all make the measurement problem extremely difficult. It often turns out that, in the design of large systems, self-checking is an effective way of solving the interference problem, using a local test subsystem that communicates digitally with an external system tester. If this is too ambitious, local digitizing, as an integral part of system design — in anticipation of testing — may provide a large ratio of benefits to cost.

B. COMMUNICATIONS AND SIGNAL ANALYSIS

In this section, we shall discuss briefly the class of converter applications that involve the generation, transmission, recovery, processing, storage, characterization, and synthesis of analog waveforms. Conceivable applications include:

Time expansion, compression, (relative) advance, and delay
Transient storage and recording
Synthesis and analysis of speech and music (and waveforms in general)
Transfer-function synthesis and analysis
Convolution
Digital filtering
Recovery of signals from noise by correlation techniques and fast Fourier transforms
Scrambling and unscrambling coded transmissions
Generation of arbitrary signals and transfer functions

Digital methods, even without a Central Processing Unit, can provide a powerful set of tools for dealing with analog functions and the transfer functions that operate on them in the time and frequency domains, as we have suggested in Chapter 4.

The key that unlocks the door is the A/D converter, which "freezes" a sample of the waveform and makes possible permanent storage without degradation. Thereafter, digital shift registers, binary rate-multipliers, memories, comparators, arithmetic functions, and control logic can perform a variety of operations entirely in digital format.

Except for errors due to the discrete (in time and amplitude) nature of the sampled signal, and approximations or roundoff errors in computation (where necessary or permitted), there is no loss of information, even though the signal be stored, multiplied, integrated, added, subtracted, correlated, or otherwise man(or machine-)ipulated. It can of course be returned to the analog domain, via D/A conversion, and subjected to further processing there, while its attributes are still retained in Memory.

The circuits and ideas that appear here, all variations on the basic theme of the shift register delay line, represent promising areas of application, but they are not necessarily new or original. Their purpose is to unleash the reader's curiosity and creativity, in the field broadly encompassed by the title of this section. We've tried to avoid, except where necessary, mathematical particularities (and the controversies they sometimes engender).

SHIFT-REGISTER DELAY LINE

The basic tool for performing many interesting functions is the shift-register delay line, mentioned briefly in Chapter 4, and shown here again for further discussion.

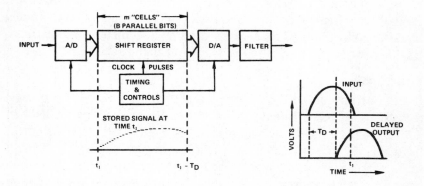

Figure 2. Parallel Shift-Register Delay Line

Suppose the analog signal is a one-shot occurrence, of which m samples have been taken, that the clock has stopped, and the conversions have ceased. The signal is now stored in the delay line in digital form, and it will remain there until it is advanced or cleared or the power has been turned off. A number of interesting things may be done with the stored signal:

Read out into memory

The stored signal can be read out, a word at a time, and stored in memory, while the line awaits another transient (Figure 3).

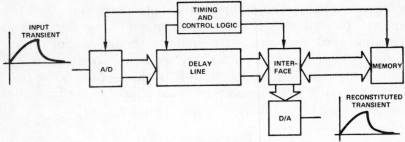

Figure 3. Transient Recorder

Read out as an analog signal

The signal can be read out and converted to an analog signal, each sample in turn, but at a rate arbitrarily determined by the choice of clock frequency. For example, the transient may have been quite rapid, but it is desired to plot it out on a chart recorder. Or, it may have been fed into the line slowly (perhaps even manually as an arbitrary waveform), to be used as a shaped stimulus for an analog process, and is to be discharged at high speed.

Recirculate

If the output end of the line is fed back to the input, it becomes a recirculating delay line (Figure 4). The stored signal will then appear at the end of the line repetitively, allowing the transient to be displayed on an ordinary oscilloscope. By loading, or "charging", with an arbitrary input signal (either analog or digital), then providing rapid recirculation and D/A conversion, it is possible to create an extremely wide range of arbitrary repetitive analog waveforms, of controllable repetition rate and amplitude.

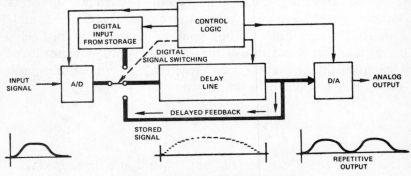

Figure 4. Recirculating Delay Line

Perform waveform averaging by addition

If the same message is sent repeatedly but arrives at the converter accompanied by (and perhaps "buried in") noise, it can be recovered by summing all the versions of the message: the coherent portions will add directly with the number of items summed, while the rms noise will tend to be "averaged out" and will increase only as the square-root of the number of items. For example, with 100 repetitions, the signal will be increased in relation to noise by a factor of 10. This can be accomplished with a delay line by summing each sample increment of the newest message with the sum of the corresponding samples of previous messages, accumulated in the delay line (Figure 5). Thus, when the second message arrives, its first sample is summed with the stored first sample, etc. When the third message arrives, its first sample is summed with the already-stored sum of the two previous first samples. Since the original messages are presumably identical, while the noise varies randomly, each iteration adds 1 unit of original signal to each sample, while the noise components tend to be averaged out.

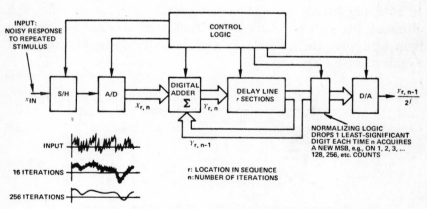

Figure 5. Waveform Averaging by Addition — Basic Scheme

In practice, computing the simple sum

$$Y_{r,n} = Y_{r,n-1} + X_{r,n}$$

where

$Y_{r,n}$ = output of the nth sample at the rth position
$X_{r,n}$ = input of the nth sample at the rth position

leads to an "open-ended" output amplitude, which is expensive to implement digitally and difficult to display on an oscilloscope during summation. It is a better idea to consider normalizing the output, i.e., dividing it by n, so that its average value tends to be constant. Since dividing digitally is not especially desirable, except for integral powers of 2, we may consider several alternatives based on the error-correcting relationship

$$Y_{r,n} = Y_{r,n-1} + \frac{X_{r,n} - Y_{r,n-1}}{n}$$

The first thing to observe is that as n becomes large, $Y_{r,n}$ and $Y_{r,n-1}$ are very nearly equal, and each additional increment causes little change, because it is divided by n. The second thing to note is that, since both terms of the difference can occur in analog form (the input and the last value of output), the difference could be taken before conversion, substituting an op amp for a digital subtractor (Figure 6). Finally, one might observe that division by n could be performed either as an analog function (counter and DAC supplying reference voltage proportional to n to the ADC), or as a digital approximation using only integral powers of 2, obtained by shifting the ADC output code one bit toward the right (dropping the last bit), as each increasingly-significant bit of n appears on a counter.

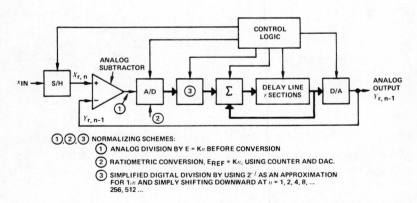

① ② ③ NORMALIZING SCHEMES:
① ANALOG DIVISION BY E = Kn BEFORE CONVERSION
② RATIOMETRIC CONVERSION, E$_{REF}$ = Kn, USING COUNTER AND DAC.
③ SIMPLIFIED DIGITAL DIVISION BY USING 2^{-j} AS AN APPROXIMATION FOR 1/n AND SIMPLY SHIFTING DOWNWARD AT n = 1, 2, 4, 8, ... 256, 512 ...

Figure 6. Waveform Averaging by Addition Using Normalized Variables

Time Compression by Sampling

In Figure 7, a shift register is advanced at a high frequency, f_c, for example 513kHz. The converter is digitizing a slowly-varying signal at a rate f_s. Suppose that the shift register has 512 steps, and that at a given instant, the 512th sample appears at the output and is fed back to the input. On the next step, starting the mth iteration, the converter output, $X_{1,m}$ is fed into the line to replace the output $X_{1,m-1}$. The line then advances for 512 steps. On the 512th step, the input is once again $X_{1,m}$, and $X_{2,m-1}$ appears at the end of the line, while $X_{2,m}$ is ready at the converter output. On the 513th step, the converter output is fed into the line to replace $X_{2,m-1}$. $X_{1,m}$ and $X_{2,m}$ are now indexed down the line, and on the 513th step, $X_{3,m}$ replaces $X_{3,m-1}$. By the time 512 conversions have occurred, in real time, the sampled signal (including new and previous values) has circulated 513 times, thus providing a 512-fold-speeded-up version of the (1.96Hz) analog input waveform at the output of the D/A converter, at the equivalent of 1ms per sample.

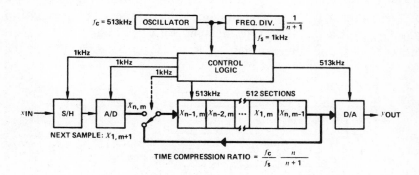

Figure 7. Time Compression by Sampling. On Next Count, $X_{n,m}$ is Introduced Into the Line to Replace $X_{n,m-1}$. At $n+1$ Additional Counts, $X_{1,m+1}$ is Introduced to Replace $X_{1,m}$.

If each cycle of the analog waveform is identical to the adjacent ones, and if the clock is synchronized to the analog signal, the output of the DAC, plotted on an oscilloscope screen, swept at 1kHz, will appear to stand still, plotting the low-frequency input, but *with no flicker.* Changes of the input signal, from iteration to iteration, will appear as progressively-appearing changes to the stationary pattern.

Since the compression ratio depends on the time required for each 512 samples, it is proportional to the clock frequency, which can be locked in at any convenient value. A typical application for time compression is in real-time spectrum analyzers.

Real-Time Correlation

For an input function, f(t), the output of the delay line over a complete circulation (in compressed time) is a set of values of $f(t - \tau_i)$. If the successive values are multiplied by the sampled value of another waveform, g(t), which, with f(t), is updated after each circulation, and if each individual product is averaged with its synchronous counterparts from previous circulations, the output of the averager will represent a sample-by-sample cross-correlation of *f* and *g* at a real-time rate, delayed by the product of the sampling period and the number of samples circulated (Figure 8).

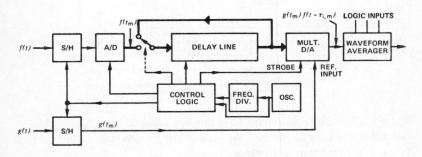

Figure 8. Real-Time Correlation Using Delay Line

Incremental Delay Line as a Filter

If the delay line consists of a number of sections, and the outputs at these taps are converted to analog form, and summed, with arbitrary coefficients, it is possible to synthesize arbitrary time-domain responses to steps, pulses, or other waveforms. Since the output bears a linear* relationship to the input, the resulting transfer function may provide amplitude and phase responses to other signal forms (over limited ranges of frequency) that can be expressed by transform integrals but are otherwise formally considered "unrealizable." In this case, the output is a function of the input only (Figure 9a).

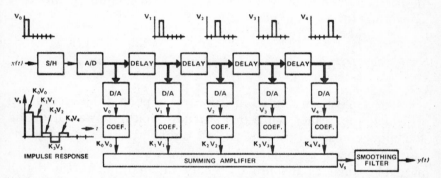

Figure 9a. Delay Line as a Filter with Programmable Real-Time Response. (Small Number of Sections Shown for Clarity)

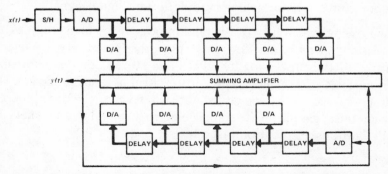

Figure 9b. Delay Line in Recursive Filtering. Coefficients (not shown) can be Applied Manually or Digitally (Multiplying DAC's).

*i.e., if the input is doubled, the corresponding output will be doubled.

Recursive Filtering

When the output is a function of input only, the number of possible responses is limited, because the output will settle within a finite time after the input has ceased to vary. However, by making the output a function of both output and input, a more-general (and more interesting) set of responses becomes possible.

Recursion may be achieved by feeding back from the output to each tap point (after it has made its contribution); but this requires an A/D converter for each tap. A more economical scheme uses a second tapped delay line, fed back (in sections – if desired) to the output summing amplifier, thus requiring only D/A converters for each tap point (Figure 9b).

CONCLUSION

Though it has been limited in scope, we hope that this section has provided the reader with an awareness of the power of digital techniques in signal processing, just through the use of delay-line storage. There are many more hard-wired processing tricks available, such as the use of binary rate-multipliers for digital frequency modulation of digital signals, counters for converting from frequencies to discrete digital values, and voltage-to-frequency converters for analog modulation of digital signals.

The growing availability of digital components of high complexity, increasing speed, and low cost, plus the possibility of overall control of the processing by CPU's and stored commands, makes the outlook for analog waveform synthesis and processing by digital techniques extremely bright, whatever the source: speech, music, noise, gas chromatographs, electroencephalograms, mechanical vibrations, to mention just a few.

C. CATHODE-RAY-TUBE DISPLAYS

In the industrial and scientific world, the close association of computer and cathode-ray tube provides an unparalleled method for speedy access to stored and real-time data. It simultaneously affords the opportunity for interactive dialogue with the computer for the purpose of actually controlling what the computer does. The recent growth of electron-beam recording (on film negative) poses a serious challenge to the centuries-old tradition of typesetting, while the ability to use computer power to adapt data to the needs of the human operator prior to presentation makes the computer-CRT display a powerful combination indeed.

While systems do exist for the sole purpose of display, the more general application of displays is in connection with data-acquisition systems and systems involving computers. Such systems may be either purely digital in nature (e.g., business systems with punched-card inputs), or they may involve A/D and D/A converters in maintaining input and output contacts with the "real world." Whatever the display's purpose, or the source of the data, many cathode ray displays involve the use of D/A converters for generating sweeps, characters, and vectors, for positioning and intensification, relying on their inherent linearity, reproducibility, and controllability by entirely digital sources of command.

Since we are concerned here primarily with display systems that employ converters — with particular emphasis on the way they are used and the factors of importance in selecting and using them — the number of systems chosen will be limited and system description brief.

In general, a cathode-ray display system consists of a display processor and the display chassis. The processor usually holds the information to be presented for update, the instructions for presenting it, the signals needed to activate the display elements, and the digital-to-analog processing hardware, and may include a *refresh memory*. The display chassis itself contains power supplies, CRT, circuitry for beam positioning intensification, nonlinearity correction, and focus.

Representative display techniques include:

> TV raster (picture and graphic displays)
> Stored-character display, e.g., Monoscope (alphanumerics)
> Dot-matrix (alphanumerics)
> Cursive: stroke and vector generators (alphanumerics and graphics)
> Rotating (PPI)

In addition, electron-beam recording (EBR) is a high-precision technique allied to the TV raster, but capable of considerably greater resolution, because it records on film, without regard for screen persistence or "flicker" problems, and can thus afford considerably greater time-per-frame.[1]

BASIC SYSTEM

Figure 10 shows the generalized system outline for an installation capable of accepting, processing, storing, and displaying information on a CRT screen. A purely clerical system would not normally involve sensors and A/D interface systems, but might, on the other hand, involve other forms of peripheral data input. An air traffic control system, based on radar data, is an example of current usage of CRT displays for interactive handling and presentation of complex information.

Further ingredients of the generalized display system are quite straightforward. The manual controls provide human interface, enabling the operator to call for a specific picture (or portion of a picture), to enter new information into the system, to command new modes of operation, and to initiate different data-processing and display functions. Bulk storage forms part of the data-processing capability; further auxiliary storage is often required, in the absence of storage-type CR tubes, for display refreshing at high speed to avoid annoying flicker. Control logic interfaces between computer data and the various peripheral devices, including displays, memories, communications links, the human operator, data-acquisition circuits, etc.

[1] *Analog Dialogue,* Vol. 6, No. 1, p. 14 "EBR uses 16-Bit DAC"

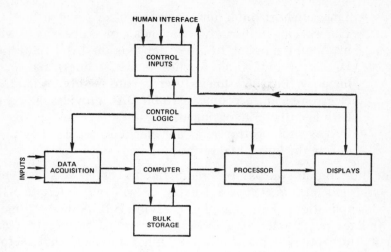

Figure 10. Display System Outline

USES OF D/A CONVERTERS IN DISPLAYS

Raster Displays

In Chapter 4, a counter-driven D/A converter was suggested as a sawtooth sweep generator. When used for displays, this scheme can provide highly-repeatable, controllable, and linear sweeps of arbitrary resolution and accuracy.

Rasters conventionally are generated by a fast horizontal scan, that is swept vertically at a slower rate that will allow a given number of lines to be generated during the period for a frame. Intensity modulation during each horizontal scan provides the pictorial information. The picture resolution is expressed in terms of the number of discernible data points per line multiplied by the number of lines. The minimum frame period is the time allowed for the horizontal scan-plus-retrace (i.e. time for 1 line) multiplied by the number of lines, plus vertical retrace time.

D/A converters are well-suited to vertical sweeps, for a number of reasons:

- Timing, controlled by a clock and logic, is quite precise and uniform.

- Lines are horizontal (analog sweeps have slight tilt).
- Line-spacing-uniformity depends on linearity, while maximum number of lines depends on DAC resolution. DAC's having 10-bit resolution (1024 lines) and 12-bit linearity (0.0125% linearity error) are readily available. In electron-beam recording, a 16-bit DAC provides 4096 lines with less than 5% spacing error.
- DAC switching transients are blanked because they occur during the horizontal retrace interval.

For horizontal sweeps, the requirements on DAC's are more severe, and analog sweeps are likely to win the cost tradeoff, in most applications. For example, to resolve 500 points per line, at 500 lines per frame, at a 30Hz frame rate, requires that each digital horizontal step settle well within 100ns, and that there be no "glitches." (Even if the display is blanked between horizontal steps, large glitches at major carries can cause deflection-amplifier transients, which distort the pattern.) While this is feasible (e.g., DAC-10DF), cost is increasing rapidly with resolution.

Raster displays using either analog or internally-synchronized digital sweeps have the weakness that the whole picture must be updated at once: specific portions cannot be singled out for local refreshing. For this reason, plus the low cost of video hardware (if it can be successfully adapted to the use at hand), a major application of raster displays is in multiple or remote monitoring, where no interaction is needed.

However, if it is necessary to update the display in local spots only, or to interact with it (for example, in editing), a form of display that allows access to specific portions of the tube face must be used.

Dot-Matrix Displays

Another name for a display in which each point to be brightened has a definite address is the highly-descriptive one: dot-matrix. While it can take the form of a raster display with both sweeps digital, the speed limitations and memory requirements make a variation of it more useful, especially for alphanumerics: the stored-character dot-matrix.

Each character might be represented by a matrix of points, e.g., 4 X 7, with each point that is defined as part of the character intensified, by either a "mini-raster" scan or a character trace. The X and Y coordinates of each point are located at addresses in two ROM's; in character tracing, the point is addressed by a word consisting of a format code for the character (e.g., ASCII) and a number from a counter indicating the order of the point in the writing sequence.

In a typical system using this presentation (Figure 11), two DAC's with outputs that are summed are used for each axis. One set of DAC's, producing sweeps in raster format, locates the index point (i.e., position) of the character. The second set produces a sequential set of outputs that rapidly move the spot from one point to the next, until the character has been traced out.

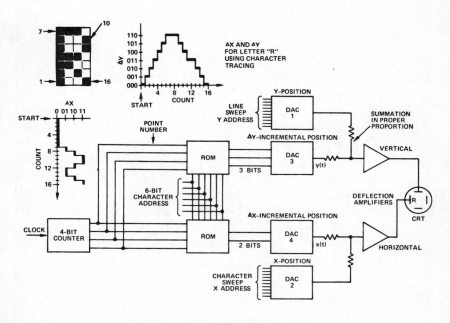

Figure 11. Dot Matrix Display Scheme

An important advantage of this scheme is that low-resolution (but high linearity) DAC's can be used to locate each character, in the same way that a typewriter indexes across a page, character by character, and down the page, line by line. Glitches are no problem because the trace is blanked in transit. The DAC's that produce the characters need only have fast response, with very modest resolution and accuracy. And the refresh memory needs to store only the character codes, rather than all points for each character.

For a purely alphanumeric display, type "point size" and "leading" could be determined by manual gain controls of the respective DAC's, to the degree allowed by the logic determining the character count per line and the amount of information to be presented in each frame.

Information can be updated incrementally by addressing specific display locations, and grossly by either displaying new frames, or by a "scrolling" or "waterfall" (in reverse) scheme in which data is advanced vertically. Old data disappears at the top as new data appears at the bottom.

Of course, the "typewriter" presentation need not be used at all. For example, in a display that combines graphics and alphanumerics, the X and Y DAC's may be set at the appropriate arbitrary address for each character of a caption, which is then supplied via the ROM. Captions may also be read along vertical lines if axes are interchanged. Although 2 and 3 bits served to display the character adequately in the example, the D/A converter may have many more bits available for handling other forms of additive input. It is important to note, though, that the accuracy and resolution of the positioning DAC must be such that its errors are less than the relatively-weighted value (taking differing scaling into account) of the least-significant bits of DAC's whose outputs are summed. Otherwise, overlapping or uneven spacing may result.

GRAPHIC DISPLAYS

The general objective in graphic displays is to provide a flickerless presentation of numerical, line-drawing, or pictorial information, with the possibility of editing, changing, storing, or isolating any element of it. If the drawing is synthesized by definable and reproducible computer operations, then any number of schemes may be used for the actual control and interaction, ranging from keyboards to "light pens."

The general problem is to start with the spot at a given point (which may be any point arrived at in the course of plotting the display, or it may be a point that has been recalled for replotting), and proceed by a straight-line increment to another point, using a programmed analog technique. (For better control of spot position, it could be done digitally by closely-spaced dots, perhaps employing a binary rate-multiplier, but, on the other hand, it may be highly desirable to reduce the amount of memory or digital manipulation involved.) It is important to avoid variations of intensity caused by velocity modulation, by either maintaining constant writing speed or by compensating for variable writing speed by appropriate intensity modulation (the former is preferable if it can be accomplished simply).

Delay-Line Integrator

In Figure 12, a single high-resolution converter is used for each coordinate. The outputs of the converters are incremented in small, equal steps of X or Y, whichever is the greater in magnitude. Between the converter output and the deflection amplifier is a "delay-line integrator," essentially a fast analog delay line tailored for step response that has a fixed delay time, and is linear with time from the initial value to the final value. It will then hold the final value until the input changes. Because the maximum input steps are equal, the delay line will maintain a constant maximum writing rate in the X or Y direction (until the other variable becomes greater). Since the larger of the two variables has been chosen, the largest possible vector change (occurring in the case where they are equal) is 1.4 times as great. The range from 1 to 1.4 is sufficiently small that only a few values (if any) of intensity-modulation voltage will be needed to provide adequate correction for changes in writing speed.

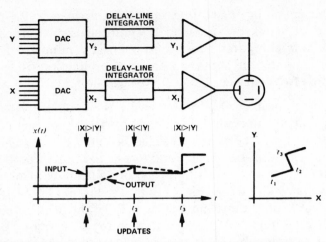

Figure 12. Delay–Line Integrator. DAC Outputs Have Just Switched to New Values, X_2, Y_2. Delay Line Outputs X_1, Y_1 Will Change to New Values Linearly.

Vectors and Segments

An obvious way of obtaining a given rate of change of voltage is to feed a constant into an integrator: the rate of change of output is proportional to the input. Thus, starting with an initial position X_0, Y_0, furnished by a DAC pair, there is added to it the output of a pair of integrators, the inputs of which are slope update outputs from another DAC pair with inputs from the refresh memory. The slope update signals may change during the configuration of a character, or they may allow long uninterrupted straight sweeps. The two major difficulties with this approach are that the integrator must be reset to eliminate drift, and there is no easy way to maintain constant trace brightness.

Another approach uses ramps instead of integrators. In the (perhaps unwieldy) circuit of Figure 13, there are two out-of-phase triangular waves, two high-accuracy DAC's for initial positioning, and four multiplying D/A converters supplying the coordinates of the points to be connected.

Starting from an initial point, determined by the X and Y position DAC's, the rates of change of X and Y are determined by multiplying the digital input values by the ramps and summing the out-of-phase values in the output amplifier, e.g., $(X_2 - X_1)$ and $(Y_2 - Y_1)$ for the positive slope of the synchronous ramp.

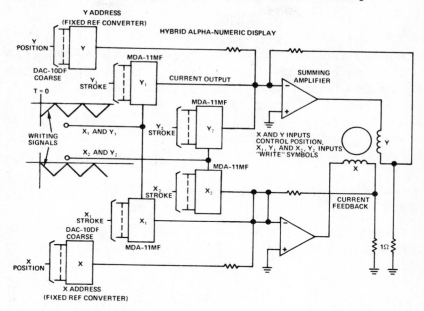

Figure 13. Display System Combines Fixed-Reference Converters for Coarse Positioning, Plus Multiplying Converters for Applying "Writing" Analog Signals to the Deflection Circuits. Method uses Common Analog Triangular Waveform for Synthesizing all Alpha-Numeric Symbols, Instead of Using a Unique Analog Waveform for each Symbol.

When updating occurs, the ramp at the same time changes slope, and the old value, i.e., X_1, Y_1 is replaced by X_3, Y_3. The new rates of change are thus determined by $-(X_2 - X_3)$ and $-(Y_2 - Y_3)$, or $X_3 - X_2$ and $Y_3 - Y_2$. Thus, each new incremental slope is determined by the difference between the new input and the previous input, always in the proper sense.

Unlike the integrator, resetting is not necessary; however, the values of X and Y should be refreshed from time to time, since the net change depends on the ramp amplitude, and tolerances build up. Also, it is necessary for the computer to determine the vector change and modulate the intensity appropriately.

There are many other schemes that could be conceived of, and a number have been described in the literature. In some recent schemes, binary rate-multipliers are used for direct digital multiplication to supplant multiplying DAC's.

In the large majority of display schemes, either a fixed-reference or a multiplying D/A converter is a key element, determining to a large extent the accuracy, linearity (except for geometrical sources of nonlinearity) and sharpness (lack of transients and flicker) of the display. The elements of DAC performance that are often necessary in other applications are *crucial* in displays because of the high visibility of defective performance. A few of these elements are:

Differential Linearity and Linearity

If differential linearity is poor, gaps, banding, and irregular line- or dot-spacing will result. Straight lines develop wobbles. If linearity is poor, it may not be especially bothersome in alphanumeric displays, but graphics become distorted. If linearity is poor in electron-beam recording for aerial photography, maps pieced together to make larger maps may suffer discontinuities at the edges.

Speed and Dynamics

Slow settling will result in unevenness in spot locations, a loss of "sharpness" in transitions. Because of the mathematics of filling space, compromises must be made between flicker, resolution, and dynamics. Glitches cause raggedness in patterns where sweeps go through major carries, and poor tracking at corners in graphic displays. Speed variations resulting from transients superimposed on linear tracks result in intensity variations due to velocity modulation of the image. Fast DAC transients that are not of themselves important (because the brief interval in which they occur can be blanked out) are rendered more important by the dynamics of the deflection system, which involves amplified energy levels and higher inertias, and can result in hundredfold prolongation of the transient interval, as well as ringing and overshoots.

The photographs show the effect of "glitches" on a typical display. About 5% of the picture area is shown. (Courtesy of The Foxboro Company, Foxboro, Mass.)

D.   COMMERCE, INDUSTRY, AND ELSEWHERE

The reader who has arrived at this point (after presumably reading all of the material in Part One) has been exposed to a large variety of circuit configurations and applications suggestions. It would not have been difficult for him to have noticed that some of the configurations looked more-or-less alike, though offered from somewhat different viewpoints.

In this section, he will not find anything especially different, from the circuit point of view, but he may find it of interest as a microcosmic glimpse of the applications of conversion devices in the workaday world. We will show here just a few applications, with the descriptive emphasis more on what they *accomplish*, rather than on how their circuits go together.

At the end of this chapter will be found a brief appendix, listing a large number of randomly-aggregated present and possible uses for conversion and the associated analog-digital technology. This list, in no sense complete, and in no wise organized in any rational way, might represent the result of a quick scan of one or two current magazines, and the recesses of one's mind. It will not impress anyone now working in the field. However, for the reader who is unaccustomed to the power of computational techniques, it may be an excellent point of departure for the development of ideas as to how they might help in his own field.

Because A/D and D/A converters were originally developed as computer interfacing devices, used primarily for getting data into and out of digital computers, the casual observer still tends to associate them with computer application alone. In reality, as Chapter 4 has demonstrated, both A/D and D/A modules have followed the operational amplifier out of the computer laboratory and into the industrial world-at-large.

Digital communications is increasingly employed for its noise immunity. Likewise, digital methods are used in testing, controlling, and measuring, owing to their ease of application, and the simplicity with which digital data can be manipulated, stored, processed, addressed, distributed, scaled, and otherwise handled.

One result is an interesting variety of applications for A/D and D/A converters, in which the unit has a life of its own, quite independent of a computer, as a component of a piece of equipment designed for a purpose.

AUTOMATIC SCALE ZEROING

The use of a D/A converter to reset zero in a weighing machine (Figure 14) is typical of a large number of uses for the D/A converter as a long-term sample-hold device, as mentioned in Chapter 4.

The purpose of the arrangement is to measure the container (or "tare") weight and feed it back to the summing point of an operational amplifier, to produce a null reading, so that when the container is filled, only the weight of the contents is read out.

The procedure is simple: The empty container is placed on the scale, with the D/A output at zero. The voltage representing the container's weight is converted to digital form by the A/D converter. Then the A/D output is strobed into the D/A converter, producing an output that is equal, but of opposite polarity, to the input, thus zeroing the summing-amplifier output. When the load is applied, another conversion is performed (but does not affect the D/A output), and the weight of the load alone is read out.

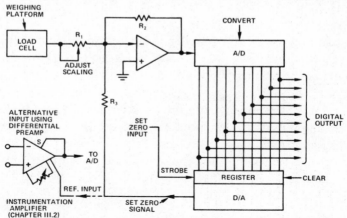

Figure 14. Weighing Device With Automatic "Push-Button" Tare Weight Compensation

The amplifier can be so scaled that the converter (which may be part of a DPM) reads out in engineering units of weight, or some function of weight, such as cost. If the A/D converter is a BCD type, the D/A converter should be similarly coded. If the input range of the A/D converter is similar to the output range of the D/A, $R_2 = R_3$, with R_1 setting the overall gain relationship. If an instrumentation amplifier is used, the DAC adjusts its reference.

The same basic idea is applicable to any situation for which push-button zeroing is desirable, usually when sophisticated equipment is being operated by untrained personnel, or when time is of the essence, as in production-line operations.

LOW-NOISE COMMUNICATIONS

Digital techniques for voice and data transmission[1] are widely used by the common carriers, NASA, the military, railroads, and many more. The purpose is to gain increased immunity to noise and to preserve the fidelity of the transmitted information in the presence of nonlinearities, analog crosstalk, etc.

Low noise communication is possible when a voice signal is converted to digital form before transmission. Analog signals pick up noise, and, though amplified in "repeater" stations along the way, tend to become progressively degraded. But if digital transmission is used, the signal can be restored by reshaping or regenerating the pulses. At the receiving end, a D/A converter reconstructs the original voice signal.

Figure 15 is a simplified diagram of such a system. The analog signal is sampled at regular intervals, converted to digital form in the A/D converter, and transmitted serially, along with the clock pulses. At the receiving end, the signals are assembled in a shift register, kept in step by the clock pulses, and converted back to the original audio signal with the D/A converter.

[1] This topic and the following one (among others) were described in *Electronics*, October 26, 1970 "Putting D/A Converters to Work. . ."

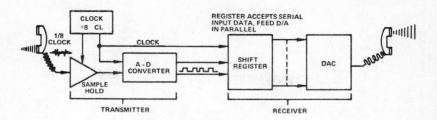

Figure 15. Digital Voice Communications

The clock frequency is divided by 8 before being applied to the sample-hold. The A/D converter thus sends one serial 8-bit word for each time the sample-hold circuit is strobed. The shift register at the receiving end assembles the words of eight bits each.

The sampling rate should be at least twice the bandwidth. Thus for 5kHz bandwidth, a 10kHz sampling rate is required. The converters thus should operate on 0.1 ms cycle times.

MUSIC DISTRIBUTION SYSTEMS

Music-distribution systems in commercial aircraft (e.g., the Boeing 747) utilize digital techniques to conserve wiring and economize on weight. As an alternative to piping eight analog channels to each seat, in parallel (with all the wiring involved, as well as the possibilities of crosstalk), the music channels are multiplexed, distributed digitally on one pair of wires, and decoded at the seat.

In Figure 16, the analog music channels are multiplexed into the sample-hold circuit. The A/D converter sends out serial words corresponding to each of the eight channels in sequence. A 3-bit address code is added to the 8 bits of analog information, and the complete word is wired to every seat in the plane. At each seat, an address decoder is linked with the channel-selector switch, and the D/A converter operates only on the digital word corresponding to the selected channel.

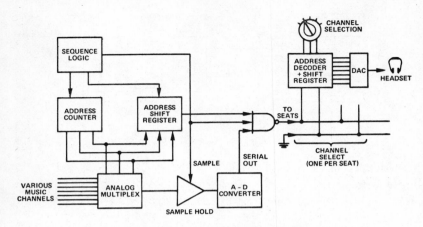

Figure 16. Aircraft Music Distribution

As in the previous application, absolute accuracy in the D/A converters is unimportant – all that counts for good sound reproduction is linearity. It's also interesting to note that only 6 bits are required for reasonably satisfactory music reproduction (6 X 6 = 36dB). ("It's a nice place to visit, but I wouldn't want to live there.")

POWER RECTIFIER MONITORING

Availability of low-cost digital computers and peripheral equipment has opened up a new field in the real-time monitoring of high-power systems, and detecting incipient danger signals in time to protect against (really) catastrophic failure. One can foresee application of the principle to large turbines, generators, engines, pumps, machine tools, and other equipment where continuous monitoring and comparison of oil pressure, bearing temperature, mechanical stresses, etc., can prevent destruction of expensive (perhaps irreplaceable) equipment and even save human lives.

Digital protection is well-suited to systems that must operate constantly and consistently, but it is perhaps even more advantageous for systems that operate over wide ranges of temperature, pressure, altitude, speed, or must be started and stopped frequently.

The concept of digital protection is exemplified very effectively by a 128-megawatt power-rectifier system used at the Lawrence Radiation Laboratory, Berkeley, California,[2] for magnet-field control in the Bevatron particle accelerator (Figure 17).

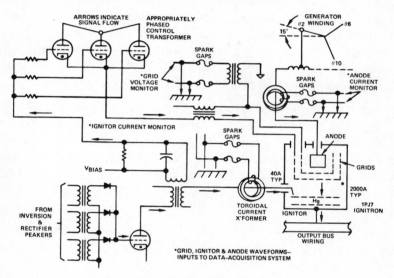

Figure 17a. Ignitron Monitoring System

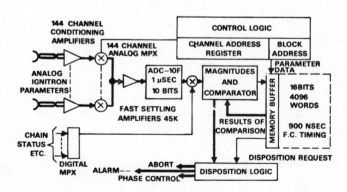

Figure 17b. Data Acquisition System

Figure 17. Bevatron Data-Acquisition System

[2] *Analog Dialogue,* Vol. 5, No. 3, "Protecting a 1/8 Gigawatt Power Supply (8kVA at 16kV) or How Do You Make a 2000A Fuse?"

The rectifier system is based on 48 mercury Ignitrons (high-power rectifiers), operating in parallel pairs, each of which handles an anode current of 2000 amperes. Output dc power is controlled SCR-fashion by adjusting the time, within each cycle of the 12-phase 60Hz excitation power, at which the individual ignitrons conduct. Firing control is accomplished by varying the phase of the drive pulses applied to each ignitron's grid. Faulty firing can obviously create havoc within the system, by simply causing one ignitron in a pair to conduct prematurely — or not at all — so that current is unequally distributed between ignitron pairs.

A fast data-acquisition system samples such waveforms as grid voltage, ignitor current, and anode current, for each tube, at a large number of intervals during each cycle and compares them with stored threshold values (perhaps obtained by processing earlier data). Any significant disparities are noted, analyzed, and appropriate action is automatically initiated, ranging from minor adjustments, to a "flag," to shutdown.

Since such anomalies can signal incipient breakdowns, this scheme can prevent the very expensive consequences of loosing large amounts of power under fault conditions, even for very short times. The method also allows observation of aging and so can effect parts replacement at appropriate, rather than arbitrary, intervals. It also provides rather obvious means of feedback of life data to parts manufacturers, who can use the information for product reliability improvement. (It's much harder to diagnose the source of failure by investigation of a hardened puddle of metal and glass, or after an explosion of suddenly-vaporized coolant.)

Although most readers of this book are unlikely to be designers of control systems for Bevatrons, a little thought will show that the monitoring principles applied in this case may prove useful elsewhere for minimizing risks of failure, and for failure analysis, in any system where catastrophic failure should be unthinkable.

APPENDIX TO CHAPTER FIVE

A random, incomplete, disorderly, and possibly presumptuous (*but, hopefully, thought-provoking*) list of present and likely areas where A/D and D/A conversion may help.

Accumulated life information
Actuators, displays, indicators
Aircraft hydraulic system testing
Air traffic control system
Angular rate, linear force, swept frequency, programmed temperature, forced vibrations, etc., generated electronically
Architectural work
Automated production processes
Automatic pushbutton zeroing by nontechnical personnel
Automatic scale zeroing
Automatic test system

Bins, putting things into
Blood, automatic chemical testing
Blood pressure monitoring in intensive care

Calibration curves
Chart-recorder overrange
Chemical plants & complexes
"Chirp" radar
Communications signals
Complete testing from several-hundred tests/min
Constant-speed alternator
Continuous blending
Controllers

Depth of cut
Digitally-controlled aircraft simulator
Digital control of steel mills
Digital speech & music transmission, multiplexed
Doppler radar, ignoring returns from stationary objects

Electrical substation
Electronic weighing
Electrochemical analyzer
Electrochemical baths
Emitted energy from bombarded target
Energy level, momentum, light intensity

Factory electrical power demand peaks
Firmware
Flow meter
Fluidic devices
Food processing operations
Foundry operations
Frequency synthesizer

Gas chromatographs
Generate ideas for rectifier improvements
Grading apples
Graphics design

Hangar and airfield testing of aircraft
High-voltage power supplies
High-power systems (real-time monitoring)
Histograms

IC semiconductor test equipment
Industrial, aeronautic, or scientific
Infrared optical pyrometers
Infra-red techniques
Instrument servos

Lasers and optoelectronics
Level indicators
Load cell

Machine shops
Maintenance scheduling
Mass spectrometers
Materials testing
Mechanical handling
Mechanical servos
Metal fabrication
Metal-removing speed
Metalworking
Monitoring oil pressure, bearing temperature, mechanical stress
Motor drive
MPX music distribution systems for passengers in 747's

Nuclear accelerators
Null balance
Numerically-controlled machine tools
N/C positioner

Oceanography
Ocean technology
On-line chemical process

Pharmaceutical plants
Plating plants
Pollution monitoring
Power-rectifier monitoring
Precision 3-phase output (synchronous motor speed control)
Pressure gages
Pressure regulators
Pressure, temperature, seismic, sonar, radar, and other transducers
Printing and graphics
Programmable power supplies
Protects against breakdown
Pulp and paper mills
Pulse-height analysis

Radar or fire-control system
Radar plan-position & moving-target indicators
Real-time process control
Relay testing
Remote or unattended monitoring
RF measurements

Seismographic experimentation
Ship's turbine, widely-differing speeds, temperature, pressure, humidity, shaft speed, torque
Signal processing in radar and sonar systems
Simulator's altimeter
Solenoid valves
Sonar returns
Spectral analysis
Speed control
Steel industry
Steel rolling mill
Stress signals
Sulfur dioxide monitors
Supersonic air blasts
Synchro-resolver

Tachometer signals
Tanks, boilers, vats, pipelines, bearings, oil burners (temperature sensing)
Tare weight compensation
Textile mills
Thermal ovens
Tone generator
Tracked air-cushion vehicle
Training simulators
Turbines, generators, engines, pumps, machine tools
Typesetting

Utility Substation

Valves and Actuators

Weather charts
Weather stations
Weighing machines
Wind tunnel

X-ray dosage

II
Understanding Converters

A/D converters translate from analog measurements, which are characteristic of most phenomena in the "real world," to digital language, used in information processing, computing, data transmission, and control systems. D/A converters are used in transforming transmitted data or the results of computation back to "real-world" variables for control, information display, or further analog processing.

ANALOG QUANTITIES

Analog input variables, whatever their origin, are most frequently converted by transducers into voltages or currents. These electrical quantities may appear as "dc" continuous direct measurements of a phenomenon, as modulated ac waveforms (using a wide variety of modulation techniques), or in some combination, with a spatial configuration of related variables to represent shaft angles. Examples of the first are outputs of thermocouples, potentiometers on dc references, analog computers; of the second, "chopped" optical measurements, ac strain gage or bridge outputs; and of the third, synchros and resolvers.

The analog variables to be dealt with in this chapter are those involving "dc" voltages or currents representing the actual analog phenomena. They may be either wideband or narrow-band. They may be either scaled from the direct measurement, or subjected to some form of analog pre-processing, such as linearization, combination, demodulation, filtering, sample-hold, etc. As part of the process, the voltages and currents are "normalized" to ranges compatible with assigned converter input ranges. Ways and means of accomplishing appropriate pre-processing are discussed in the chapters on applications and system accessories. Analog output voltages or currents from D/A converters are direct and in normalized form, but they may be subsequently post-processed (e.g., scaled, filtered, boosted, etc.).

Synchro-to-digital and digital-to-synchro converters, while widely-used in some control applications, are not included within the scope of this chapter. Some relevant material on this topic will be found in the applications chapters of Part 1.

DIGITAL QUANTITIES

Digital numbers are represented by the presence or absence of essentially fixed voltage levels referred to "ground," either occurring at the outputs of logic gates, or applied to their inputs. The digital numbers used are all basically binary. That is, each "bit," or unit of information has one of two possible states. These states are "off," "false," or "0," and "on," "true," or "1." *Words,* or groups of levels representing digital numbers, may appear simultaneously in *parallel,* on groups of gate inputs or outputs, or in *series* (or time sequence) on a single line.[1]

The most widely-used choice of levels at this writing, applicable to the class of products to which this book is devoted (i.e., converters manufactured by Analog Devices), are those used in TTL (transistor-transistor logic), in which positive true, or "1," corresponds to a minimum output level of +2.4V (inputs respond unequivocally to "1" for levels greater than 2.0V); and false, or "0" corresponds to a maximum output level of +0.4V (inputs respond unequivocally to "0" for anything less than +0.8V). A unique parallel or series grouping of digital levels, or a *number,* or *code,* is assigned to each analog level which is quantized (i.e., represents a unique portion of the analog range). A typical digital code would be this array:

$$1\ 0\ 1\ 1\ 1\ 0\ 1\ 0\ 1$$

---

[1] In series data transmission, if the levels return to ground between successive bits, they are denoted RZ (return-to-zero); if they change only when the leading edge of a clock pulse is present, and remain until the next leading edge, they are denoted NRZ (non-return-to-zero).

It is composed of nine bits. The "1" at the extreme left is called the "most significant bit" (MSB, or Bit 1), and the one at the right is called the "least significant bit" (LSB, or bit n: 9 in this case). The meaning of the code, either as a number, or as a representation of an analog variable, is unknown until the *code* and the *conversion relationship* have been defined.

THE BINARY CODE

The best-known code is *natural binary*. In a natural binary fractional code having n bits, the MSB has a weight of $1/2$: (2^{-1}), the second bit has a weight of $1/4$: (2^{-2}), and so forth down to the LSB, which has a weight of 2^{-n}. The value of a binary number is obtained by adding up the weights of all non-zero bits. As an example, Table 1 lists the 16 permutations of 4-bits' worth of 1's and 0's, with their binary weights, and the equivalent numbers expressed as both decimal and binary fractions.

Decimal Fraction	Binary Fraction	Code			
		MSB (x1/2)	Bit 2 (x1/4)	Bit 3 (x1/8)	Bit 4 (x1/16)
0	0.0000	0	0	0	0
$1/16 = 2^{-4}$ (LSB)	0.0001	0	0	0	1
$2/16 = 1/8$	0.0010	0	0	1	0
$3/16 = 1/8 + 1/16$	0.0011	0	0	1	1
$4/16 = 1/4$	0.0100	0	1	0	0
$5/16 = 1/4 + 1/16$	0.0101	0	1	0	1
$6/16 = 1/4 + 1/8$	0.0110	0	1	1	0
$7/16 = 1/4 + 1/8 + 1/16$	0.0111	0	1	1	1
$8/16 = 1/2$ (MSB)	0.1000	1	0	0	0
$9/16 = 1/2 + 1/16$	0.1001	1	0	0	1
$10/16 = 1/2 + 1/8$	0.1010	1	0	1	0
$11/16 = 1/2 + 1/8 + 1/16$	0.1011	1	0	1	1
$12/16 = 1/2 + 1/4$	0.1100	1	1	0	0
$13/16 = 1/2 + 1/4 + 1/16$	0.1101	1	1	0	1
$14/16 = 1/2 + 1/4 + 1/8$	0.1110	1	1	1	0
$15/16 = 1/2 + 1/4 + 1/8 + 1/16$	0.1111	1	1	1	1

Table 1. Fractional Binary Codes

When all bits are "1" in natural binary, the number value is $1 - 2^{-n}$, or normalized full-scale less 1 LSB ($1 - 1/16 = 15/16$ in the example). Strictly speaking, the number that is represented, written with an "integer point," is 0.1111 (= 1 - 0.0001). However, it is almost universal practice to write the code simply as the integer 1111 (i.e., "15") with the fractional nature of the corresponding number understood ["1111" → $1111/(1111 + 1)$, or 15/16].

For convenience, Table 2 lists bit weights in binary, for numbers having up to 20 bits. The practical range for the vast majority of applications is about 16 bits; for larger numbers of bits than 20, continue to divide by 2.

(handwritten notes: $\frac{.4v}{100}$ 10 v input $= .04v$ F.S $= 40 mv$ resolution)

BIT	2^{-n}	$1/2^n$ (Fraction)	"dB"	$1/2^n$ (Decimal)	%	ppm
FS	2^0	1	0	1.0	100	1,000,000
MSB	2^{-1}	1/2	−6	0.5	50.	500,000
2	2^{-2}	1/4	−12	0.25	25	250,000
3	2^{-3}	1/8	−18.1	0.125	12.5	125,000
4	2^{-4}	1/16	−24.1	0.0625	6.2	62,500
5	2^{-5}	1/32	−30.1	0.03125	3.1	31,250
6	2^{-6}	1/64	−36.1	0.015625	1.6	15,625
7	2^{-7}	1/128	−42.1	0.007812	0.8	7,812
8	2^{-8}	1/256	−48.2	0.003906	0.4	3,906
9	2^{-9}	1/512	−54.2	0.001953	0.2	1,953
10	2^{-10}	1/1,024	−60.2	0.0009766	0.1	977
11	2^{-11}	1/2,048	−66.2	0.00048828	0.05	488
12	2^{-12}	1/4,096	−72.2	0.00024414	0.024	244
13	2^{-13}	1/8,192	−78.3	0.00012207	0.012	122
14	2^{-14}	1/16,384	−84.3	0.000061035	0.006	61
15	2^{-15}	1/32,768	−90.3	0.0000305176	0.003	31
16	2^{-16}	1/65,536	−96.3	0.0000152588	0.0015	15
17	2^{-17}	1/131,072	−102.3	0.00000762939	0.0008	7.6
18	2^{-18}	1/262,144	−108.4	0.000003814697	0.0004	3.8
19	2^{-19}	1/524,288	−114.4	0.000001907349	0.0002	1.9
20	2^{-20}	1/1,048,576	−120.4	0.0000009536743	0.0001	0.95

Table 2. Binary Bit Weights or Resolution

The weight assigned to the LSB is the *resolution* inherent in numbers having n bits. The "dB" column represents the logarithm (base 10) of the ratio of the LSB value to unity (full scale), multiplied by 20, in the popular manner. Each successive power of 2 represents a change of 6.02dB [i.e., $20 \log_{10} (2)$] or "6dB/octave."

In natural binary, the normalized numerical value of the code 1 0 1 1 1 0 1 0 1, a 9-bit code, would be

0.5000	MSB	1/2	=	256/512	
0.1250	Bit 3	1/8	=	64/512	
0.0625	Bit 4	1/16	=	32/512	
0.0312	Bit 5	1/32	=	16/512	
0.0078	Bit 7	1/128	=	4/512	
+0.0020	Bit 9 (LSB)	1/512	=	+ 1/512	
0.7285				373/512	= 0.7285

BASIC CONVERSION RELATIONSHIPS

Perhaps the most fruitful way of indicating the relationship between analog and digital quantities involved in a conversion is to plot a graph. Since there are two complementary conversion relationships to be discussed, two graphs must be plotted, one for A/D conversion, the other for D/A conversion.

Figure 1 shows the graph for an ideal 3-bit D/A converter. A 3-bit converter has 8 discrete coded levels, thus a total of 8 different inputs and 8 corresponding outputs, ranging from zero to 7/8 of "full scale." Since no other levels can exist with this coding, it is plotted as a bar graph.

In practical D/A converters, the zero bar may not be exactly zero (offset error). The range from zero to 7/8 F.S. may not be exactly as specified (gain error), the differences in heights of the bars may not be equal or changing uniformly (nonlinearity), and − in fact − if the nonlinearity is great enough, one or more values of analog output may be less than the values corresponding to codes having smaller weight (non-monotonic due to excessive *differential nonlinearity*). These errors (and others), the means of specifying

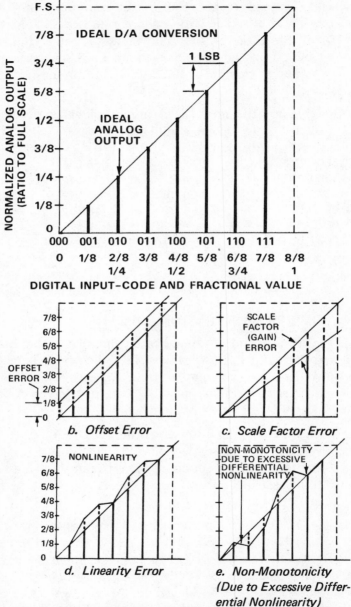

Figure 1. Conversion Relationship in a 3-Bit D/A Converter
a. Ideal Relationship
b, c, d, e. Typical Sources of Error

and testing them, and some of the design techniques for keeping them small, are discussed in chapters 2, 3, and 4.

To visualize the ideal performance of converters having larger number of bits, one may intensify this pattern by interpolating additional bars between the bars on this graph. For example, a fourth bit would require 8 additional bars with heights halfway between the levels indicated. The value of the LSB would be F.S./16, and the maximum value would be $7/8 + 1/16 = 15/16$ F.S. The next bit would interpolate 16 additional bars, the new LSB would be F.S./32, and the maximum value would be 31/32, etc. The straight line connecting the tops of the bars is the locus of the *envelope* of the ideal conversion relationship.

Figure 2 shows the graph for an ideal 3-bit A/D converter. Since all values of the analog input are presumed to exist, they must be *quantized* by partitioning the continuum into 8 discrete ranges. All analog values within a given range are represented by the same digital code, which corresponds to the nominal mid-range value. These mid-range values correspond to the bar heights of the *D/A* converter.

There is, therefore, in the A/D conversion process, an inherent *quantization uncertainty* of ±½ LSB, in addition to the conversion errors analogous to those existing for the D/A converter. The only sure way to reduce this quantization uncertainty is to increase the number of bits. (There are, of course, statistical interpolation tricks that may be performed in the digital processing or in analog filtering following subsequent D/A conversion, which will fill in missing analog values for large, rapidly-varying signals, but they will do nothing to indicate the variations within a quantum for an apparently-constant digital number.)

Since it is easier to determine the location of a *transition* than it is to determine a mid-range value, errors and settings of A/D converters are defined and measured in terms of the analog values at which transitions occur, in relation to the ideal transition values. Like D/A converters, A/D converters have offset error: the first transition may not occur at exactly +1/2 LSB; scale-factor (or gain) error: the difference between the values at which the first transition

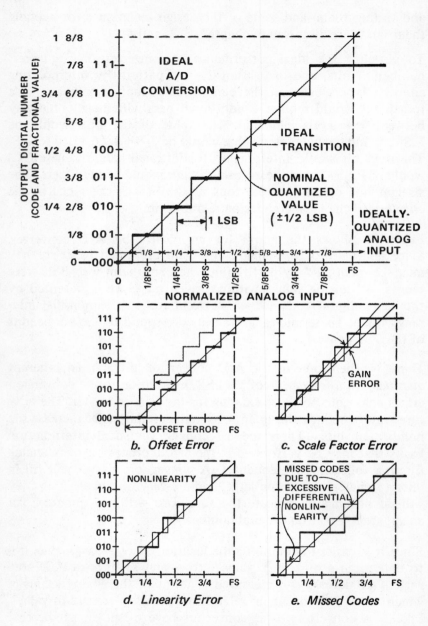

Figure 2. Conversion Relationship in a 3-Bit A/D Converter
a. Ideal Relationship b, c, d, e Typical Sources of Error

and the last transition occur is not equal to (F.S. − 2LSB); and *linearity* error: the differences between transition values are not all equal or uniformly changing. If the *differential linearity* error is large enough, it is possible for one or more codes to be missed (the counterpart of non-monotonic D/A conversion).

An important factor in the conversion relationship is the choice of "Full Scale," the LSB magnitude, and the transition points. For a great many converters, full scale is in the vicinity of 10 volts: either exactly 10V or 10.24V. For 10V, the bit values are easily expressed as negative powers of 2, multiplied by 10; for 10.24V, the LSB can be expressed in "round" numbers, being a multiple or submultiple of 10mV.

No. of Bits n	LSB	10V Full Scale			10.24V Full Scale			
			A/D Transitions				A/D Transitions	
		All 1's (Volts)	To LSB (1/2 LSB)	To All 1's (Volts)	LSB	All 1's (Volts)	To LSB (+1/2 LSB)	To All 1's (Volts)
1	5V	5.0	2.5V	2.5	5.12V	5.12	2.56V	2.56
2	2.5V	7.5	1.25V	6.25	2.56V	7.68	1.28V	6.40
3	1.25V	8.75	625mV	8.13	1.28V	8.96	640mV	8.32
4	625mV	9.38	312mV	9.07	640mV	9.60	320mV	9.28
5	312mV	9.69	156mV	9.53	320mV	9.92	160mV	9.76
6	156mV	9.84	78.1mV	9.76	160mV	10.08	80mV	10.00
7	78.1mV	9.92	39.1mV	9.88	80mV	10.16	40mV	10.12
8	39.1mV	9.961	19.5mV	9.941	40mV	10.20	20mV	10.18
9	19.5mV	9.980	9.77mV	9.970	20mV	10.220	10mV	10.21
10	9.77mV	9.990	4.88mV	9.985	10mV	10.230	5mV	10.225
11	4.88mV	9.9951	2.44mV	9.9927	5mV	10.235	2.5mV	10.232
12	2.44mV	9.9976	1.22mV	9.9964	2.5mV	10.2375	1.25mV	10.2362
13	1.22mV	9.9988	610µV	9.9982	1.25mV	10.2388	625µV	10.2382
14	610µV	9.9994	305µV	9.9991	625µV	10.2394	312µV	10.2391
15	305µV	9.99970	153µV	9.99955	312µV	10.23969	156µV	10.23953
16	153µV	9.99985	76µV	9.99977	156µV	10.23984	78.1µV	10.23976
17	76µV	9.99992	38µV	9.99988	78.1µV	10.23992	39.1µV	10.23988
18	38µV	9.999962	19µV	9.999943	39.1µV	10.239961	19.5µV	10.239941
19	19µV	9.999981	9.5µV	9.999971	19.5µV	10.239980	9.77µV	10.239970
20	9.5µV	9.999990	4.8µV	9.999985	9.77µV	10.239990	4.88µV	10.239985

Table 3. LSB and (FS − LSB) Values for 10V and 10.24V Conversion

Table 3 lists the LSB values, the "all 1's" value (i.e., F.S. − 1 LSB), and the A/D converter transition values at 1/2 LSB (for zero adjustment) and all 1's (F.S. − 1½ LSB, for scale factor adjustment) for resolutions to 2^{-20}, for both 10V and 10.24V full scale. If full scale is 5V (also a popular value), simply divide the appropriate numbers by 2.

OTHER CODES

Although binary is the most commonly-used code, there are a number of other popular codes used at system interfaces, depending on signal range and polarity, conversion technique, specially-desired characteristics, and origin or destination of digital information.

BINARY-CODED DECIMAL (BCD)

This is a code in which each decimal digit is represented by a group of 4 binary-coded digits. The LSB of the most significant group, or "quad," has a weight of 0.1, the LSB of the next has a weight of 0.01, the LSB of the next has a weight of 0.001, etc. Each quad has 10 permissible levels with weights 0 to 9. Group values in excess of 9 are not permitted. For example, Table 4 shows BCD coding for a variety of numbers between 0 and 0.99.

A/D converters with the BCD code are used primarily in digital voltmeters and panel meters, since each quad's output may be decoded to drive a numeric display using the familiar decimal numbers. If the display is of a BCD digitally transmitted or processed number, or if the input is via a thumbwheel switch, a D/A converter that responds to BCD may be used to furnish an analog output from the same digital input.

BCD is somewhat wasteful, in the sense that each BCD quad has 10/16 the resolution of a comparable natural binary quad. Table 5 shows the relative resolution capability.

OVERRANGING

Many BCD A/D converters have an additional bit with weight equal to full scale, in a position "more significant" than the MSB.

Decimal Fraction		BCD Code	
		MSQ (x1/10) x8 x4 x2 x1	2nd Quad (x1/100) x8 x4 x2 x1
0.00 = 0.00 + 0.00		0 0 0 0	0 0 0 0
0.01 = 0.00 + 0.01		0 0 0 0	0 0 0 1
0.02 = 0.00 + 0.02		0 0 0 0	0 0 1 0
0.03 = 0.00 + 0.03		0 0 0 0	0 0 1 1
0.04 = 0.00 + 0.04		0 0 0 0	0 1 0 0
0.05 = 0.00 + 0.05		0 0 0 0	0 1 0 1
0.06 = 0.00 + 0.06		0 0 0 0	0 1 1 0
0.07 = 0.00 + 0.07		0 0 0 0	0 1 1 1
0.08 = 0.00 + 0.08		0 0 0 0	1 0 0 0
0.09 = 0.00 + 0.09		0 0 0 0	1 0 0 1
0.10 = 0.10 + 0.00		0 0 0 1	0 0 0 0
0.11 = 0.10 + 0.01		0 0 0 1	0 0 0 1
:			
0.20 = 0.20 + 0.00		0 0 1 0	0 0 0 0
:			
0.30 = 0.30 + 0.00		0 0 1 1	0 0 0 0
:			
0.90 = 0.90 + 0.00		1 0 0 1	0 0 0 0
0.91 = 0.90 + 0.01		1 0 0 1	0 0 0 1
:			
0.98 = 0.90 + 0.08		1 0 0 1	1 0 0 0
0.99 = 0.90 + 0.09		1 0 0 1	1 0 0 1

Table 4. Examples of 2-Digit BCD Weighting

Number of Bits	Least Significant Bit		Number of Binary Bits Needed For Same Resolution as BCD
	Binary	BCD	
4	0.062	0.1	4
8	0.0039	0.01	7
12	0.00024	0.001	10
16	0.000015	0.0001	14
20	0.000001	0.00001	17
24	0.0000002	0.000001	20

Table 5. Relative Resolution of BCD and Binary

This additional bit provides a maximum of 100% "overrange" capability. Additional "super-significant" bits would provide binary 300% (2 bits) and 700% (3 bits) overrange capability (or extend the range to nearly 800% of the BCD "full scale.") The overrange bit is most commonly used in digital voltmeters and panel meters to indicate that nominal full scale has been exceeded and that the visual reading may be erroneous.

Overrange bits need not be restricted to BCD. They are useful as "flags" in any conversion process for which an overrange input would give an ambiguous reading, or where an overrange input indicates anomalous analog system behavior. The overrange bit must of course be of suitable accuracy, since it is, in effect, the MSB.

2-4-2-1 BINARY-CODED DECIMAL

This is a code that is still in common use, in which the bit in the MSB position in each quad has a weight of 2 instead of the usual 8 that is normal for BCD. It is found, for example, at the digital output of some Hewlett-Packard digital voltmeters. The relative weights within a quad are given in Table 6.

			$2^{\star}$ (x2)	4 (x4)	2 (x2)	1 (x1)
0.0			0	0	0	0
0.1	=	0.1	0	0	0	1
0.2	=	0.2	0	0	1	0
0.3	=	0.1 + 0.2	0	0	1	1
0.4	=	0.4	0	1	0	0
0.5	=	0.1 + 0.4	0	1	0	1
0.6	=	0.2 + 0.4	0	1	1	0
0.7	=	0.1 + 0.2 + 0.4	0	1	1	1
0.8	=	0.2 + 0.4 + 0.2	1	1	1	0
0.9	=	0.1 + 0.2 + 0.4 + 0.2	1	1	1	1

Table 6. 2-4-2-1 BCD Bit Weights Within Each Quad

This code was more economical to implement in the days before integrated-circuit logic became common, still has the advantages of having all 1's for (full scale − LSB) and requiring a smaller range of resistance in D/A-converter ladder networks based on binary conductance values.

GRAY CODE

This is a binary code in which the bit position does not signify a numerical weighting; however, in converters using it, each code still corresponds to a unique portion of the analog range. It is easily translatable into natural binary (Table 7):

Decimal Fraction	Gray Code				Binary Code			
0	0	0	0	0	0	0	0	0
1/16	0	0	0	1	0	0	0	1
2/16	0	0	1	1	0	0	1	0
3/16	0	0	1	0	0	0	1	1
4/16	0	1	1	0	0	1	0	0
5/16	0	1	1	1	0	1	0	1
6/16	0	1	0	1	0	1	1	0
7/16	0	1	0	0	0	1	1	1
8/16	1	1	0	0	1	0	0	0
9/16	1	1	0	1	1	0	0	1
10/16	1	1	1	1	1	0	1	0
11/16	1	1	1	0	1	0	1	1
12/16	1	0	1	0	1	1	0	0
13/16	1	0	1	1	1	1	0	1
14/16	1	0	0	1	1	1	1	0
15/16	1	0	0	0	1	1	1	1

Table 7. Comparison of 4-Bit Binary and Gray Codes. Underlined Bits Indicate Changes as Number Increases.

In Gray code, as the number value changes, the transitions from one code to the next involve only one bit at a time. The bits that change as the numbers increase are underlined in the table.

The conversion from binary to Gray code occurs as follows: If the binary MSB is zero, the Gray code MSB will be zero. Then, continuing to read from MSB to LSB, each change produces a "1," each non-change produces a "0." For example, 11 in binary, 1011, becomes 1110 in Gray code (1 → 1, 1-to-0 → 1, 0-to-1 → 1, 1-to-1 → 0). Another example: the 12-bit binary number 101111000101 becomes 111000100111. Fig. 3 shows one way in which binary to Gray code conversion may be mechanized.

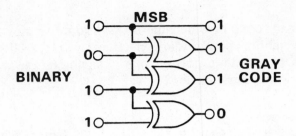

Figure 3. Binary to Gray Code Conversion Using Exclusive — or Gates

The conversion from Gray code to binary is just the reverse of the conversion from binary to Gray code: The binary MSB will be the same as the Gray code MSB. Then, continuing to read from MSB to LSB, if the next bit is 1, the next binary bit is the complement of the previous binary bit. For example, if the Gray code is 1110, the corresponding binary is 1011 (1 → 1, 1 → 1-to-0, 1 → 0-to-1, 0 → 1-to-1). Another example, the 8-bit Gray code 01110000 is 01011111 in binary. A mechanization of Gray code-to-binary conversion appears in Figure 4.

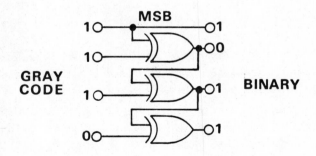

Figure 4. Gray Code to Binary Conversion

Gray code is useful for shaft encoders (angle-to-digital converters) because the change of only 1 bit for each increment eliminates false intermediate codes that could occur in natural binary conversion. Here, for comparison, are Gray code and binary developed optical shaft encoders for 4-bit resolution.

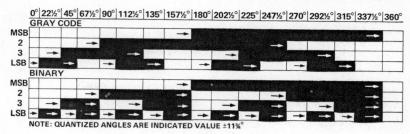

Figure 5. Gray vs. Binary Encoding

Note that, with the Gray code converter, there is only one bit change at each transition. If the edge of a shaded area is slightly out of line, the coding will be in error by a small fraction of an LSB. In the binary converter, *all four bits change at once* at the 180° and 360° transitions. If bit 2's shaded area were to end a little to the left of the 180° transition, the code, in a small region, would be 0011, indicating the 67½° range, or a fictitious progression from 157½° to 67½° to 180°. We leave the catastrophic implications of this to the reader.

The shaft encoder is a *simultaneous* converter: all bits appear at once and can be read in parallel at any time. There is an electrical equivalent form of simultaneous A/D converter having a Gray code output. It employs a chain of biased comparators, the outputs of which provide a quantized indication of the analog input level: all comparators above it are 0, all comparators below it are 1. Multi-input logic gates then make the decisions necessary to obtain a parallel Gray code output. Such converters are quite fast, some being capable of producing 10M meaningful conversions per second, but they require a number of comparisons that is a geometric function of the required resolution, (i.e., $2^n - 1$), as well as logic gates having large numbers of inputs.

A variation of this scheme, the cyclical converter, which also has Gray code output, uses fewer comparators, with more-accurate output states, but it requires more time to perform the conversion. It continuously tracks the analog input.

The use of Gray code in fast converters that provide continuous conversions has the same rationale as for the shaft encoder. Any Gray code output value that is latched into a register will always be within ±1 LSB of the correct value, even if the latching occurs just as a bit is switching. With binary, however, where many bits can switch at a single transition, it is possible to latch in mid-flight, and, because of the "skew" between turn-on and turn-off speeds, lock in an utterly false code.

COMPLEMENTARY CODES

The actual mechanization of some forms of converters, (for example, D/A converters using the μDAC® monolithic quad switches) may require codes, such as natural binary or BCD, in which all bits are represented by their complements. Such codes are called complementary codes.

In a 4-bit complementary-binary converter, 0 is represented by 1111, half-scale (MSB) by 0111, and full scale (less 1LSB) by 0000. It can be easily obtained from the "Q̄" outputs of a register, of which "Q" is the normal output sense.

Similarly, for each quad of a BCD-coded converter, *complementary BCD* is the code obtained by representing all bits by their complements. In complementary BCD, 0 is represented by 1111, and 9 is represented by 0110. As an example, Table 8 lists the equivalents for 1 through 11 in complementary binary and complementary BCD (with overrange bit).

Decimal Number	Natural Binary	Complementary Binary	BCD	Complementary BCD
0 BIN DEC	0000	1111	00000	11111
1, 1/16, 1/10	0001	1110	00001	11110
2, 2/16, 2/10	0010	1101	00010	11101
3, 3/16, 3/10	0011	1100	00011	11100
4, 4/16, 4/10	0100	1011	00100	11011
5, 5/16, 5/10	0101	1010	00101	11010
6, 6/16, 6/10	0110	1001	00110	11001
7, 7/16, 7/10	0111	1000	00111	11000
8, 8/16, 8/10	1000	0111	01000	10111
9, 9/16, 9/10	1001	0110	01001	10110
10,10/16,10/10	1010	0101	10000	01111
11,11/16,11/10	1011	0100	10001	01110

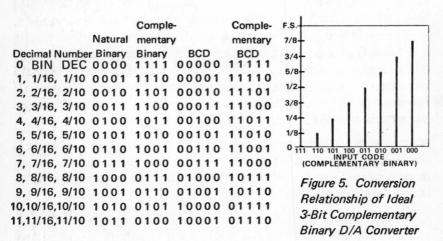

Figure 5. Conversion Relationship of Ideal 3-Bit Complementary Binary D/A Converter

Table 8. Complementary Codes

If a natural binary input were applied to a D/A converter coded to respond to complementary binary, the output would be in reverse order, i.e., zero output for all 1's, and F.S. − 1 LSB for all 0's.

The complementary codes discussed above involve complementing *all bits*, for convenience in implementing the conversion relationship using certain kinds of switches (i.e., those that respond to complementary logic). We could just as well have left the logic unchanged but redefined it as "negative true." However, for consistency in elucidation, we define all logic in terms of "positive true" TTL (or DTL), as explained at the beginning of the chapter. It is important to understand that, for purposes of this discussion, these complementary codes have nothing to do with representation of the *analog polarity* relationship, a matter that will be discussed next.

ANALOG POLARITY

So far, the conversion relationships mentioned have been unipolar: the codes have represented numbers, which in turn represent the normalized *magnitudes* of analog variables,[2] without regard to polarity. A unipolar A/D converter will respond to analog signals of only one polarity, and a unipolar D/A converter will produce analog signals of only one polarity.

The analog signal polarity is determined either by using a converter whose reference and switches (or specifications) are compatible with the desired analog polarity, or (if for reasons of economy or availability, a converter is available having predetermined polarity) by operating on the analog signal before A/D conversion − or after D/A conversion − to invert its polarity, and also perform any necessary scale changes, if range must be adapted too.

BIPOLAR CODES

For conversion of bipolar analog signals into a digital code that retains sign information, one extra bit − the "sign bit" − is necessary. This "most significant bit" doubles the analog range and halves the peak-to-peak resolution. In some cases, the sign bit

---

[2] Gray code is an exception. Since it is not quantitatively weighted, it can represent any arbitrary range of magnitudes of any polarity.

is provided by re-interpreting the existing MSB, in which event the analog *range* may still be doubled, but the *resolution* is twice as coarse. For example, if a 10-bit converter's resolution is 1/1024, for the range 0–10V, we may use a bipolar code having 11 bits, with peak-to-peak resolution of 1/2048 and range of ±10V, or retain a code having 10 bits, but "stretch" the range to ±10V, in which case the peak-to-peak resolution remains 1/1024, which doubles the magnitude of the LSB. It must be emphasized that, because the sign digit doubles both the range *and* the number of levels, the LSB's ratio to full scale in either polarity is $2^{-(n-1)}$, not 2^{-n}.

The most-often-used binary codes in bipolar conversion are: Sign-magnitude (magnitude plus sign), Offset binary, Two's complement, and One's complement. Table 9 shows each of these codes expressed for 4 bits (3 bits plus sign).

	— Decimal Fraction —					
	Positive	Negative	Sign +	Two's	Offset	One's
Number	Reference	Reference	Magnitude	Complement	Binary	Complement
+7	+7/8	−7/8	0 1 1 1	0 1 1 1	1 1 1 1	0 1 1 1
+6	+6/8	−6/8	0 1 1 0	0 1 1 0	1 1 1 0	0 1 1 0
+5	+5/8	−5/8	0 1 0 1	0 1 0 1	1 1 0 1	0 1 0 1
+4	+4/8	−4/8	0 1 0 0	0 1 0 0	1 1 0 0	0 1 0 0
+3	+3/8	−3/8	0 0 1 1	0 0 1 1	1 0 1 1	0 0 1 1
+2	+2/8	−2/8	0 0 1 0	0 0 1 0	1 0 1 0	0 0 1 0
+1	+1/8	−1/8	0 0 0 1	0 0 0 1	1 0 0 1	0 0 0 1
0	0+	0−	0 0 0 0	0 0 0 0	1 0 0 0	0 0 0 0
0	0−	0+	1 0 0 0	(0 0 0 0)	(1 0 0 0)	1 1 1 1
−1	−1/8	+1/8	1 0 0 1	1 1 1 1	0 1 1 1	1 1 1 0
−2	−2/8	+2/8	1 0 1 0	1 1 1 0	0 1 1 0	1 1 0 1
−3	−3/8	+3/8	1 0 1 1	1 1 0 1	0 1 0 1	1 1 0 0
−4	−4/8	+4/8	1 1 0 0	1 1 0 0	0 1 0 0	1 0 1 1
−5	−5/8	+5/8	1 1 0 1	1 0 1 1	0 0 1 1	1 0 1 0
−6	−6/8	+6/8	1 1 1 0	1 0 1 0	0 0 1 0	1 0 0 1
−7	−7/8	+7/8	1 1 1 1	1 0 0 1	0 0 0 1	1 0 0 0
−8	−8/8	+8/8		(1 0 0 0)	(0 0 0 0)	

Table 9. Commonly-Used Bipolar Codes

Because the analog signal now has a choice of polarity, we must be careful about the relationship between the code and the polarity of the analog signal. "Positive reference" indicates that the analog signal[3] increases positively as the digital number increases. "Negative reference," on the other hand, indicates that the analog signal decreases towards negative full scale as the digital number increases. Conversion relationships for bipolar A/D and D/A converters are shown graphically in Figures 6 and 7.

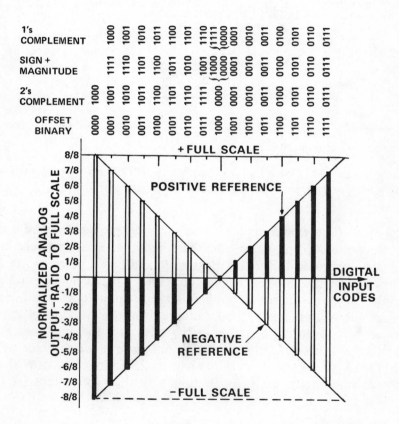

Figure 6. Ideal D/A Conversion Relationship for 4-Bit (3-Bit-Plus-Sign) Offset Binary, 2's Complement, Sign-Magnitude, 1's Complement Codes

[3] A/D converter input or D/A converter output.

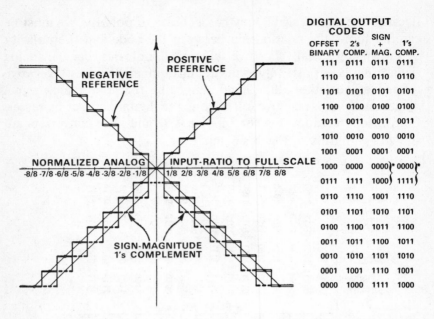

Figure 7. Ideal A/D Conversion Relationship for 4-Bit (3-Bit-Plus Sign) Offset Binary, 2's Complement, Sign Magnitude, 1's Complement Codes

Sign-Magnitude would appear to be the most straightforward way of expressing signed analog quantities digitally. Simply determine the code appropriate for the magnitude and add a polarity bit. It is used advantageously in D/A converters that operate in the vicinity of zero, where the application calls for smooth and linear transitions from positive small voltages to negative small voltages. As can be seen in the example in the table, it is the only code for which the three magnitude bits do not have a major transition (all 1's to all 0's, or equivalent) at zero. Sign-magnitude *BCD* is almost universally used for bipolar digital voltmeters (A/D converters).

---

*In sign-magnitude and 1's-complement A/D converters, the ambiguous zero must be dealt with. In some units, one of the codes is "forbidden," (DVM's generally read "+0" only), in others, the ±½ LSB zero region is divided into two regions (0 to +½ LSB, and 0 to −½ LSB), one of which produces one code, the other the other code. This is a more useful approach in codes having a sequential continuum of numbers, such as 1's complement.

It does have some shortcomings, though. In data-processing applications, the *other* codes are more-readily usable for computation with a minimum of translation. One of its problems is that it has two codes for zero. For this reason, sign-magnitude is harder to interface with digitally, because it requires either software, or additional equipment. In addition, the converter circuitry for sign-magnitude is usually somewhat more complicated and costly than for some other codes.

Offset binary is the easiest code to embody with converter circuitry. An examination of the offset binary code for three bits plus sign will show that it is really a natural binary code for four bits, except that its zero is at negative full scale, the LSB is 1/16 of the whole bipolar range, and the MSB is turned on at analog zero. Therefore, to make an offset binary 3-bits-plus sign converter out of a 4-bit D/A converter having 0-to-10V full-scale range, we have only to double its scale factor (20V range), and offset its zero by one half of the full range (–10V), an operation which is neither difficult nor expensive. Similarly, for an A/D converter, one would attenuate the input by one-half, and add a bias of one-half the full range.

Besides its ease of implementation, offset binary has the further advantage that it is compatible with computer inputs and outputs, it is easily changed to the more-computationally-useful two's complement (just complement the MSB), and it has a single unambiguous code for zero. The all-zeros negative full scale code (0000), though not used in computing (because – (F.S. – 1 LSB) is the most negative value defined in computing), is nevertheless useful as a converter checking and adjustment code.

The principal drawback of offset binary is that a major bit transition occurs at 0 (all bits change, from 0111 to 1000). This can lead to "glitch" problems dynamically (the difference in speed between bits turning on and off can lead to large spikes – see the index for "glitches") and to linearity problems statically (the largest linearity errors are most likely to occur at major transitions, because the transition is essentially a difference between two large numbers). Also, in offset binary, zero errors may be greater than with sign-magnitude, because the zero analog level is usually obtained by taking a difference between the MSB (½ full range) and a bias (½ full range), again, two large numbers.

Two's complement, for conversion purposes, consists of a binary code for positive magnitudes (0 sign bit), and the two's complement of each positive number to represent its negative. The two's complement is formed arithmetically by complementing the number and adding 1 LSB. For example, the two's complement of 3/8 (0011) would be its complement plus 1 LSB, or 1100 + 0001 = 1101.

Two's complement is a useful code computationally because it can be thought of as a set of negative numbers. Therefore, addition can be used instead of subtraction. For example, to subtract 3/8 from 4/8, add 4/8 to −3/8, or 0100 to 1101. The result is 0001 (disregarding the extra carry), or 1/8.

If the two's complement code and the offset binary code are compared, it can be seen that the only difference between them is that the MSB of one is replaced by its complement in the other (Nature's way of helping converter manufacturers and users). Since both a digit and its complement are available from most flip-flops, an offset-binary-coded converter may be used for 2's complement, just by using the MSB's complement at the output of an A/D converter or at the output of a D/A converter's input register. And vice versa.

Two's complement has the same disadvantages as offset binary, since the conversion process is identical.

One's complement is a means of representing negative numbers sometimes used by computers. One's complement is obtained arithmetically by simply complementing all of a number's digits. Thus, the one's complement of 3/8 (0011) is (1100). When a number is subtracted by adding its 1's complement, the extra carry (that is disregarded in 2's complement), if present, causes 1 LSB to be added to the total ("end-around carry.") Thus, subtracting 3/8 from 4/8, 0100 + 1100 = 0000 + 0001 = 0001 (or 1/8). A one's complement code can be formed by complementing each positive value to obtain its corresponding negative value, including − alas − zero, which is then represented by two codes, 0000 and 1111.

Besides its ambiguous zero, another disadvantage of this code in conversion is that it is not as readily implemented as is 2's complement. If it is not converted to 2's complement before a D/A conversion, by adding 1 LSB digitally when the MSB is 1 (indicating a negative number), then the easiest way to implement the conversion is by performing a 2's complement conversion, and adding the *analog* value of 1LSB, if the MSB is 1. Adding the extra analog bit can be done simply and elegantly (if not accurately) by resistively dividing the digital MSB logic level down to the LSB's analog value and summing this attenuated signal.

CODE CONVERSION

Since code conversion may be desirable, either after A/D conversion or before D/A conversion, in order to make it possible to use a converter that produces the best results at the lowest cost, the matrix of Table 10 briefly outlines the relationships among the codes.

To Convert From / To ↓	Sign Magnitude	2's Complement	Offset Binary	1's Complement
Sign Magnitude	NO CHANGE	If MSB = 1, complement other bits, add 00 .. 01	Complement MSB If new MSB = 1, complement other bits, add 00 .. 01	If MSB = 1, complement other bits
2's Complement	If MSB = 1, complement other bits, add 00 . . . 01	NO CHANGE	Complement MSB	If MSB = 1, add 00 . . . 01
Offset Binary	Complement MSB If new MSB = 0 complement other bits, add 00 . . . 01	Complement MSB	NO CHANGE	Complement MSB If new MSB = 0, add 00 . . . 01
1's Complement	If MSB = 1, complement other bits	If MSB = 1, add 11 . . . 11	Complement MSB If new MSB = 1, add 11 . . . 11	NO CHANGE

Table 10. Relations Among Bipolar Codes

OTHER BIPOLAR CODES

The list of bipolar codes mentioned above may seem quite complete and coherent from the tutorial point of view, but it does not fully reflect the ingenuity and diversity of the computer and converter industries. There are a number of variations in more-or-less widespread usage that should be mentioned here because they will inevitably be encountered. Fortunately, they are based on codes we have already discussed and may be easily described.

Modified sign-magnitude: This is a version of sign-magnitude in which the MSB is complemented (1 for positive, 0 for negative).

Modified one's complement: Like modified sign-magnitude, a version in which the MSB is complemented (1 for positive, 0 for negative).

Both of the above codes have polarity bits that are the same as for offset binary — which is the lone standout in table 9. Since offset binary is popular among converter manufacturers, it stands to reason that other codings should be available with compatible sign bits, for the sake of uniformity, even though they may take us one step away from the basic natural binary rationale.

Complementary everything: All of the above-mentioned codes may be completely complemented to form complementary sign-magnitude, complementary offset binary, complementary 2's complement, and complementary 1's complement. (These are, as explained on page 17, this chapter, "negative true" versions.) Such codes, although they may make life a little more complex, are necessary to take advantage of some of the best monolithic switching hardware available today (the μDAC® quad switches). Fortunately, A/D converters and D/A converters that are supplied with registers perform the complementarity internally, so that the user never suspects the complexities that lie within.[4] However, users of

---

[4] Since both polarities of logic are usually available, complementary inputs (or outputs) can *simplify* loading, and wiring, and fanout problems. For example, if an A/D converter uses a conversion process involving a complementary-input D/A converter, the complementary logic outputs may be applied to the D/A converter, and the uncomplemented outputs to the outside world.

μDAC components and D/A converters without registers should be prepared to adjust their thinking (and especially their test equipment) to include the possible application of complementary codes.

For the sake of completeness, Table 11 lists the codes mentioned above, for 3-bits-plus-sign.

			COMPLEMENTARY CODES			
Number	Modified Sign-Magnitude	Modified 1's Complement	Comp. Sign-Magnitude	Comp. Offset Binary	Comp. 2's Complement	Comp. 1's Complement
+7	1 1 1 1	1 1 1 1	1 0 0 0	0 0 0 0	1 0 0 0	1 0 0 0
+6	1 1 1 0	1 1 1 0	1 0 0 1	0 0 0 1	1 0 0 1	1 0 0 1
+5	1 1 0 1	1 1 0 1	1 0 1 0	0 0 1 0	1 0 1 0	1 0 1 0
+4	1 1 0 0	1 1 0 0	1 0 1 1	0 0 1 1	1 0 1 1	1 0 1 1
+3	1 0 1 1	1 0 1 1	1 1 0 0	0 1 0 0	1 1 0 0	1 1 0 0
+2	1 0 1 0	1 0 1 0	1 1 0 1	0 1 0 1	1 1 0 1	1 1 0 1
+1	1 0 0 1	1 0 0 1	1 1 1 0	0 1 1 0	1 1 1 0	1 1 1 0
0+	1 0 0 0	1 0 0 0	1 1 1 1	0 1 1 1	1 1 1 1	1 1 1 1
0-	0 0 0 0	0 1 1 1	0 1 1 1	0 1 1 1	1 1 1 1	0 0 0 0
-1	0 0 0 1	0 1 1 0	0 1 1 0	1 0 0 0	0 0 0 0	0 0 0 1
-2	0 0 1 0	0 1 0 1	0 1 0 1	1 0 0 1	0 0 0 1	0 0 1 0
-3	0 0 1 1	0 1 0 0	0 1 0 0	1 0 1 0	0 0 1 0	0 0 1 1
-4	0 1 0 0	0 0 1 1	0 0 1 1	1 0 1 1	0 0 1 1	0 1 0 0
-5	0 1 0 1	0 0 1 0	0 0 1 0	1 1 0 0	0 1 0 0	0 1 0 1
-6	0 1 1 0	0 0 0 1	0 0 0 1	1 1 0 1	0 1 0 1	0 1 1 0
-7	0 1 1 1	0 0 0 0	0 0 0 0	1 1 1 0	0 1 1 0	0 1 1 1
-8				1 1 1 1	0 1 1 1	

Table 11. Modified and Complementary Bipolar Codes

ARBITRARY BIASING AND SCALING

The conversion relationships discussed so far have been either strictly one-sided (0 to full scale) or symmetrical (±full scale). The reason for this emphasis is that most commercially-available converters are built that way — as general-purpose devices.

However, since the principal relationship between the analog variable and the digital number is *proportionality,* the repertoire of codes corresponding to a given resolution may represent any portion of the analog voltage or current range. For example, if one wished to encode the voltage range from 4 to 7 volts in binary, using a 0–10V A/D converter, one could simply apply the voltage without any transformation, using only 0.3 of the available number of bits. However, a more efficient alternative would be to offset the input by 4 volts, amplify by 3.33, and apply the resulting 0–10V signal to the converter, thereby making use of the entire range of available codes and improving resolution by a factor greater than 3. In a sense, the conversion relationship between the original input and the digital output is an *offset binary* code. The subsequent digital processing would take this transformation into account via the software.

Another sort of arbitrary scaling might result if the analog signal were proportional to a temperature range of (for example) 0° to 70°C, and one desired a direct readout of temperature on a digital voltmeter. A typical approach might be to scale the voltage directly to the temperature numbers (e.g., 10°/V) and apply it to a DVM, with the location of the decimal point re-interpreted. The DVM would then provide a readout in *engineering units.*

In offset binary and 2's complement coding, a converter's output is asymmetrical, because a code exists for –F.S. (i.e., – 1), but not for +F.S. ($1 - 2^{-(n-1)}$ is maximum). Since a computer will not use the code for –F.S., the remaining codes are symmetrical for computing purposes, and the –F.S. code is unused, and – in effect – lost. For some purposes, such as data transmission, it may be desirable to retain the information in *all* codes, and achieve full scale and symmetry as well. This can be accomplished by biasing the analog signal by F.S./$(2^n - 1)$, and multiplying the reference by $1/(1 - 2^{-n})$.[5] The only drawback of this scheme is that a D/A converter output, though providing a complete, symmetrical full-scale swing, will not have an analog zero state. (Fig. 8).

[5] These are b and m, respectively, in the equation $y = mx + b$.

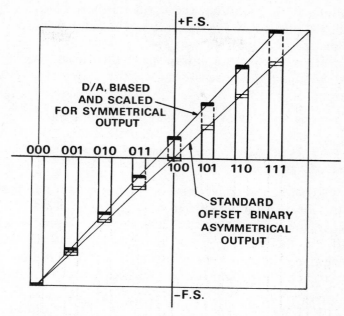

Figure 8. Conversion Relationship for a 2-Bit-Plus-Sign D/A Converter Biased and Scaled for Symmetrical Analog Output. Note that there is no Code that gives Analog Zero.

DAC's AS MULTIPLIERS AND ADC's AS DIVIDERS

The D/A converter can be thought of as a digitally-controlled potentiometer that produces an analog output (voltage or current) that is a normalized fraction of its "full scale" setting. The output voltage or current depends on the reference value chosen to determine "full scale" output. If the reference may vary in response to an analog signal, the output is proportional to the product of the digital number and the analog input. The product's polarity depends on the analog signal polarity, and the digital coding and conversion relationship. 4-quadrant multiplication is available if the D/A converter accepts reference signals of both positive and negative polarities, and the digital response is bipolar. A typical conversion relationship for a 4-quadrant multiplying DAC having 3-bit-plus-sign 2's complement coding is shown in Figure 9, interpreting the Multiplying DAC as a digitally-controlled variable-gain amplifier.

In another interpretation, the envelope of the ideal bipolar D/A converter output in Figure 6 could be seen as proportional to the analog signal input, starting from full scale "Positive Reference," being attenuated as the analog signal is reduced, passing through zero, and increasing negatively to the "Negative Reference" envelope.

Multiplying D/A converters may be 4-quadrant, two-quadrant (single polarity of either analog or digital variable), or one quadrant. They may even be fractional-quadrant, if the reference has a limited range of variation.

In analog-to-digital converters, the digital output number depends on the ratio of the quantized input to the "full-scale" reference. If the reference is allowed to change in response to a second analog input, the digital output will be proportional to the ratio of the analog signal to the reference signal. Thus, the "ratiometric" A/D converter can be thought of as an analog divider with digital output.

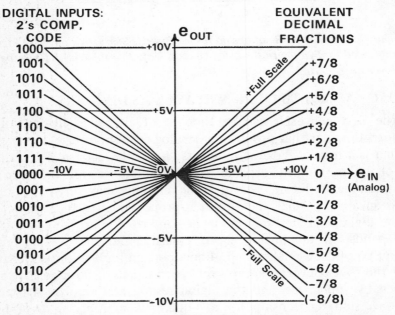

Figure 9. D/A Converter as Four-Quadrant Multiplier of Analog Voltage and 3-Bit-Plus-Sign 2's Complement Digital Number. Analog Output vs Analog Input as a Function of Digital Input Code.

ELECTRICAL INTERFACES WITH CONVERTERS

Converters may have associated with them five families of electrical inputs and outputs: analog signal, digital code, power, control, and reference. Table 12 indicates some of the properties of these interfaces, and the text that follows adds further detail.

	D/A Converters	A/D Converters
ANALOG SIGNAL	Output: Voltage or Current Polarity Magnitude	Input: Usually Voltage Polarity Magnitude
DIGITAL CODE	Input: Buffered or Direct Serial or Parallel Code Logic Levels	Output: Serial or Parallel Code Logic Levels Timing
POWER	Analog: Usually ±15V Digital: +5V (or other)	Analog: Usually ±15V Digital: +5V (or other)
CONTROL	Input: Strobe(s)	Input: Convert Command Outputs: "Status" Clock
REFERENCE	Internal or External Fixed or Variable Polarity	Internal or External Fixed or Variable Polarity

Table 12.

Figure 10 is a block diagram showing typical connections to a converter. There may be yet other connections, such as a clock synchronization input or output, complementary logic inputs or outputs, and connections that are essentially internal but are brought out for the sake of optional flexibility, such as bipolar offset reference terminals.

Block diagrams used in this book (and much of the literature), for facility of communication, tend to depict only those interfaces that are of specific relevance to the point under discussion. However, the reader should be aware that "out of sight" should not mean "out of mind."

GROUND RULE

The experienced circuit designer will recognize the feeling of wariness provoked by the presence of two supplies, and several classes of signals, all needing return "to ground." Grounding is indeed important to system performance; discussions of the essentials of grounding practice will be found (as appropriate) in several places in this book (see "Ground" in the Index); however, for clarity in the present exposition, we will consider that all grounds are always at true zero potential with respect to all input and output signals. Accordingly, the discussions that follow will everywhere employ the inverted triangle, which represents ideal signal ground.

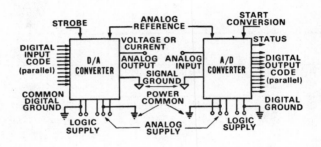

Figure 10. Converter Connections

POWER SUPPLIES

The choice of power supplies for use with converters is governed by their effect on conversion accuracy, system noise, size and weight, reliability, and cost. Supply capacity is determined by the choice of system philosophy: one main supply feeding all elements, vs. a number of satellite supplies or regulators sharing a common primary source (which might itself be a dc voltage derived from the ac mains). For most commercially-available modular converters, supply voltage used for operational amplifiers is usually adequately regulated to provide rated performance. Converter performance specifications as a function of dc variation of power supply voltage are almost always provided by the manufacturer.

DIGITAL LOGIC LEVELS

There are a variety of voltage levels and current-drive capacities corresponding to logic "0" and logic "1." This variety is a result of historical compromises between the need for speed, reliable differentiation between the logic states, circuit complexity, fanout capability, and the limitations of circuit/processing technology. They are described by such sets of initials as RTL, DTL, HTL, ECL. Most of the modern modular conversion system products are designed to be compatible with TTL, which is the most widely-used logic system at present.

In TTL, as mentioned on page 2, this chapter, a gate must respond to "0" if the input to it is 0.8 volts or less, and it must respond to "1" if the input is 2.0 volts or greater, up to the maximum and minimum voltage ratings. In order to provide a measure of immunity to noise, including dc voltage drops, occurring in transmission, gate outputs (within their current ratings), must furnish a minimum of 2.4 volts to signify "1" and a maximum of 0.4 volts to signify "0."

Within the TTL system, there are further classifications by fanout (the number of gates that can be driven) and speed. For convenience, input or output currents are normalized in terms of the standard *TTL load,* which is a positive current of $40\mu A$ for "1" and $-1.6mA$ (sink current) for "0."

In addition to the *bipolar* transistor logic circuitry, there is now coming into increasing use *MOSFET* logic (e.g., CMOS). Because CMOS logic can operate at higher voltages, with greatly-increased noise immunity, and because of its low power consumption and accordingly higher circuit-packing density, it will find increasing use in remote and portable system elements. The Analog Devices ADC-12QL is an example of an A/D converter specifically designed for such applications, using CMOS, but compatible with TTL.

Products designed for TTL logic can be used with other logic schemes by performing appropriate transformations (level-shifting, gain-or-attenuation, sign-inversion). D/A converters designed for TTL logic will inherently accept DTL inputs.

CONTROL LOGIC: THE *STATUS* OUTPUT

Most types of A/D Converters – except for those that perform continuous conversions – require a time interval, that may be either fixed or variable, to perform the conversion. During this time, the outputs may be changing and may bear no relationship to the final result. If a converter is interrogated during conversion, erroneous information will be transmitted. For this reason, the control output called *Status* (or "busy," "ready," etc.) changes state in response to the Convert Command to define the beginning of conversion and does not return to the original state until conversion is completed. It may be used to inhibit readout or to activate a *buffer* output register that holds the previous output word. It may also serve to prevent another conversion from beginning until the previous one is accomplished.

CONTROL LOGIC: THE *STROBE*

Most D/A converters – except for serial types, such as those that depend on charging of capacitors – have basic circuitry that responds immediately and continuously to whatever digital signals are applied. It is often desirable to isolate the basic circuitry from the source of digital information by a register, and update all bits simultaneously, upon command. The command input is called the *strobe* (or "clock" or "enable.")

ANALOG SIGNALS

Inputs to A/D converters are usually in the form of voltage. Outputs from D/A converters are often in the form of voltage, at low impedance, from an operational amplifier (an example is DAC–10Z). However, many converters provide an output *current* instead of a voltage (for example, MDA–10Z). As will become clear in the sections that follow, the basic conversion process may inherently develop a current output that is quite fast, linear, and free from offset. A built-in operational amplifier may be used to convert that current to voltage, but at the present state-of-the-art, low-cost IC op amps having submicrosecond settling time to useful resolution are not available. As a result of the inevitable design tradeoffs, the amplifier will tend to limit converter performance, primarily by increasing settling time. If the current is made available directly, the speed of response is under the control of the user, through the choice of an appropriate external output amplifier. He can also choose the inverting or the noninverting mode. For example, the full-scale settling time of the current output from MDA–10Z to 0.05% (½LSB of 10 bits) is 300 nanoseconds. The same basic circuit in DAC–10Z, using a general-purpose I.C. operational amplifier for voltage output, has settling time of 5µs to the same resolution (for the same price).

Converters that have current outputs or "soft" voltage outputs (directly from resistive ladders) may be considered as either voltage generators with series resistance or current generators with parallel resistance (Figure 11). They are used with operational amplifiers in either the inverting or the noninverting connection (Figure 12). Some types, such as the MDA–10Z have one or more internal feedback resistors (for appropriate output voltage scaling) that track the ladder resistors, to minimize temperature variations of gain in inverting configurations. Also present is a terminating resistor, to develop passively a noninverted output voltage, which may be amplified with a noninverting amplifier. The gain-determining feedback resistances (R_1, R_2) do not have to track the converter's internal resistors, only one another.

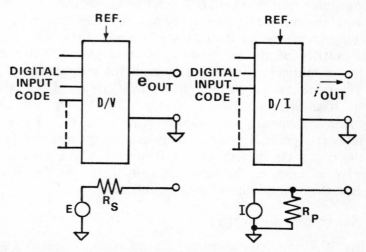

Figure 11. Digital-to-Analog Converters as Voltage or Current Generators

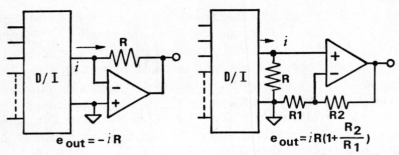

Figure 12. Current-to-Voltage Conversion Using Operational Amplifier

Using current-output converters, the inverting connection is the preferred connection, for a number of reasons: With current output, the internal impedance of the D/I converter is usually high. Thus, the loop gain will tend to remain near unity, essentially independently of the value of feedback resistance, minimizing amplifier-contributed errors, such as voltage drift. Furthermore, the output swing of the D/I converter (at the amplifier's negative input terminal) will be negligible, minimizing loading of the current output — and any associated problems, such as voltage-dependent nonlinearity and variation of internal impedance with temperature. Finally, common-mode rejection is not important, since there is no common-mode swing.

The conversion relationship of D/I converters is "positive reference" (Fig. 6) if the current flowing *out of the converter* increases as the value represented by the digital code increases, irrespective of the actual polarity of the converter's reference element. If a non-inverting amplifier configuration is used, the output voltage will have the same normalized conversion relationship as the output current. If an inverting connection is used, the voltage will have a conversion relationship of opposite output polarity. Figure 13 illustrates this point, for both binary and complementary binary unipolar codes. On the other hand, if current flowing *towards the converter* increases as the value represented by the digital code increases, the relationship is "negative reference."

D/A CONVERTER CIRCUITS

A basic D/A converter consists of a reference, a set of binary-weighted precision resistors, and a set of switches (Figure 14).

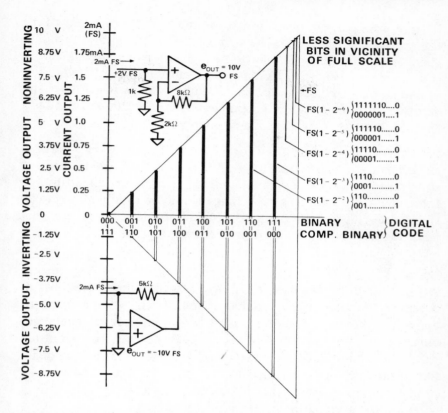

Figure 13. Ideal Conversion Relationships for 3 Most-Significant Bits in Positive Reference Unipolar D/I Converter with Noninverting and Inverting Amplifier Connections, and Binary vs. Complementary Binary Codes

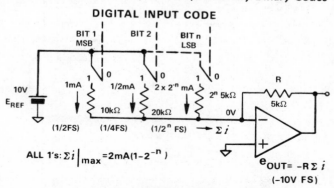

Figure 14. Simple D/A Converter

In this example, an operational amplifier holds one end of all the resistors at zero volts. The switches are operated by the digital logic, open for "0," closed for "1." Each switch that is closed adds a binary-weighted increment of current E_{REF}/R_j via the summing bus connected to the amplifier's negative input. The negative output voltage is proportional to the total current, and thus to the value of the binary number.

In practical applications, say for 12-bit D/A conversion, the range of resistance values would be 4,096:1, or 40MΩ for the LSB. If the resistors are to be manufactured in thin- or thick-film, or integrated-circuit form, such a range would be totally impractical. If discrete resistors are used, cost and size are increased, tracking advantages are lost, and inventory becomes a problem.

Resistance Ladders

A way to reduce the resistance range is to use a limited number of repeated values, with suitable attenuation. One convenient approach, shown in Figure 15, is to use a binary resistance quad, consisting of the first four values (i.e., 2R, 4R, 8R, 16R) for each group of 4 bits, with attenuation of 16:1 for the second quad, 256:1 for the third quad, etc. As an additional benefit, the proper relative quad weighting for *BCD* conversion is achieved by changing the attenuation between quads to 10:1.

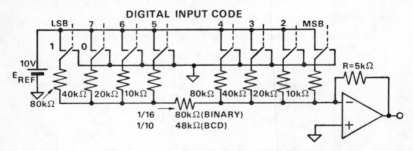

Figure 15. 8-Bit D/A Converter Using Two Equal-Resistance Quads With Attenuation for the Less-Significant Quad

Carrying this reduction of resistance values all the way, one arrives at the R-2R ladder, another convenient — and very popular — form, depicted in Figure 16, which shows its use with

an inverting operational amplifier. If all bits but the MSB are off"
(i.e., grounded), the output voltage is $(-R/2R)E_{REF}$. If all bits
but Bit 2 are off, it can be shown that the output voltage is
$\frac{1}{2}(-R/2R)E_{REF} = 1/4\ E_{REF}$: The lumped resistance of all the
less-significant-bit circuitry (to the left of Bit 2) is $2R$; the
Thévenin equivalent looking back from the MSB towards Bit 2
is the generator, $E_{REF}/2$, and the series resistance $2R$; since
the grounded MSB series resistance, $2R$, has virtually no influence —
because the amplifier summing point is at virtual ground — the
output voltage is therefore $-E_{REF}/4$. The same line of thinking
can be employed to show that the nth bit produces an increment
of output equal to $2^{-n}E_{REF}$.

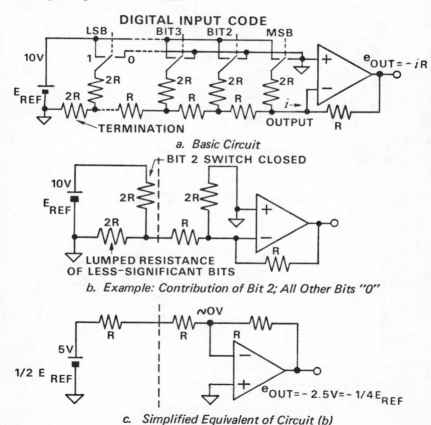

a. Basic Circuit

b. Example: Contribution of Bit 2; All Other Bits "0"

c. Simplified Equivalent of Circuit (b)

Figure 16. D/A Converter Using R-2R Ladder Network in Current Mode

The R-2R network can be employed to give unattenuated non-inverting output simply by connecting the output terminal to a high-impedance load, such as the input of a follower-connected operational amplifier (Figure 17). If the line of reasoning described in the preceding paragraph is followed, it can be seen that the MSB output is $\frac{1}{2} E_{REF}$ (2R-2R divider), Bit 2 is $1/4 E_{REF}$ ($\frac{1}{2} E_{REF}$ equivalent generator and 2R-2R divider), etc. Since the entire network may be considered to be an equivalent generator having an output voltage $N E_{REF}$ where N is the fractional digital number) and an internal resistance R, the output may be scaled down accurately by connecting precise resistance values to ground. Because of its symmetry and self-duality, the R-2R network may be used in other configurations. Figure 18 shows one example, in which the input and output leads, as depicted in Figure 16, are interchanged, for use in *current*-switching conversion.

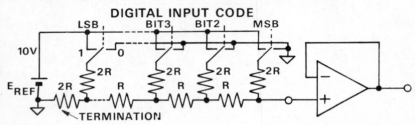

Figure 17. D/A Converter Using R-2R Ladder Network in Voltage Mode

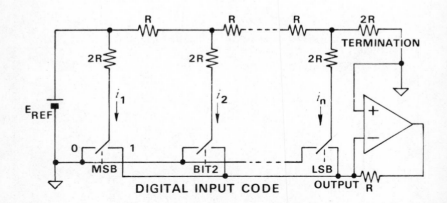

Figure 18. Inverted R-2R Ladder in Current-Switching Mode

Switching

A thorough description of the variety of voltage and current switches actually used in converters would be beyond the scope of this chapter. However, the use of monolithic quad switches in converter design is discussed in Chapter 2; and detailed information on typical voltage (AD555) and current (AD550 and AD551) switch quads will be found in the Analog Devices' *Product Guide*. Voltage switches are used in the manner indicated in Figures 16 and 17, switching between the reference and ground, in order to maintain constant impedance. The monolithic quads, used with thin-film R-2R ladder networks[6] are capable of 12-bit resolution with appropriate accuracy. Since they accept reference voltage of either polarity, they may be used in 4-quadrant multiplying DAC's.

Current switches are used to steer current between an amplifier summing point and ground. They are capable of considerably higher speeds than voltage switches, because the reference current is not interrupted, and the only significant voltage changes appear at the output, (in response to code changes) but not across the switches. A simplified form of current switch, first employed in the MDA–U Minidacs®, is shown in Figure 19. In this scheme, the switching transistors, in effect isolate the weighting resistors from the output line (and its attenuators).

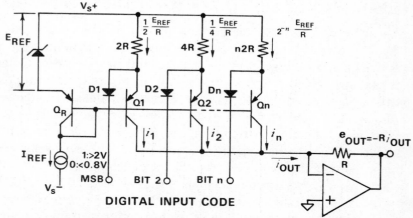

Figure 19. D/A Converter Using Basic Current Switching Technique

[6] See *Analog Dialogue*, Vol. 5, No. 2, p. 3, for a complete discussion of this application.

To understand the switching scheme of Figure 19, consider the transistor Q1. If its base-emitter voltage is equal to that of Q_R, the voltage across 2R will be equal to E_{REF}. The current through the resistor will therefore be $\frac{1}{2}E_{REF}/R$, and (assuming no current through the diode, and very high β) this same current will flow through to the collector circuit (i.e., the output). In order for this to happen, the cathode of the diode must be above the anode potential (i.e., logic "1.")

If the base line is at 1.4V, and assuming 0.6V diode conduction voltage, an anode voltage of 2V (minimum for TTL logic "1") would be sufficient for this condition. If the anode of D1 is now switched to "0" (0.8V or less), Q1 will be cut off, because D1 will steal all its current, clamping the emitter of Q1 at or below the base potential, and eliminating Q1's contribution to the output. Since the current is not interrupted, and the voltage change is small, switching time is quite short, with settling to within 1 LSB typically of the order of 200 nanoseconds.

If Q1 and Q_R are matched for V_{BE} and have equal currents flowing through their emitter circuits, the voltage across 2R will track E_{REF} with temperature, making the MSB current essentially independent of temperature, except for β variations. The lesser-order bits operate in similar manner, except that the switching transistors are matched to the reference at the appropriate binary-weighted current levels. Tracking with temperature at these levels is adequate.

The switches and resistors are grouped in quads, with repeated 2R, 4R, 8R, 16R resistance values and 8:1 maximum range of bit currents. The less-significant bit currents are attenuated in the output line (Figure 20). An important benefit of the quad structure is that there are only four different current values, considerably reducing the dimensions of the current-matching problem, and maintaining adequate switching speed for the less-significant bits. Because of the attenuation, the tolerances on the resistor values and transistor tracking in the less-significant quads are greatly relaxed relative to the most significant quad. In monolithic quads, such as the AD551, the switching transistors have emitter areas bearing power-of-two relationships, so as to inherently maintain constant current density and hence equal (and tracking) V_{BE} and β. The reference transistor, on the same chip, is identical to one of the switching transistors.

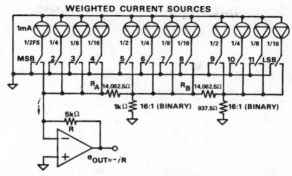

Figure 20. Block Diagram of 12-Bit Current-Switching D/A Converter, Showing Weighted Attenuation of Quad Output Currents for Binary Coding. For BCD, R_A and R_B become 8,132.5Ω and 8,437.5Ω, and R becomes 4kΩ, and the Interquad Attenuations are 10:1.

References

The most widely-used reference device is the temperature-compensated zener diode, often used with operational amplifiers for operating-point stabilization, unloading, or transducing to current (Figure 21). Some useful reference circuits are discussed in chapter 2.

Bipolar Conversion

For bipolar current-switching D/A conversion, using offset binary or two's complement codes, an offset current equal and opposite to the MSB current is added to the converter output. This may be accomplished with a resistor and a separate offset reference, but more usually, it is derived from the converter's basic reference, in order to minimize drift of the output zero with temperature.

The gain of the output inverting amplifier must be doubled, in order to double the output range, e.g., from 0 – 10V to ±10V. As indicated earlier, (Figure 6) zero output corresponds to offset binary 1 0 0 . . . 0 0, or two's complement 0 0 0 . . . 0 0.

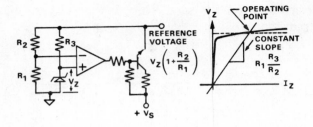

a. Amplifier Adjusts Feedback Current to Stabilize Zener Operating Point Independently of V_s or Load Variations

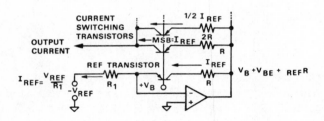

b. Amplifier Converts Reference Voltage to Reference Current in Current-Switching Converter

Figure 21. Examples of Use of Operational Amplifiers in Generating Reference Voltage and Current

Figure 22 shows an example of a current-switching converter connected for bipolar output. Note that because the amplifier is connected for sign inversion, the overall conversion relationship is "negative reference," i.e., +F.S. for all 0's (offset binary), −F.S. (1 − LSB) for all 1's.

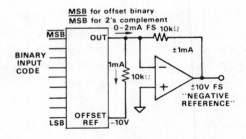

Figure 22. Bipolar Connection of Current-Switching D/A Converter for Offset Binary or 2's Complement Codes

For non-inverting applications, the same values of offset voltage and resistance are used, but the proper value of output voltage scale factor depends on the load presented by the parallel combination of the internal resistance, the offset resistance, and the external load. (Figure 23)

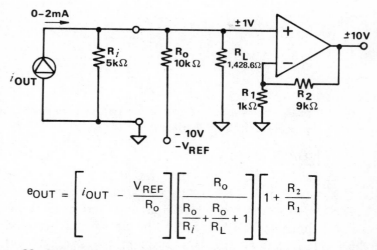

$$e_{OUT} = \left[i_{OUT} - \frac{V_{REF}}{R_o} \right] \left[\frac{R_o}{\dfrac{R_o}{R_i} + \dfrac{R_o}{R_L} + 1} \right] \left[1 + \frac{R_2}{R_1} \right]$$

Figure 23. Non-inverting Output from Current-Switching D/A Converter

For bipolar D/A conversion using the voltage switches and R-2R ladder network of Figures 16 and 17, and offset binary or 2's complement coding, one approach is to drive those network terminals that are normally grounded for unipolar operation (one side of the switches and the LSB termination) with the reference signal in the opposite polarity. If the LSB termination is allowed to remain grounded, the output will be symmetrical, resembling the conversion relationship of Figure 8, with no code for analog zero but with normalized gain reduced to $1 - 2^{-(n+1)}$

For sign-magnitude conversion, the converter's current output may be inverted, using a current inverter. Switch circuitry, operated by the MSB, determines whether the output amplifier's input is direct or via the current inverter. One way of accomplishing this is shown in Figure 24.

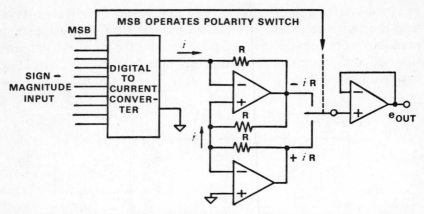

Figure 24. Sign-Magnitude Bipolar D/A Conversion Using Unipolar DAC and Switched Outputs of Operational Amplifiers

Registers on DAC's *(FIGURE 25)*

The basic parallel-input D/A converter circuits considered so far have the common property that the analog output continually reflects the state of the logic inputs. If the basic conversion circuitry is preceded by a register, the device will respond only to the inputs gated into it. This property is especially useful in data distribution systems, in which data is continually appearing, but it is desired that a DAC respond only at certain times, then hold the analog output constant until the next update. In this sense, a DAC with buffer storage may be viewed as a sample-hold with digital input, analog output, and (conceivably) infinite "Hold" time.

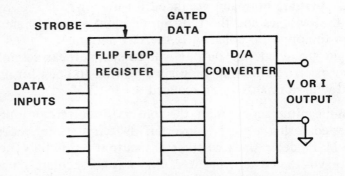

Figure 25. D/A Converter with Buffer Register

The register is controlled by a *strobe* signal, which causes it to update. The limiting rate at which the strobe may update is determined by two factors: the settling time of the DAC, and the response time of the logic. In general, settling time of the analog portion of the D/A converter is at least an order of magnitude slower than the response time of modern high-speed TTL logic circuits and is thus the limiting factor on update rate.

The only time when the speed of the digital portion of a D/A converter is of importance is when the "glitch" (See Index) caused by unequal turn-on and turn-off times is an important factor in the application. The digital inputs to a DAC come from digital logic circuits, which exhibit *skew,* or unequal turn-on and turn-off times. The switches used in DAC's also exhibit skew; however, even if the switch circuitry is specifically designed to minimize skew, the additional skew of the digital logic will constitute an irreducible minimum. In such circuit applications, glitch energy can be minimized by using high-speed logic.

A/D CONVERTER CIRCUITS

There are a vast number of conceivable circuit designs for A/D converters.[7] There are a much more limited number of designs available on the market in small, modular form at low cost, specifically designed for incorporation as components of equipment. The most popular of these are:

> Successive-approximation types
> Integration (single- and dual-slope) and V-to-f types
> Counter and "servo" types
> Parallel and modified-parallel types

Each approach has characteristics that make it most useful for a specific class of applications, based on speed, accuracy, cost, size, versatility.

---

[7]See *Electronic Analog/Digital Conversions,* by H. Schmid (Van Nostrand Reinhold, 1970) for an encyclopedic panoply of A/D (and D/A) converter circuit designs.

Successive-Approximation

Successive-approximation A/D converters are quite widely used, especially for interfacing with computers, because they are capable of both high resolution (to 16 bits: ADC-16Q), and high speed (to 1 MHz throughput rates: ADC-10F). Conversion time is fixed and independent of the magnitude of the input voltage. Each conversion is unique and independent of the results of previous conversions, because the internal logic is cleared at the start of a conversion.

The conversion technique consists of comparing the unknown input against a precisely-generated internal voltage at the output of a D/A converter. The input of the D/A converter is the digital number at the A/D converter's output. The conversion process is strikingly similar to a weighing process using a chemist's balance, with a set of n binary weights (e.g., 1/2lb, 1/4lb, 1/8lb, 1/16lb (= 1oz), 1/2oz, 1/4oz, etc., for unknowns up to 1 lb.)

After the conversion command is applied, and the converter has been cleared, the D/A converter's MSB output (1/2 full scale) is compared with the input. If the input is greater than the MSB, it remains ON (i.e., "1" in the output register), and the next bit (1/4FS) is tried. If the input is less than the MSB, it is turned OFF (i.e., "0" in the output register), and the next bit is tried. If the second bit doesn't add enough weight to exceed the input, it is left ON ("1"), and the third bit is tried. If the second bit tips the scales too far, it is turned OFF ("0"), and the third bit is tried. The process continues in order of descending bit weight until the last bit has been tried. The process completed, the *status* line changes state to indicate that the contents of the output register now constitute a valid conversion. The contents of the output register form a binary digital code corresponding to the input signal.

Figure 26 is a block diagram of a successive-approximations A/D converter, accompanied by a time history of a simple 3-bit conversion, in terms of the D/A converter output (the weight added to the balance pan). Note that, to place the D/A converter output in the center of each ideal output quantum, a 1/2-LSB "thumb" is placed on the scale (see Figure 2, this chapter), in order to locate the transitions precisely at the 1/2LSB points.

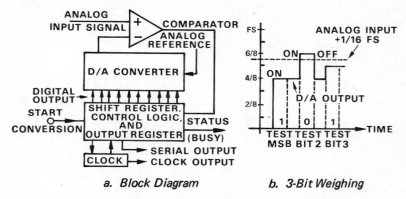

a. Block Diagram   *b. 3-Bit Weighing*

Figure 26. Successive-Approximation A/D Converter

Note that the input does not change during conversion in the example of Figure 26b. If the input were to change during conversion, the output number could no longer accurately represent the analog input unless the new value were larger than the sum of the weights already present by an amount less than the sum of the untried weights. Since this is a not-often-fulfilled requirement, it is usual to employ a sample-hold device ahead of the converter to retain the input value that was present at a given time before the conversion starts, and maintain it constant throughout the conversion. The *status* output of the converter could be used to release the sample-hold from its *hold* mode at the end of conversion. A sample-hold may not be needed if the signal (by itself, or with filtering) varies slowly enough and is sufficiently noise-free that significant changes will not be expected to occur during the conversion interval.

Accuracy, linearity, and speed are primarily affected by the properties of the D/A converter (and its reference), and the comparator. In general, the settling time of the D/A converter and the response time of the comparator are considerably slower than the switching time of the digital elements. The differential nonlinearity of the D/A converter will be reflected in the differential nonlinearity of the resulting A/D converter. If the D/A converter is non-monotonic, one or more codes may be missing from the A/D converter's output range. Bipolar inputs are dealt with by using a D/A converter with bipolar output and offset binary coding, and appropriate input scaling.

Integration (Ramp and V-to-f Types)

This family of converters is also quite popular. Its members perform an *indirect* conversion, by first converting to a function of time, then converting from the time function to a digital number using a counter. The *dual-ramp type* is especially suitable for use in digital voltmeters and those applications in which a relatively-lengthy time may be taken for conversion to obtain the benefits of noise reduction through signal averaging.

Here's how the dual-ramp type works: The input signal is applied to an integrator; at the same time a counter is started, counting clock pulses. After a predetermined number of counts (a fixed interval of time, T), a reference voltage having opposite polarity is applied to the integrator. At that instant, the accumulated charge on the integrating capacitor is proportional to the average value of the input over the interval T. The integral of the reference is an opposite-going ramp having a slope V_{REF}/RC. At the same time, the counter is again counting from zero. When the integrator output reaches zero, the count is stopped, and the analog circuitry is reset. Since the charge gained is proportional to $\overline{V_{IN}}T$, and the equal amount of charge lost is proportional to $V_{REF}\Delta t$, then the number of counts relative to the full count is proportional to $\Delta t/T$, or $\overline{V_{IN}}/V_{REF}$. If the output of the counter is a binary number, it will therefore be a binary representation of the input voltage. If the input is attenuated and offset by half the reference voltage, the output will be an offset binary representation of a bipolar input, suitable as an input for computer systems. Figure 27a shows a dual-ramp A/D converter for bipolar signals with offset-binary output.

Dual-slope integration has many advantages. Conversion accuracy is independent of both the capacitor value and the clock frequency, because they affect both the up-slope and the down-ramp in the same ratio. Differential linearity is excellent, because the analog function is free from discontinuities, the codes are generated by a clock and counter, and all codes can inherently exist. Resolution is limited only by analog resolution, rather than by differential nonlinearity; hence, the excellent fine structure may be represented by more bits than would be needed to maintain a given level of scale-factor accuracy. The integration provides rejection of high-frequency noise and averaging of changes that occur during the

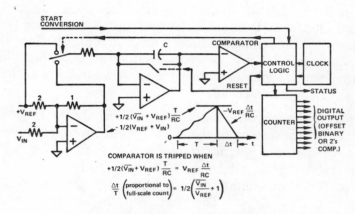

a. Dual-Ramp A/D Converter for Bipolar Input

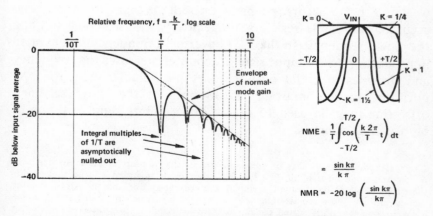

b. Worst-Case Normal-Mode Response of Dual-Slope A/D Converter

Figure 27. Voltage-to-Time-to-Digital Converters

sampling period. The fixed averaging period also makes it possible to obtain "infinite" normal-mode rejection[8] at frequencies that are integral multiples of $1/T$ (see Figure 27b).

Throughput rate of dual-slope converters is limited to somewhat less than $1/2T$ conversions per second. The sample time, T, is determined by the fundamental frequency to be rejected. For example, if one wishes to reject 60Hz and its harmonics, the minimum integrating time is 16-2/3 ms, and the maximum number of conversions is somewhat less than 30/s. Though too slow for fast data acquisition, dual-slope converters are quite adequate for such transducers as thermocouples and gas chromatographs; and they are the predominant circuit used in constructing digital voltmeters. Since DVM's use sign-magnitude BCD coding, bipolar operation requires polarity sensing and reference-polarity switching, rather than simple offsetting.

Other conversion approaches in this class include the single-ramp type and V/f converters. In the single-ramp converter, a reference voltage, of opposite polarity to the signal, is integrated (while a counter counts clock pulses) until the output of the integrator is equal to the signal input. At that time (Δt) the output of the integrator is $E_{REF}\Delta t/RC$. Therefore, Δt − hence, the number of counts and the corresponding digital number − is proportional to the ratio of the input to the reference. This process has the weakness that its accuracy depends on both the capacitor (extremely-accurate and stable resistors are relatively easy to come by) and the clock frequency. In the V/f converter, a frequency is generated in proportion to the input signal; a counter measures the frequency and provides a digital output code, the value of which is proportional to the input signal. In both of the above schemes, offsetting may be used to obtain offset binary representation of bipolar analog inputs.

---

[8] *Normal-mode* noise consists of unwanted signals that appear on the input line, even if common-mode error is nil. If a low-frequency or dc quantity is to be converted in the presence of a high-frequency ripple, a successive-approximations A/D converter, even if preceded by a sample-hold, will convert the instantaneous values of signal-plus-noise, producing a noisy digital signal. On the other hand, an integrator will inherently attenuate high frequencies, producing smoothing, and, if combined with a fixed averaging period, will null out those frequencies that have whole numbers of cycles during the averaging period.

Counter and "Servo" Types

Figure 28 is a block diagram of a counter-comparator A/D converter, which is analogous to the single-ramp type, but it is independent of the time scale. The analog input is compared with the output of a D/A converter, the digital input of which is driven by a counter. At the start of conversion, the counter starts its count, which continues until the D/A output crosses the input value. At that point, conversion ceases, and the converter is ready to perform the next conversion after the counter has been cleared and its output dumped into a storage register. The number of counts appears in the output register. For bipolar inputs, a bipolar D/A converter is used, and the count is an offset binary representation of the input, starting from negative full-scale.

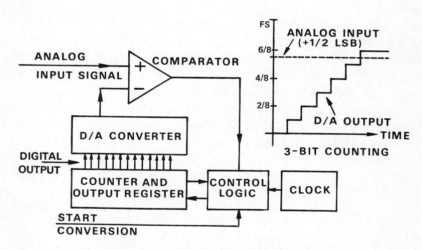

Figure 28. Counter-Comparator A/D Converter

Though quite simple in concept, this converter has the disadvantage of limited speed for a given resolution, since the conversion time for a full-scale change is equal to the clock frequency divided into the maximum number of counts. For example, if the clock frequency is 10MHz, the maximum throughput rate for 10-bit resolution (1024 counts) is something less than 10kHz (100μs per conversion). A variation of this converter is the "servo" type, in which an "up-down" counter is used. (See Figure 15, in the chapter on Sample/Holds).

If the output of the D/A converter is less than the analog input, the counter counts up. If the D/A output is greater than the analog input, the counter counts down. If the analog input is constant, the counter output "hunts" back and forth between the two adjacent bit values. This converter can follow small changes quite rapidly (it will follow 1 LSB changes at the clock rate), but it will require the full count to acquire full-scale step changes. Since it seeks to "home in" on the analog value, the analogy to a servomechanism is quite evident. It seeks to convert continuously, which may be a disadvantage in tying it in with a fast data-acquisition system, since it can give a valid "conversion complete" report only during the clock period immediately following a change in state of the comparator (which in general occurs at irregular intervals). A buffer storage register may be used to store the previous count, while the counter is seeking the next value. By stopping the count (following a completed conversion) at an externally-determined instant, the servo-type converter may be used as a sample-hold with arbitrarily-long *hold* time (with no droop). If the "up" or the "down" count is disabled, the converter will act as a valley follower or a peak follower, counting in the appropriate direction only when the analog input exceeds the previous extreme value. Both the analog and the digital stored values are available.

Parallel Types

Figure 29 shows a parallel 3-bit converter with Gray code output. It has $2^n - 1$ comparators, biased 1 LSB apart, starting with +1/2 LSB. For 0 input, all comparators are off. As the input increases, it causes an increasing number of comparators to switch on. For a given bit position in the code, e.g., Bit 2, those comparator outputs that should give logic "1" for a given input level are connected to the first *nor* gate, and those that should be zero are connected to the second *nor* gate, thus generating the appropriate code. (Natural binary could be implemented in the same way, using an appropriate table).

The evident advantage of this approach is that conversion occurs in parallel, with speed limited only by the switching time of the comparators and gates. As the input changes, the output code changes. Thus, this is the fastest approach to conversion.

Unfortunately, the number of elements increases geometrically with resolution. For 4 bits, 15 comparators, and 7 8-input gates are required. For 5 bits, 31 comparators, and 9 16-input gates are necessary. As linear and digital integrated-circuit elements of increasing complexity become available, increased levels of resolution will tend to approach the threshold of practicality. But high resolution and the fastest speeds at low cost are still some time away.

By combining parallel conversion for small numbers of bits with iteration (to wit, successive approximations taking several bits at a time), it is possible to strike a compromise that gives better resolution than a parallel approach, with less complexity, and improved speed over the successive-approximations approach.

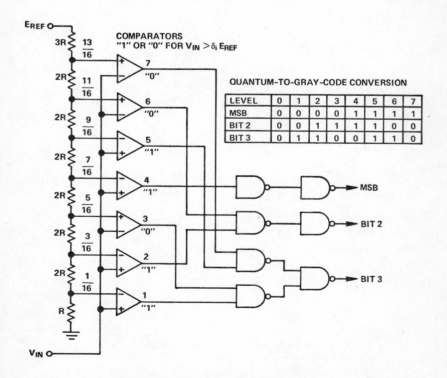

QUANTUM-TO-GRAY-CODE CONVERSION

LEVEL	0	1	2	3	4	5	6	7
MSB	0	0	0	0	1	1	1	1
BIT 2	0	0	1	1	1	1	0	0
BIT 3	0	1	1	0	0	1	1	0

Figure 29. Parallel 3-Bit A/D Converter with Gray Code Output

CONCLUSION

In this chapter, we have attempted to provide the fundamentals for a basic understanding of converters. In the chapters that follow, we will discuss further some of the considerations faced by the converter designer, provide an understanding of and a guide to specification of converters, and explore the elements of successful system design using converters. For more details on any specific topic mentioned in this chapter, we suggest that you consult the bibliography. Though not comprehensive, the references provided do "fan out" to additional references that can lead to exhaustive — if not exhausting — coverage of specific topics.

Designing Converters

In Chapter 1, "Understanding Converters," there is included a hasty survey of the more-popular converter design approaches. The intention of this chapter is to provide more-detailed and practical information on the design and construction of D/A and A/D converters for the benefit of both users and designers.

While one could recall the approaches described in the earlier chapter, but cover them in much greater depth, it is manifestly evident that to do justice to a number of the most popular designs would require more space than is available here. We have therefore decided to focus on one approach and attempt to treat it thoroughly.

The design approach chosen for D/A conversion uses quad current switches of the AD550 family and a monolithic thin-film resistor network of the AD850 type. The A/D conversion example uses this D/A converter in a successive-approximation device.

This practical example will serve the reader's purposes well, and for a number of reasons. First, it represents an approach actually used for the construction of converters in production quantities, to be sold at competitive prices, with resolutions ranging from 8 to 16 bits. In addition, it has speed adequate for most purposes; the appropriate components are accessible to the designer at reasonable cost from at least one source (Analog Devices); and, having moderate complexity, it is an excellent starting point for understanding other designs of both greater and lesser complexity.

With this view of the inner workings of products engineered for OEM users (probably the first time a module manufacturer has ever "told all"), users of converters may gain better insight into the devices they are using, and design engineers may gain some ideas or principles that will help them in their future designs.

CONVERTER DESIGN

Many writers on this subject claim that a high-precision D/A converter is the most-difficult-to-design section of any device using it, including an A/D converter. This is only partially true; the added design elements, circuiting, and physical layout involved in using a D/A converter in an A/D converter should not be slighted. The increase of difficulty in building A/D converters of high speed and accuracy, even with a well-designed basic D/A-converter building block, can be massive.

The difficulties of designing D/A converters increase rapidly with the useful resolution sought in the design. 8-bit D/A converters are relatively easy to design and manufacture, since the allowable uncertainty is of the order of 0.2%. Ten-bit converters are much more difficult to design, since the resolution sought is 0.05%. By the time one reaches 12 bits of resolution (0.0125%), the design and manufacturing problems become acute. And 16-bit converters should be left entirely alone by the do-it-yourselfer.

In most cases where the make-or-buy decision involves large numbers of units, it may be comforting to follow the example of the mass-transportation officials who suggest: " . . . leave the driving to us," for reliable, economical, and carefree arrival at one's destination.

REVIEW OF D/A TECHNIQUES

Figure 1 reproduces the current-weighting D/A converter depicted in Figure 14 of "Understanding Converters." This is perhaps the simplest approach to performing a digital-to-voltage conversion. A set of binary-weighted currents flows through a 5kΩ feedback resistor, producing an analog output voltage proportional to the sum of those currents that are turned on.

While this approach looks simple, the problems of manufacturing a converter of this type are large. The two most difficult problems are the switching speed and resistor T.C. matching. For a 12-bit con-

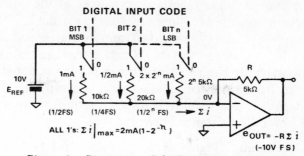

Figure 1. Elementary D/A Converter Circuit

verter using a $10k\Omega$ resistor for the most significant bit (MSB), the least-significant-bit resistor would be $40.96M\Omega$. This range of resistance cannot be obtained from a consistent film material, so that resistance temperature coefficients cannot even be approximately matched. Furthermore, the switching speed of a current switch depends upon the current available to charge the stray capacitances. Since the LSB is $0.5\mu A$, if the stray capacitance is 10pF, then the settling time for 1LSB is $200\mu s$. Obviously, if all currents could be of the order of 1mA, the conversion time for all bits will be uniformly shortened.

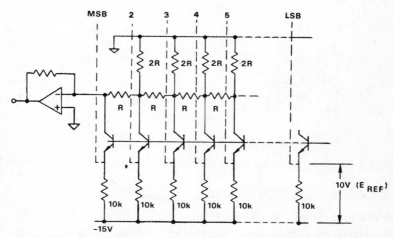

Figure 2. D/A Converter Using Equal Current Sources and R–2R Ladder Attenuator

Figure 2 shows a way in which this is commonly accomplished. Basically, the NPN current sources are all made equal to 1mA.

The individual currents from the collectors of the current source transistors are subjected to binary weighting via the R–2R network. D/A converters of this type yield extremely high speed conversions (e.g., the MDA–10F settles in 50ns). Other advantages of this circuit are evident: the resistance range is very reasonable and the selection of transistors for matched V_{BE} is simplified. However, a disadvantage of this circuit is that it requires *two* accurately-trimmed low-T.C. resistance networks.

A third technique (Figure 3) combines good features of both techniques. Commonly known as the quad current-source approach (see Figure 20 in the preceding chapter), the technique relies on binary-weighted current sources, in groups of four, with currents ranging from 1mA (MSB) to 1/8mA. Three such quads provide 12 bits of resolution. The currents from the third quad are resistively attenuated by 16:1 before summing with the currents in the second quad, and this sum is again attenuated by 16:1 before summing with the first quad's currents. Much of the circuitry, being repetitive, is highly amenable to monolithic integration, as exemplified by Analog Devices' AD550/AD850 monolithic μDAC conversion components.

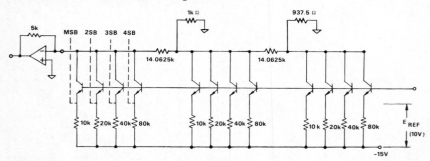

Figure 3. D/A Converter Using Binary-Weighted Quad Current Sources

THE IMPORTANCE OF LOGIC BUFFERING

The manner in which the switching signals from logic circuits are buffered from the analog circuitry of D/A converters, though of great importance, is not commonly well-understood. There are many ways (some good, some not so good), to turn electronic switches on and off. The simplest is the single diode approach shown in Figure 4 (see also Figure 19 in the preceding chapter).

Here the common base line of the current sources is biased at a midrange value of the TTL threshold (1.4V). When the data inputs are low ("0"), the diodes are forward-biased and draw the bit current away from the PNP current source. This, in effect, back-biases the PNP emitter-base junction, turning the transistor off. When the logic input goes high ("1" — greater than 2.0V), the diode is back-biased and the transistor current source is turned on.

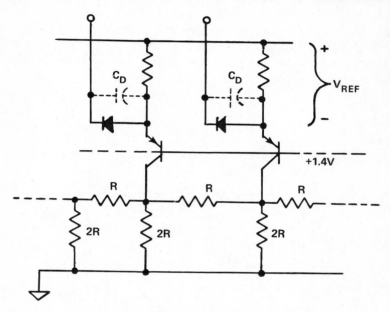

Figure 4.   Diode Switching in D/A Converter

Two major error sources are characteristic of this simple approach. The first is leakage current in the diode. 10nA may sound negligible at room temperature, but at 70°C this figure is in the neighborhood of 1μA, an appreciable error. Similarly, when the switch is in the high state, the diode is back-biased; logic transients on the data input side, though not of sufficient magnitude to affect the switch state, are coupled through the diode capacitance, to the emitter of the current source, thereby producing transient errors in the weighted current.

Figure 5 shows a much-improved way to electronically switch current sources on and off. This buffered scheme involves essentially two D/A converters. The first, using Q1–Q4, performs the actual high-accuracy conversion. The second D/A, composed of Q5–Q8, accepts the digital inputs and applies back-bias to the emitters of the appropriate switching transistors, Q1–Q4, as required by the input code (which must be complementary to the input code required by the circuit in Figure 4). For example, when the input logic at Q5 is high, the diode is reverse-biased and Q5 conducts. Its positive collector current biases the emitter of Q1 high and effectively diverts the flow of I_1. When the logic input is low, the diode shuts off Q5's collector current, which allows I_1 to flow normally in the collector circuit of Q1. The buffered scheme solves both problems of the single-diode approach.

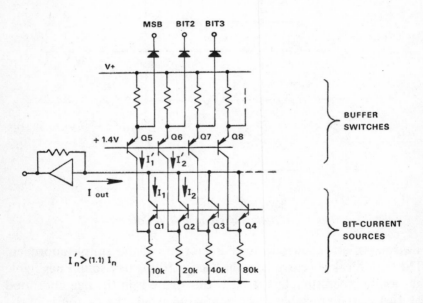

Figure 5. Buffered Switches in D/A Converter

Often overlooked in the buffer design is how much swing must be provided at the emitter of Q1 to toggle the switch fully from *on* to *off*. The following exercise may be revealing:

$$\Delta V_{BE} = \frac{kT}{q} \ln \frac{I_{ON}}{I_{OFF}}$$

For 12-bit resolution, with 1/10LSB uncertainty,

$$\frac{I_{ON}}{I_{OFF}} > 10 \times 2^n \cong 40,000$$

Since ln (40,000) $\cong$ 10.5, at 70°C (343°K)

$$\Delta V_{BE} = 29mV \times 10.5 = 300mV$$

and, at 125°C,

$$\Delta V_{BE} = 33mV \times 10.5 = 350mV$$

If one considers that the standard TTL input logic thresholds are 0.8V for "0" and 2.0V for "1", and that diode drops, while conducting I_{ON}, may approach 0.7V, it is evident that the base line must be held within a narrow range of voltage, especially at higher temperatures.

MONOLITHIC COMPONENTS

The basic monolithic conversion components to be discussed in connection with the circuitry encountered in the remainder of this chapter are the AD550 monolithic quad switches and the AD850 monolithic thin-film resistor network.

The key factor establishing the accuracy of the quad switches is the binary weighting of the current-source transistors, Q1–Q4 in Figure 6. It is well known that two matched transistors, operating at current densities that cause the V_{BE} drops of the transistors to be equal, will exhibit theoretically perfect tracking with temperature.

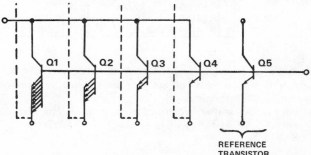

Figure 6. Binary-Weighted Current Source Transistors

If two perfectly-matched paralleled transistors together draw twice the total emitter current of a third matched transistor, their V_{BE}'s will nevertheless be equal.

The current switches Q1–Q4, though conducting currents in the ratio 1:2:4:8, have similarly-weighted emitter areas, hence equal current densities, and will therefore exhibit equal V_{BE}'s. If the V_{BE} drops of the current sources are equal, then errors in current due to variations of V_{BE} in series with the measuring resistors track perfectly for all four switches.

The finite β of the current-source transistors represents another source of conversion error, since the base current, $I_E/(1 + \beta)$ subtracts an increment from the emitter current. Monolithic construction leads to initial β-matches within ±5%. When used with the reference transistor, Q5, the effects of both V_{BE} and β variation with temperature can be fully compensated, resulting in extremely low temperature coefficients for the conversion.

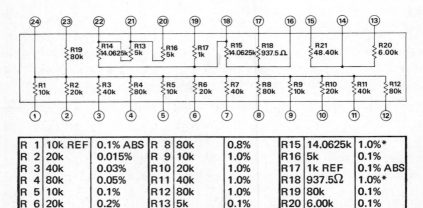

R 1	10k REF	0.1% ABS	R 8	80k	0.8%	R15	14.0625k	1.0%*
R 2	20k	0.015%	R 9	10k	1.0%	R16	5k	0.1%
R 3	40k	0.03%	R10	20k	1.0%	R17	1k REF	0.1% ABS
R 4	80k	0.05%	R11	40k	1.0%	R18	937.5Ω	1.0%*
R 5	10k	0.1%	R12	80k	1.0%	R19	80k	0.1%
R 6	20k	0.2%	R13	5k	0.1%	R20	6.00k	0.1%
R 7	40k	0.4%	R14	14.0625k	0.1%*	R21	48.40k	0.1%

NOTES:
All resistors ratio to R1 except R14, R15, R18 which ratio to R17. Tolerances shown are for 12-bit accuracy and degrade by factor of four maximum for 10-bit accuracy.
Total positive or negative "contribution to error" is less than 0.012%
BCD network, AD851, is: $R_{13} = R_{16} = 4k\Omega$; $R_{14} = 8.1325k\Omega$;
$R_{15} = 8.4375k\Omega$.

Figure 7. Typical Monolithic Thin-Film Resistor Network (AD850)

The companion AD850 thin-film resistor network is shown schematically in Figure 7. Included in this network are:

Bit-weighting resistors (R1 − R12)

Reference compensation resistor (R19)

Interquad divider resistors (R13, R14, R15, R17, and R18)

Gain resistors (feedback resistor in D/A's, input resistor in A/D's) (R13 and R16)

Reference input resistors (R21 and R20)

When used for all its indicated circuit functions, this resistor network has the interesting property that, as long as the resistors track one another as temperature changes, the output voltage error due to absolute resistance changes for any given code combination will be nil. The reason is that absolute resistance changes of *all* resistors in the network make little difference − the tracking *between* resistors is the only item of importance. For the AD850, temperature coefficient of tracking error is ±1 ppm/°C.

COMPONENT TOLERANCE

Save for the reference and output amplifier, the errors produced by the analog components used to build a D/A converter can be mainly attributed to errors caused by the bit switches and resistance tolerances. The V_{BE} and β mismatch errors in the quad current switches have already been briefly touched upon. Naturally, the tracking of these parameters with temperature influences errors measured when temperature changes.

The Analog Devices AD550 is classified into numerous parametric categories. On the data sheet, 30 of these categories are shown. The three main subdivisions relate to the relative contribution to error by each bit. The "J" grade (±1%) is used in the least-significant-quad position. The "K" grade (±0.1%) is used in the middle quad of 10- or 12-bit converters. The "L" grade (±0.01%) is used in the most significant quad position. The other 10 subdivisions result from sorting these units by V_{BE} at rated current. The V_{BE} range from 600mV to 700mV is subdivided into the 10mV categories denoted by the integers 0 to 9 (i.e., 6$\underline{00}$−6$\underline{09}$, 6$\underline{10}$−6$\underline{19}$, etc.)

Interquad V_{BE} matching is required to minimize errors between bits in the first quad and bits in the second quad. If the V_{BE} difference between Quad 1 and Quad 2 were 100mV, then the apparent error in bit 5 relative to full scale would be 0.03%. When the three AD550's used in a 12-bit converter are assembled, the V_{BE} groupings of at least the L and K grades must match.

Internally, at ADI, the product breakdown is even more detailed than is indicated on the AD550 data sheet. The AD550L, which fortunately has quite respectable yields, is itself graded and further subdivided into higher-accuracy groups designated as follows:

Switch Contribution to Error
(Relative to MSB)

Grade Designation	Switch Matching Error
LA	0.01%
LB	0.007%
LC	0.005%
M	0.002%

The errors listed for each grade are maximum, as measured in an actual conversion circuit. Thus, they are a composite of V_{BE} and β tracking errors, and take advantage of compensation, where it occurs. As indicated, these subdivisions are mainly for internal manufacturing purposes, but the user of AD550's may be comforted to know that when he orders an "L" grade unit, he nearly always gets, in actuality, an *LC*. The M-grade unit is used for the most-significant quad in the DAC–16QM (and ADC–16QM).

The resistor specifications listed in the table (Figure 7) are often misinterpreted. It is imperative that a D/A-circuit designer understand the meaning of the tolerance specifications, and their effect on a given resistor's contribution to the total error. The most-significant-bit resistor, R1, is used as the reference resistor for ratio-matching purposes; all the other resistors are referred to it. The second-bit resistor, R2, is shown as having a ratio tolerance of 0.015%. Some persons automatically interpret this as meaning that the second-bit resistor could contribute an error of 0.015% *relative to full scale*. This interpretation is wrong. Since the MSB (R1) has a weight of ½F.S., the second-bit contribution to error has a weight of ¼F.S. This means that a ratio tolerance of 0.015% for R_2/R_1 will cause bit 2 to have a contribution to full-scale error of 1/8 LSB of 12 bits (0.00375%).

Applying a tolerance analysis to the specifications, one might be led to expect that a 12-bit set of AD550's and an AD850, when assembled (with the best of care) will always yield a 12-bit-linear D/A converter, with no bit-trimming necessary. The overall error actually depends upon a statistical distribution of the errors of both sets of components. In the very worst case, it is possible for some code combinations to be outside the 12-bit linearity expected. For this reason, we recommend certain final-trimming procedures, which will be described later. Besides being occasionally necessary, they lead to improved temperature-margins and a sense of confidence that each assembled unit is well within specifications.

THE INTER-QUAD DIVIDER

The inter-quad division network of the AD850 functions quite simply. The basic idea is depicted in Figure 8a, where a current source delivers its current to the node joining a 15kΩ resistor and a 1kΩ resistor. Since the 15kΩ unit is terminated in virtual ground (the amplifier summing junction), the voltage across both resistors will be equal. Hence, 15/16 of the original current (I) goes off to signal ground via the 1kΩ resistor, while the remaining

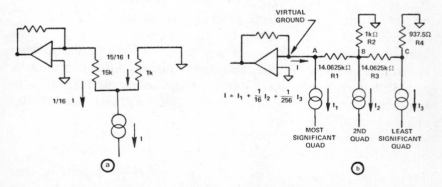

Figure 8a. Current Attenuation to 1/16

Figure 8b. Current Attenuation of Three Sources to 1, 1/16, 1/256

1/16 I is added at the summing point via the 15kΩ resistor. The problem is just a little more complicated when the multiple-current-source situation depicted in Figure 8b exists.

In Figure 8b is a simplified diagram of the AD550 outputs and the interquad weighting resistors of the AD850. The 3 current sources I_1, I_2, I_3, represent the common collector lines of the three quads. The current from the most-significant quad (MSQ) flows directly into the summing node of the op amp (virtual ground). The second quad's current is split 16:1 by the following means: As the current enters node "B", 15/16ths of I_2 goes to signal ground through the parallel combination of R2 with (R_3 + R_4). The remaining 1/16 goes off through R1 to the summing node "A". Note that the parallel combination of R_2 and R_3 + R_4 is 937.5 ohms. Thus, the inter-quad current split effected at node "B" is precisely 16:1.

The inter-quad current division at node "C" is a little more difficult to understand. It is easiest to analyze the two interquad dividers as a single network and solve for a 256:1 attenuation of I_3 as it reaches node "A". By a straightforward analysis, one can learn that the current entering node "B" from node "C" is $1/17 I_3$. At this point, it is further split, in the ratio 15.0625:1, by R1 and R2. The product of 15.0625 and 17 is, as desired, 256.

One should note that, in the practical situation, the current sources depicted at Figure 8 are the collectors of common-base NPN transistors. The designer must be aware of the fact that when all bits are turned on, a voltage drop appears at nodes "B" and "C" of the order of – 1.8V. For this reason, the common base line of the current sources should be operated below – 2.0V, in order to keep the transistors well within their linear region. Also, it should be noted that the output resistance of the collectors in the most-significant quad can be as low as 30MΩ without significantly affecting divider accuracy.

REFERENCE LOOP

The overall gain and accuracy of a D/A converter depend on that of a stable current reference. The AD550/AD850 system is designed to use the common 6.2V "zero-T.C." zener reference diodes.

Figure 9 shows one such diode, the 1N829A, used in a circuit that provides it with an essentially constant-current drive. Low-T.C. zeners require 7.5mA of constant bias current to maintain minimum temperature coefficient. Furthermore, variations of the current with temperature or supply voltage will alter the zener voltage, due to the drop across the diode's R_{on} (about 10Ω). The circuit of Figure 9 provides excellent power-supply rejection and a sufficiently accurate 7.5mA bias current, plus the 1.125mA taken by the input current of the converter's reference amplifier and the bipolar offset, used in the recommended AD550/AD850 combination. The $2.2k\Omega$ resistor at the output of the AD741 op amp helps maintain the amplifier in its linear region by reducing its output load, which it shares with the +15V supply. It also avoids latchup.

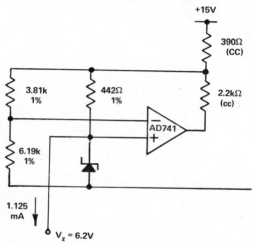

Figure 9. Constant-Current Excitation of Precision Reference Zener Diode

The basic reference loop for the D/A converter is shown in Figure 10. The reference transistor of the most significant quad (see Figure 6) is used to monitor changes in the V_{BE} and current gain of all the bit switches (since it is identical to them and operating under virtually identical conditions). The zener voltage, developed as in Figure 9, is connected to pin 14 of the AD850 ladder network.

A trim resistor, placed in series with the $48.4k\Omega$ (R21) reference-current resistor, allows the current supplied, via the op amp's summing junction, to the collector of the MSQ reference transistor, to be adjusted to just 1/8mA. Since the reference transistor has the same geometry as each elementary bit-transistor, the resistors are precisely weighted, and all transistors share a common voltage-reference supply, then when the reference loop has adjusted the base voltages such that 0.125mA flows in the collector of the reference transistor, the properly-weighted currents will automatically flow through the collector circuits of all turned-on bit-switches.

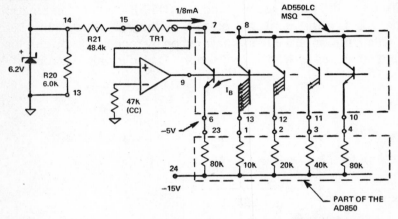

Figure 10. Reference Circuit Using Non-inverting Amplifier Input

As the V_{BE}'s and current gains of the transistors change with temperature, the reference loop will adjust the base voltages to track and maintain 1/8mA at all times into the reference transistor's collector, and correspondingly proportional currents through all the other collectors. Adjusting the value of the trim resistor TR1 will adjust the absolute value of the reference current and hence all of the individual bit weights in proportion. The 48.4kΩ reference current resistor R21 is designed to produce 1/8mA with a minimum zener voltage of 6.05V, with $TR_1 = 0$.

The configuration of Figure 10 is simple and can be easily described; however, it is prone to latch up under certain conditions because it uses the op amp's positive input. For certain sequences of power-supply turnon, it is possible for the amplifier output to become positive with respect to ground, thereby forward-biasing the base-collector junction of the reference transistor and latching the amplifier in its positive feedback mode. The inverting configuration of Figure 11 avoids this problem by adjusting the common side of the supply, instead of the base line, to close the loop.

Here the common base line is biased by the 1N746 at −3V. The inverting op amp drives the resistors' common rail via a buffer and level shift circuit. Another advantage of this circuit is improved immunity to noise in the −15V supply. Unfortunately, it has the disadvantage that it is difficult to prevent the circuit from bottoming on the −15V rail, since the base of the PNP buffer is within 0.6V of the −15V line.

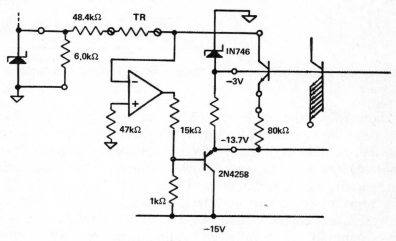

Figure 11. Reference Circuit Using Inverting Input

In Figure 12, the basic non-inverting configuration of Figure 10 is revised to include an anti-latchup circuit — CR2 and the 4.7kΩ resistor. It also includes frequency-response shaping to prevent transient voltages from upsetting the reference loop, as follows: In junction-isolated IC's, such as the AD550, capacitive coupling from the collector of one NPN transistor to the collector of another NPN transistor exists via the depletion capacitance of the substrate. When the input bit combination changes, the DAC's output amplifier will usually be driven in a slewing condition, resulting in a fast rising voltage edge on the common collector line of the AD550. This fast-moving edge is coupled to the collector of the reference transistor on the same chip. Since the collector of the reference transistor looks at a high impedance (48.4kΩ), the coupled transient is applied to the noninverting terminal in the circuit of Figure 10. This, in turn, can upset the reference loop for a period of microseconds.

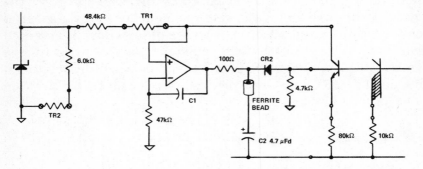

Figure 12. Reference Circuit With Frequency Shaping and Anti-Latchup Circuit

In the configuration of Figure 12, we can see a means by which this behavior can be controlled. The voltage from the common base rail of the AD550 to $-15V$ is kept from changing instantaneously by a 4.7μF capacitor. However, since a 4.7μF capacitance can by itself cause the reference amplifier to oscillate, a 100Ω isolation resistor provides a predictable time constant. C1, together with the 4.7kΩ common-mode bias-compensation resistor, rolls off the response of the amplifier on a 6dB/octave slope, which intersects unity open-loop gain at the breakpoint of the 100Ω $\times$ 4.7μF combination. CR2 and the 4.7kΩ resistor prevent the latchup mode mentioned earlier. The ferrite bead is added to prevent the common-base bit-switches (with f_t's of approximately 500MHz) from oscillating in the 100–200MHz region.

The 6.0kΩ resistor on the AD850 (R20) is shown connected to signal ground in Figures 10, 11, and 12. R20 provides 1mA offset current in bipolar offset-binary D/A converters, when it is connected to the output current terminal of the converter. This resistor should be grounded when the unipolar configuration is desired, so that the zener diode (Figure 9) runs at constant current. Ignoring this consideration — leaving R20 open — can result in a gain error of 0.2%. Of course, with an external reference, or with a circuit in which the reference voltage is applied via a low impedance (e.g., the emitter of an inside-the-loop follower) it would not matter greatly whether or not R20 were terminated.

TRIMMING HIGH-ACCURACY CONVERTERS

One should be always aware that, however easily we may talk of 12-bit accuracy, it still represents *total error* of the order of 0.01%, which many circumspect engineers still consider uncomfortably-close to the limits of the state-of-the-art. Second- and third-order tolerance buildups can become highly significant, as can inadvertent errors in interfacing a converter with its analog output circuit or a measurement circuit.

For 12-bit (and better) linearity, the designer of converters should always seek *the best-possible resolution,* and should make provisions for final trim of the highest-order bits in order to attain it. In addition, he must provide both coarse and fine trims of the overall "gain" (i.e., scale factor) of the converter, offset-bias-current trim for bipolar converters, and overall zero adjustment of the output amplifier.

Let us start with the bit-trimming procedures. The AD550 and AD850, in combination, are amenable to highly-accurate and stable trimming. Figure 13 is a fairly-complete schematic of the first

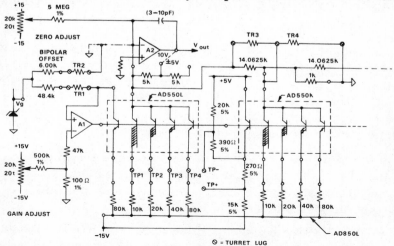

Figure 13. Connections for Trimming a D/A Converter for 12-Bit Accuracy

8 bits of a 12-bit D/A; it will illustrate the discussions to follow on trimming and adjustment.

For final trim of the first 4 bits, a number of nanoamperes of current must be added to or subtracted from the emitter current of each switch to bring it to its calibrated relative value. To do this, we use the conveniently-available reference transistor of the second quad (AD550K) to establish two small offset voltages, which will be centred about the emitter voltage of the bit-switches. In Figure 13, the AD550's reference transistor is biased by approximately 1/8mA; ordinary carbon composition resistors may be used. The voltage at TP+ is 200mV *below* the emitter voltages, while that at TP– is 200mV *above* the emitters. These arbitrary designations are for convenience in trimming.

If the bit being adjusted does not have sufficient weight (measured at the output, using instrumentation of adequate precision), a current ΔI is added to that bit by connecting a resistor of appropriate value ($R = 200mV/\Delta I$, or conductance 2.5 micromho/LSB) from the emitter of the bit switch in question to TP+. Similarly, if the bit weight is too high, it can be decreased by connecting an appropriate resistance between the emitter and TP–. It should be noted that, as temperature varies, the V_{BE} of all the transistors will also vary. But the trim voltages will remain fairly constant and centred around the nominal emitter voltage of the AD550k's reference transistor.

To minimize the effects of slight mismatches between the first two quads, due to either V_{BE} or β differences, one should provide for slight trimming of the first interquad divider (i.e., the relative weight of the second quad). If, after trimming the first four bits, the fifth bit differs from ½ the fourth bit by a significant amount, the following procedure may be followed:

If bit 5 is too *low* in weight, install a trim in the TR3 position (usually of the order of megohms). If bit 5 exhibits *too much* weight, it can be attenuated with a trim in position TR4 (typically of the order of 100kΩ or more).

Normally, 1/8W carbon-composition resistors can be used in these positions, since only very small quantities of current are drawn through them. The carbon-composition-resistor temperature coefficients are attenuated by both their overall weight relative to the resistors they parallel, and the bit weight, relative to full scale. This effect is negligible.

To trim the overall gain of a converter, trim-position TR1 is utilized. First center the gain-adjust pot (10 turns from one end). Install a decade-resistance box for TR1, and turn on the first four bits (00001 . . . 1 in complementary binary). With the 5kΩ resistor serving as the feedback resistor for the output amplifier, the proper output voltage should be 0.3750 (unipolar mode) for best adjustment of TR1. Replace the indicated decade resistance by the nearest standard precision-film-resistance value. (R20 of the AD850 should be grounded during this operation). Final gain trim can now be accomplished with the trim resistance installed in TR1. The resistance values shown in Figure 13 provide a mean adjustment of ±0.25%.

To adjust zero in unipolar converters, turn off all bits (1 1 1 . . . 1 in complementary binary), and adjust "Zero Adjust" for 0.0000V out. In bipolar converters, to trim the bipolar offset (±5V full-scale output range), center the 20-turn "zero-adjust" pot and connect the bipolar offset resistor to the output amplifier's summing point, as indicated in Figure 13. Using a decade box in TR2, and leaving all bit switches off, adjust the decade box for −5.0000V out. Install the nearest value of trim resistance to the reading of the decade box in the TR2 position. Final offset trim can now be performed with the MSB only on (0 1 1 1 . . . 1 in complementary offset binary) using the "zero-adjust" pot.

Further details on testing procedures and trimming of D/A and A/D converters can be found in chapter 3, "Testing Converters." An additional detail of the design of the circuit of Figure 13 is worth mentioning:

The feedback capacitance (3 to 10pF) around the output amplifier compensates for the capacitance of the common collector rail of the AD550L, the input capacitance of the output amplifier, and circuit strays. Circuit wiring capacitances should, of course, be minimized to keep the value of feedback capacitance low, since it tends to increase the output settling time. It is adjusted for "optimum" response: minimum transients *and* settling time. Its omission may cause oscillations, or instability.

TEMPERATURE VARIATION EFFECTS

Reiterating an earlier statement, if all resistors in the AD850 network track perfectly, then even if their absolute value changes, say at a rate of 50ppm/°C, the output voltage will remain constant (assuming constant V_Z). This can be shown by the following example: If the reference-current resistor (R21, 48.4kΩ) increases by 2%, the reference current would be decreased by 2%. However, the feedback resistor around the output amplifier is also increased by 2%, increasing the gain by 2% to compensate, with no net error. Since the bipolar offset resistor, R20, also increases in proportion, there is no net error in bipolar applications. Variation of the current-weighting resistors is compensated by similar variation of the resistance in series with the emitter of the reference transistor. And finally, the interquad attenuation resistors track one another and maintain constant attenuation of the outputs from the less-significant quads.

This example describes the ideal situation. In practice, the resistance values will track ratiometrically to only about 1ppm/°C. Further, the discrete metal-film resistors used for TR1 and TR2 will undoubtedly have temperature coefficients that differ from those of the ladder resistors. Since their effect on total resistance is incremental, the effect of their T.C. on circuit performance is reduced. However, one should always perform a calculation to be sure that they can be safely neglected. Here is an example:

The absolute TCR of the AD850 is within ±25ppm/°C. Assume that TR1 and TR2 have an absolute TCR range of ±50ppm/°C. The effect of these mixed TCR's is dependent upon the absolute value of V_Z. The greater V_Z is, the larger the value of TR1 (and TR2). For V_Z = 6.5V, at the high end of a +5% tolerance range, the worst case of TCR mismatch will be approximately 5ppm/°C for a 50ppm/°C TCR of TR1. If the TCR of TR1 is reduced to ±10ppm/°C, this drift mismatch is reduced to 2.5ppm/°C. If the zener voltage is at its nominal value, 6.2V, and TR1 is ±10ppm/°C, then gain drift is reduced to approximately 1ppm/°C. Suffice it to say that the closer V_Z is to the low end of its allowable tolerance range (6.05V), and the lower the TCR of the trim resistors is kept, the lower the effect of temperature on gain T.C. Then, scale factor (or gain) drift becomes almost entirely dependent on the Zener diode's voltage T.C.

Another contributor to gain drift is the offset drift, with temperature, of the reference amplifier, A1. Both offset voltage and bias current drifts must be considered. As an example, suppose that the total effect amounts to $15\mu V/°C$. This will contribute roughly 2.5ppm/°C to gain drift ($15 \times 10^{-6}/6.2 = 2.5$ppm). Gain drift error can also result from a reduction in open-loop gain of the output amplifier. For instance, a gain change, in A2, from 20,000 to 10,000, can result in an error contribution of 0.005%. It is therefore very desirable for A2's open-loop gain to be greater than 40,000 at room temperature.

CURRENT VS VOLTAGE OUTPUT

A converter can be built to produce either an analog current output or an analog voltage output. The AD550/AD850 combination produces a basic current output, which is externally converted to a voltage using an additional output amplifier. However, since the op amp must slow down the response, some users prefer a current output for their application, or a passively-derived (small) voltage output.

Since the drift of the current output is not compensated by a tracking feedback resistor, the drift of current output from the D/A circuit in Figure 13, with the amplifier removed, is subject to the absolute TCR of the resistance ladder network, and can be as great as ±25ppm/°C. The current output terminal of the D/A can be terminated in a resistive load to ground. However, one must observe the range over which this kind of loading is applicable. A total load resistance of 1kΩ, with 2mA full-scale output current, will produce an output voltage of –2V full scale. Higher-value resistors will drive the common collector bus into saturation, producing excessive non-linearity.

Though it might appear at first glance that the interquad division ratios might be disturbed by using a resistive load instead of a virtual ground, vigorous application of Norton's theorem will show that only the overall scale factor is affected. With a resistive load, the overall scale factor is determined by the external load, in parallel with the resistance looking back toward the interquad dividers (and — in the case of bipolar converters — the offset current resistor (R20)).

If the output voltage developed across a passive load is to be amplified, attention must be paid to the common-mode and offset drift requirements of the output configuration and the choice of resistor ratio in the amplifier feedback circuit, especially if large amounts of gain are desired. The problem of gain temperature coefficient due to non-compensation of the absolute TCR by the unused built-in feedback resistor may be solved to a degree by using a discrete $48\text{k}\Omega$ resistor, matching the TCR of the external load resistor, to set the reference current (and another matching resistor to replace R20 for bipolar applications). Though the loading effect of the interquad resistances will tend to worsen it, the gain-temperature coefficient will be greatly improved by good discrete-resistor tracking.

ON ERROR BUDGETS

One can see, from the above discussion, that there are many sources of error. As desired resolution and linearity increase, and as first-order errors are decreased, the many sources that contribute 2nd and 3rd-order errors become more important. One way that some designers keep these sources in mind and try to account for their probable contributions is to use some form of error-budget analysis.

This consists of listing all the anticipated sources of error, with their expected worst-case and probable contributions, and using some form of linear or root-sum-of-the-squares summation to estimate the total error.

Error budget analysis, used as an intelligently-applied checklist, is at its most-useful in pinpointing those sources of error that must be minimized, either by circuit design, by trimming, by component selection, or by performing some cost tradeoff.

As a means of predicting total error, error budgets are no better than the assumptions made, both about the individual error sources and about the way they will occur and combine when the circuits are assembled in production quantities. A too-conservative design for no-rejects, based on straight summation of worst-case errors, may result in greater overall cost of production than a less-conservative but more-clever design (utilizing some insight into how errors might combine), even though the less-costly design may (nay, *should*) produce (an acceptable number of) rejects in testing. (The cost of rejects can be reduced by recycling.) On the other hand, it is possible to defeat the best estimate of overall error by poor layout or component choice, or the best estimate of cost by requiring excessive tweaking or rejects.

LAYOUT CONSIDERATIONS

Up to this point, we have dealt strictly with the electrical circuit design of digital-to-analog converters. We have discussed some of the finer points of error and drift compensation. Now let us turn our attention to those factors that do not show up in the schematic.

Sources of both static and dynamic errors must be considered when designing the layout of the converter. Static errors are most often caused by voltage drops in "ground loops" and result from carelessness in the layout process. To give an appreciation for how easily this problem can arise, consider a hypothetical example. Suppose an analog ground line has 50 milliohms of resistance between two points. Suppose the current variation through that piece of track is 0 to 10mA for various code combinations in the converter. The resulting change in ground potential is 0.5mV. If this ground happens to be in common with the output signal, this type of error can be disastrous in converter designs calling for 12-bit and better resolutions.

Furthermore, the selection of input/output sockets and pins is very important. It is not difficult to pick up 100mΩ of contact resistance in an improperly-chosen connector. Suffice it to say that all lines carrying analog output currents must be carefully located, and calculations should be performed to ensure that lead-resistance and ground-loop errors are minimal. Never try to second-guess. Improper layout can also cause dynamic errors. To avoid them, the current-output bus of current switches (whether discrete or integrated) must be as short as possible and carefully laid out from three standpoints.

First, the longer the run from the current-summing point of the bit switches to the summing point of the output amplifier, the more likely it is to pick up extraneous EMI signals. Second, the longer the track from the output current bus to the summing point, the greater is its distributed capacitance. Third, the longer that track, the higher the inductance. This can lead to high-frequency oscillations, as mentioned previously. (NPN common-base current-sources, with f_t's of 500MHz, can easily oscillate in the 200–300MHz region.)

Because converters interface high-speed, high-energy digital signals with high-resolution analog signals, great care is needed to minimize stray coupling of digital waveforms into the analog circuitry. For example, some D/A converters contain buffer registers to store the digital input words. All digital information is transferred with fast-rising edges of voltage and fast-changing currents. These produce radiation, which must be kept away from critical points in the analog section. A primary design rule is that the digital and analog sections be separated physically with (if at all possible) some sort of ground plate between them.

In addition, the 5V supplies used for TTL logic should be kept apart from the ±15V supplies normally used for analog signal processing. In particular, the ground lines from the converter to the two supplies should be kept separate and terminated only at the the power supplies themselves. This will tend to keep the fast-rising current edges in the logic sections away from the relatively stationary currents encountered in the analog sections. It is generally true that the critical points in the analog sections of the converter are of relatively high impedance. Hence they are very prone to electrostatic pickup. Even though the foregoing discussion would appear to be applicable where speed is important, high-speed transients can sometimes cause dc shifts through rectification, ringing in marginally-stable circuits, and will often require filtering of the analog output.

The faster the desired analog response, the more critical such things as digital feedthrough become, because the analog output is not ready for use until the digital transients have died away. Even though the basic electrical design goal for settling time is several hundred nanoseconds, transients coupled to the output by poor layout may result in 1μs or greater settling time.

In the design of high-speed D/A converters for CRT display applications, digital transients due to stray coupling must be kept to very low levels. Also, the "glitches" due to intermediate states in code switching must be minimized. In Figure 14 is shown a DAC–10DF, a high-speed D/A converter specifically designed for CRT applications. It includes a sample-hold network to hold the output during switching, while the glitch-causing intermediate codes occur. Of greater relevance to this section, is the attention paid to layout considerations.

The digital section is separated from the analog sections as though a physical barrier existed on the board of the MDA–10F D/I converter module. All the input lines enter through an edge connector on the digital side of the printed-circuit card. All those lines that pass into the analog section are prefiltered by a ferrite-bead, ceramic filter-capacitor combination. For complete isolation, the analog output is not brought back to the edge connector, since it would have to pass through the digital section once again. Instead, a 90-ohm-cable connector is provided at the analog end of the board. The additional module shown in the photograph is the "deglitcher" circuit that minimizes transients resulting from the

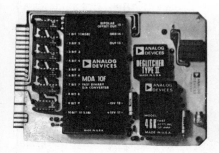 

Figure 14. Deglitched High-Speed Display D/A Converter

unavoidable glitches that occur at the switch outputs during code changes.

SUCCESSIVE-APPROXIMATION A/D CONVERTERS

Of all the techniques for analog-to-digital conversion in use today in data acquisition systems, "successive approximations" is perhaps the most widely used. A simplified block diagram of a converter using this technique is shown in Figure 15. The basic idea of successive approximation is simple, as explained in the preceding chapter. In somewhat more detail:

When the appropriate logic signal is applied to the *convert command* input terminal, the D/A switches are set simultaneously to their "off" state, except for the most significant bit (MSB), which is set to logic "1". This turns on the corresponding D/A switch,* which applies the analog equivalent of the MSB to the comparator. Simultaneously an internal clock is released from the *inhibit* state and allowed to free-run. Until the first clock-pulse edge arrives, the MSB is being compared with the analog voltage. (The scheme shown is only one of several ways). When the first clock pulse arrives, the MSB has shown itself to be either too "heavy" or too "light."

If the analog input voltage is less than the MSB weight, the MSB will be switched off at the first leading edge of the clock pulse; if the analog input is greater than the MSB, the "1" will remain in the register. Besides enabling the MSB decision, the clock pulse simultaneously turns on the second bit. During the period of the second pulse, the sum of the result of the first choice and the second bit is being compared with the analog input voltage. The comparator's state, when gated by the next clock pulse, will cause the register to either accept or reject that bit. In a similar manner, succeeding clock pulses cause the bits, in order of decreasing significance, to be tried, and accepted or rejected, until the LSB is finally accepted or rejected.

During this conversion time, the output of a *status* flip-flop is in its "busy/not valid" state, indicating that a conversion is taking place;

---

*If complementary logic is necessary, as is typical of D/A converters using the AD550 μDAC elements, this would be "0," as discussed in "Complementary Codes" in the preceeding chapter.

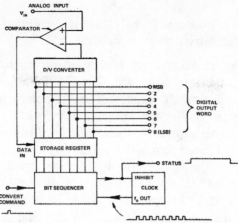

Figure 15. *Block Diagram of Successive-Approximations A/D Converter*

it signals the end of a conversion by returning to its "ready/ conversion valid" state.

Data from the parallel output lines of a successive-approximation converter are not valid until the end of conversion. However, in some applications, it is desirable to read out the data serially. When this is done, as it is in many successive-approximation converters, one must be careful to accept the serial data only as each bit becomes valid (such as on the leading edge of each clock pulse). Hence, after each bit decision is made, the data becomes valid, and the bit can be immediately shipped serially down a data line. Serial data can also be obtained at any later time if the parallel data is "jammed" into a shift register which can then be interrogated at will. Serial data should not be taken from the comparator output, unless it is bistable, since ambiguous levels (comparator in the linear range) can cause erroneous serial output if the internal/flip-flop and external shift register have different thresholds. Ignoring this consideration will result in errors as large as ½F.S.

THE LOGIC SEQUENCER

Since modern integrated-circuit logic families are continually in a state of change, it is difficult to say that any one particular logic scheme is "best." A number of criteria determine suitability of a logic scheme for a given application. For example, it may be necessary to minimize the number of logic elements used; or to minimize the cost, no matter how much real estate is consumed by the logic elements; or to minimize power dissipation, etc.

The scheme in Figure 16 can be considered representative among A/D converter designs now in use. The 7496 shift registers are parallel-entry-type 5-bit shift-registers. The 7474 elements are dual-D edge-triggered flip flops. The way this scheme works is: At the leading edge of the input *convert command,* the 7496 shift registers are preset to a 011 . . 1 condition. The 0 preset into the MSB immediately presets the Q output of the most significant bit flip-flop. This Q output* is applied to the MSB logic input of the D/A, so that at the start of conversion, the MSB immediately begins its comparison with the input voltage. On the first clock pulse to the shift register, the 0 is shifted to the second bit position, and the MSB is backfilled with a 1 (1011 . . 1). As the second-bit flip-flop is preset and the second bit is turned on in the D/A, the second flip-flop's Q output is coupled back to the *clock* input of the first flip-flop. Hence, the level appearing on the data (D) line of the first flip-flop is retained "forever" in that flip-flop. Similarly, on the 3rd clock pulse, the zero in the shift registers is shifted into the 3rd-bit position (1101 . . 1), causing the third D-type flip-flop to

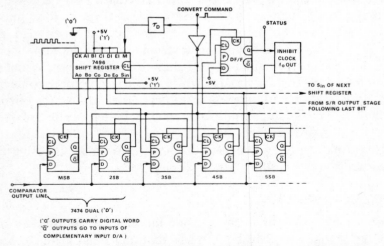

Figure 16. Logic Diagram of Successive-Approximations ADC

*Complementary logic

preset. As previously, its Q, going to the 1 state, clocks data on the D line into the 2nd-bit flip-flop. And so the sequence goes until the LSB is reached, at which time the *status* flip-flop trips and terminates the conversion (and inhibits the internal clock).

A new logic scheme, of growing popularity, hinges on the use of 8-bit addressable latches, recently available from several logic manufacturers. Basically, this MSI element consists of 8 latch-style flip-flops. The individual flip-flops are addressed by a 3-bit input code to the MSI element. This address simply enables the D line to that particular flip-flop. To sequence this arrangement, a 3- or 4-bit counter is used. A note of caution, however:, the timing between clock pulses is somewhat more critical, because the addressable latch must be disabled and enabled between address changes to avoid changing the data in intermediate states in the addressable latch.

COMPARATORS: THE MOST CRITICAL ELEMENT

Many IC comparators are available on the market today, and the number continues to increase. Simple in concept, but tricky in practice, these intriguing circuits are a never-ending challenge to IC designers and users alike.

The ideal comparator would have infinite gain and zero comparison time. Practical comparators are limited by parameters similar to those of op amps: open-loop gain, slew rate, bandwidth, and dc and dynamic differential input characteristics. Beyond these, comparators are further distinguished by the availability of such features as *enable* terminals and output drive capability.

There are basically two different ways in which a comparator can be used: To compare voltage, differentially, and to compare current. In the voltage mode, the analog output of the D/A converter is in a voltage form (for instance, from the output of an amplifier) and is presented at the inverting input of the comparator. The analog input voltage is connected to the noninverting terminal. Comparators used in this scheme must have high common-mode input range and excellent common-mode rejection. For instance, a 12-bit converter should have at least 96dB of CMR to keep common-mode error well below 1/10LSB. The voltage mode is generally used in situations where the analog output from the D/A is restricted to the zero-to-1-volt region (e.g., by taking the output from a resistive load on a current-output D/A). The analog input is scaled down by the proper amount and applied to the + input of the comparator, while the 1-volt D/A output is applied at the minus input.

The use of comparators in the *current* mode is perhaps more common these days, because it allows better speed and temperature tracking, and places no severe requirements on the comparator's common-mode rejection. This is, particularly well-implemented with the quad-current-switching D/A's discussed earlier in this chapter. Figure 17 shows why. The 5kΩ gain resistors that are normally used as the op amp feedback element to convert current to voltage in a DAC are used as the input scaling resistors. The summing point (pin 22, AD850) is connected to the minus input of the comparator. The plus input is returned to analog signal ground through an appropriate bias-current cancellation resistor (5 or 10kΩ ‖ 15kΩ, for single-ended converters, additional ‖ 6kΩ for bipolar converters). By doing this, we make use of the temperature tracking of the resistors of the AD850L network to retain near-perfect gain tracking.

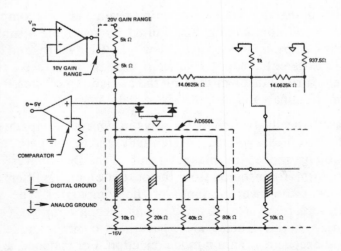

Figure 17. ADC Using Comparator in the Current Mode

The "window" determines the conversion accuracy one can obtain with any given comparator. The *window* is that range of input voltage over which the comparator output is traversing the linear region, between logic thresholds, and as such is a measure of the open-loop gain of a comparator circuit. For example, if the analog input is from 0 to +10V, and it is desired to perform a 12-bit conversion, the window must be less than 1mV for the conversion to be within one-half LSB (neglecting quantization uncertainty). Since the output of the comparator must swing between 0.4 and 2.4V to effect logic changes (TTL), the open-loop gain required for 12 bits is at least 2000. However, in practice, this figure should be at least 5000 to minimize the errors due to finite open-loop gain.

Besides gain, dc offset and drift, and impedance level, another spec that must be carefully considered in the selection of a comparator is its *speed*. The typical performance of integrated circuit comparators available today is specified by means of response diagrams on data sheets. A typical plot is shown on Figure 18; it can be seen that the speed is sharply influenced by the amount of over-drive of the comparator. The amount of overdrive applied to a given comparator in an A/D application depends on the input voltage range used and the resolution sought. The designer must be careful to plan for the minimal amount of overdrive appropriate to any given application.

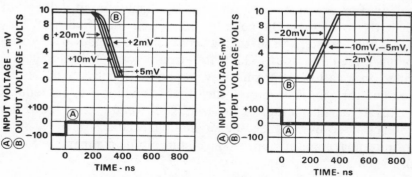

Figure 18. Comparator Response as a Function of Input Overdrive (Type AD351)

The most troublesome aspect of using any comparator, be it discrete or integrated, is the problem of maintaining frequency stability while within the linear region (i.e., in the "window"). Although the comparator is like an operational amplifier with no overt feedback, it is operating at high gain-bandwidth, with minimal feedback compensation. Even small amounts of parasitic feedback, either directly around the device, or via the power supply leads, can cause oscillation. These oscillations are generally caused by improper layout, for example, in separating the fast-rising output edges from the high-impedance input points. It is intuitively obvious that capacitive coupling of fast edges to the negative input could develop ringing or sustained oscillation when the net input is in the "window" region.

For this reason, it is recommended that adequate shielding, e.g., by ground plane, be used between the input and output. Also, it is wise to keep the digital ground terminal (normally returned to the output transistor of a comparator) away from the analog input grounds and signal lines. Furthermore, for IC comparators (whether the data sheet suggests it or not), it is a wise idea to buffer the load driven by the comparator output with a discrete transistor. This not only leads to a higher gain in the comparator, but will also lighten the changes in power dissipation in the internal output transistor, thereby eliminating thermal feedback effects.

The effect of an oscillating comparator on the A/D conversion is: as the analog input approaches the edge of a quantization level, the codes become indecisive, and in fact, exhibit non-monotonic behavior. For example, one can raise the analog input voltage sufficiently to increase the code by 1LSB, and then find that, for a slight further increase in analog input, the code goes back to the original digital output. This often-troublesome behavior can be cured in a rather surprising way — elimination by "size." If the comparator gain is *increased*, such that the window size is reduced to a very small fraction of the total LSB weight, then the region of each code over which the oscillation occurs is reduced to an infinitesimal amount, approaching a magnitude comparable to that of the circuit background noise.

OTHER CONSIDERATIONS IN A/D CONVERTER DESIGN

The additional error sources that can occur when a D/A converter is used in A/D conversion are primarily centered around the comparator's input and gain characteristics. In particular, offset drift and input bias-current drift are important in the selection of a comparator. Further errors are introduced by extraneous noise pickup in the analog sections due to fast-rising and changing edges of nearby digital logic.

Hence it is most important that much consideration and effort be given to adequate separation between digital and analog components in the circuit layout. Once again, the digital power supply should be kept entirely separate from the analog power supply, the analog input signals, and the D/A output section. This separation should be physical as well as electrical. One should take great care to minimize the *number* of digital signals that must be brought into or near the analog sections.

Another aspect that can spell trouble if not anticipated is the adequacy and use of the conversion time. Two factors place lower limits on this to a significant degree: one is the settling time of the D/A output, the other the switching time of the comparator.

Since the D/A output is driving the comparator towards its new value, the switching times of both elements are accumulated, but not in purely additive fashion. A useful trick is to use the fact that the most-significant bits take much longer to settle to their final values than do the LSB steps of a successive-approximations converter. Hence, to speed the overall conversion time one can use a frequency-modulated clock having decreasing period as the conversion progresses.

Testing Converters

Chapter 3

INTRODUCTION

The methods and test fixture configurations used to test DAC's and ADC's are influenced by a number of factors relating to converter applications, nature and speed of tests to be performed, and skill of test personnel involved. The relative importance of various converter performance specifications is dependent on each particular application, and the converter user is naturally interested in testing those parameters which significantly influence his system performance to a greater extent than those which have little effect on this performance. Two typical applications illustrate how usage influences the relative importance of various performance parameters:

Differential linearity, fast settling time, and small switching transient (glitch) amplitude are generally of great concern when DAC's are used as cathode-ray tube vector generators, since display quality is critically dependent on these parameters. Small absolute calibration errors or zero drift are generally of little consequence, since they cause only small display size and position shifts, which can be corrected easily by operator display adjustments.

By contrast, a DAC used as a programmable stimulus generator in an automatic checkout system might require good absolute calibration and zero-stability, while not requiring fast dynamic response, transient-free switching, or exceptional differential linearity. Converter test circuit configuration and degree of automation is influenced by: the purpose of the test, e.g., engineering performance evaluation, incoming inspection, functional checks only, etc., its versatility, measurement speed, data reduction and display capability, and skill level required for its operation. Simple test fixtures designed to test relatively few converter parameters can be implemented easily and inexpensively. These generally must be operated by relatively skilled persons, and test data obtained usually must be reduced to extract meaningful performance information.

Versatile automatic testers are of necessity complex and are generally costly. A general-purpose automatic tester generally performs tests faster, and can be operated by less-skilled personnel, however. High-resolution converters have a potentially large number of data points which must be examined to extract meaningful converter performance information. A 12-bit DAC or ADC, for example, has 2^{12}, or 4096 possible input/output combinations. Fortunately, by knowing the type of converter errors, or deviations from ideal performance that are commonly encountered, one can devise tests which permit useful performance data to be gained by investigating significantly fewer than the 2^n possible input/output combinations associated with an n-bit converter.

Converter performance parameters that are generally of importance are: calibration accuracy (both absolute and relative to full-scale), linearity (both cumulative and differential), offset, noise, conversion time, and, in the case of DAC's, output switching transient amplitude-time product. Also of concern are stability of these parameters with variations in time and temperature. The purpose of this chapter is to illustrate common converter errors and deviations from ideal performance, and to outline test schemes, for evaluating converter performance, that can be adapted to both manual and automatic testing.

LINEARITY

D/A CONVERTERS

The analog output of the n-bit binary DAC shown in Fig. 1a is related to its input binary number in the following manner:

$$E_0 = E_{NFS} (B_1 \, 2^{-1} + B_2 \, 2^{-2} + B_3 \, 2^{-3} + \ldots B_n \, 2^{-n}) \qquad (1)$$

where the digits $B_1 \ldots B_n$ of the binary number N each have the value 0 or 1, and E_{NFS} is the nominal full-scale output. Since

$$\sum_{i=1}^{n} 2^{-i} = 1 - 2^{-n}, \qquad (2)$$

the relation between the output with all bits "1", and nominal full-scale output E_{NFS} is

$$E_0 \Big|_{B_1, \ldots B_n = 1} = E_{NFS} (1 - 2^{-n}) \qquad (3)$$

and, since $2^{-n} = 1\,LSB$, E_{FS}, the output with all bits "1" is the nominal full-scale output minus $1\,LSB$. That is

$$E_{FS} = E_{NFS} [1 - LSB] \qquad (4)$$

The analog values associated with each of the bits acting individually can be found by setting the desired bit B_i to logic "1" and all other bits to "0". Then

$$E_0 \Big|_{B_i} = E_{NFS} \, 2^{-i} \qquad (5)$$

Relation (1) indicates a linear relationship between analog output and digital input. It follows that the sum of the analog output values obtained for any combination of bits acting individually should equal the analog output obtained when all bits of this combination are applied simultaneously. This forms the basis for a simple and effective linearity test: Various combinations of bits are turned on and the associated analog output noted. Each bit of this combination is then applied independently and its output recorded. The algebraic sum of these outputs is then compared to that obtained for all bits of the chosen combination turned on together. The difference is the linearity, or summation, error.

With most converters, the maximum linearity error occurs at full-scale. In this case, "all bits on" is the worst-case bit combination.

Converter linearity errors are independent of scale-factor calibration or gain errors. Accurate linearity measurements can be made, even on an uncalibrated DAC. The nonlinearity of the measurement device must be significantly less than that being measured. A 12-bit DAC having a nonlinearity of the order of ±½ LSB (= 1 part in 8192) requires a 5-digit DVM for meaningful linearity measurements in the circuit of Figure 1a. In addition, one should note that a zero error (non-zero output for zero input) must be corrected, so as not to introduce an error in the linearity measurement, since it is added once for each output reading taken. Consider the inequality,

$$E_0 (B_1 + B_2 + \ldots + B_n) + \epsilon_{LIN} + \epsilon_Z \neq E_0 B_1$$
$$+ E_0 B_2 + \ldots E_0 B_n + n\epsilon_Z \qquad (6)$$

where ϵ_{LIN} is the full-scale linearity error and ϵ_Z is the zero error. The left side of inequality (6) has the zero error added once (all bits on), while the right side has the zero error added n times (n individual readings). Converters using a half-scale offset to accomplish bipolar operation (e.g., offset-binary coding) must be tested for linearity (by this method) in the unipolar operating mode (half-scale offset disconnected) to prevent large errors similar in nature to those indicated by relation (6), but greater in magnitude. When making linearity (or gain) measurements, there is less possibility for computational error if the zero error is recorded and subtracted from each subsequent bit reading before any linearity or gain calculations are made. The simplest way to correct for zero (computationally, at least) is to electrically zero the converter before data are taken.

A/D CONVERTERS

The process of ascertaining linearity of an ADC is similar to that described above for a DAC. Consider the ADC of Fig. 1b, having its output binary number N related to its input analog signal E_{IN} in the following manner:

$$E_{NFS} (B_1 2^{-1} + B_2 2^{-2} + B_3 2^{-3} + \ldots + B_n 2^{-n}) = E_{IN}$$
$$\pm ½ \text{ LSB (quantizing uncertainty)} \qquad (7)$$

where the definitions associated with relation (1) apply. The analog input E_{IN} required to turn each bit on can be found by setting each bit except the desired one to zero in the relation (7). That is,

$$E_{IN}\big|_{N\,=\,B_i2^{-i}} = E_{NFS}\,2^{-i} \tag{8}$$

ADC linearity can be evaluated by applying each of the analog input values required to turn on only one bit of a particular bit combination to be examined for linearity. The sum of these analog inputs, when applied to the ADC input, should turn on all bits of the selected combination, and no others.

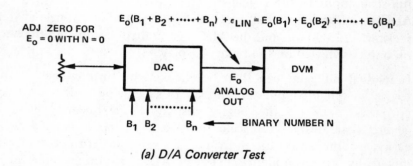

(a) D/A Converter Test

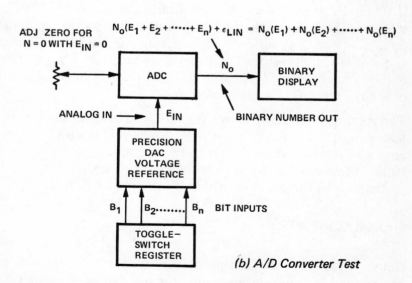

(b) A/D Converter Test

Figure 1. Linearity (Summation) Test

The most convenient method of generating binarily-scaled analog reference values, with which to test ADC's for gain calibration or linearity, is by means of a precision reference DAC and associated toggle switch register, as shown in Fig. 1b. To simplify linearity measurement, the ADC is first calibrated in the following manner: all bits of the reference DAC are turned off; this applies zero analog input to the ADC. The ADC zero control is adjusted for digital zero on the binary display. (The reference DAC and ADC are assumed to have identical scale factors so that ideally, the ADC, when properly adjusted, will have a full-scale output for full-scale input to the toggle-switch register. For convenience, the ADC is calibrated at half-scale. Bit 1 (MSB) of the toggle switch register is turned on, and the ADC gain control is adjusted for bit 1 on only, as viewed on the binary display.

Individual bit gains can then be checked by turning each of the toggle switch bit inputs on and off in succession and looking for correspondence on the binary display. Since linearity error is generally greatest at full-scale, nonlinearity can be checked quite easily, assuming that the individual bit gains are correct, as determined by correspondence between ADC output and reference DAC input for each individual bit. Starting at the most-significant reference-DAC bit-input, each bit, in descending order, is turned on and left on. Any difference between the displayed ADC output and toggle-switch-register input codes, as full-scale is approached, is then caused by an ADC nonlinearity (assuming the nonlinearity of the reference DAC to be neglibible).

The methods described above for ADC calibration and linearity testing tacitly assume that the ADC can be calibrated so that each analog calibration value is centered in the respective quantization band corresponding to the desired output code. Methods for accomplishing this are described in the section on ADC testing.

GAIN CALIBRATION

Converter accuracy can be specified in two ways: (a) absolute and (b) relative to full-scale. In testing for (a), one is concerned with ascertaining the calibration of any bit or combination thereof with respect to some absolute external standard. In testing for (b), one is concerned only with ascertaining calibration accuracy relative to the converter's full-scale value. Since, in most instances, the converter's internal calibration reference consists of a temperature-compensated zener reference diode, which might age at the rate of 0.01%/1000hrs. operation, one usually accepts the fact that high-accuracy converters require periodic recalibration to maintain rated absolute calibration accuracy.

Testing for converter accuracy relative to full-scale is generally of greater interest, since this tests the stability and ratio accuracy of the converter's precision weighting network and active switching elements; weighting network ratio adjustments are normally not provided on contemporary modular converters (whereas full-scale adjustment is, because of the realities mentioned above.) The evaluation of converter gain accuracy can be expedited by normalizing gain to some convenient reference value. In the case of converters having *zero* and *gain* adjustments, this is simply accomplished by calibrating zero and full-scale before recording the various bit (or combination of bits) readings. The evaluation of gain accuracy relative to full-scale for units having no external calibration adjustments can be expedited by normalizing gain prior to recording the data.

Two methods for accomplishing gain normalization external to the DAC under test are shown in Figs. 2a and 2b. In both figures, it is assumed that the relative accuracy of the individual bit gains and the linearity of the converter are to be tested.

In Figure 2a, a DVM, operated in the ratio mode, is used to read the DAC output. The DAC zero output is first adjusted (all bits off). Bit 1 is then turned on. The value of a stable dc precision reference standard applied to the DVM ratio reference input is adjusted to make the DVM read +5.0000V (nominal full-scale assumed to be +10V).

In Figure 2b, a precision potentiometer is used to measure the DAC output as a fraction of some reference voltage applied to the high side of the potentiometer. At any bit setting, the position of the potentiometer arm is varied until the pot output voltage equals that of the DAC, as indicated by a zero reading at the null detector. The measurement is first normalized at any desired DAC setting —half-scale in the example of Figure 2b— by adjusting the reference voltage for null at the corresponding potentiometer setting.

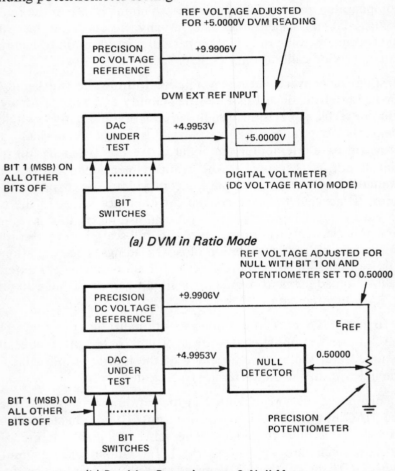

(a) DVM in Ratio Mode

(b) Precision Potentiometer & Null Meter

Figure 2. DAC Gain Normalization Methods

If the converter is nonlinear, the peak linearity error is dependent upon the point chosen for gain calibration or normalization, as illustrated in Figure 3. In Figure 3a, a peak error of 1 bit is assumed to exist at some point on the device transfer function when the unit is calibrated at full-scale. In Figure 3b the device gain has been adjusted to minimize the peak error — in this case, to ±½ bit. In practice, it is generally found that peak linearity error (deviation from a "best straight line") will be minimized if the converter gain is calibrated at roughly 3/4 scale. If the device nonlinearity is less than ¼ bit, the exact point chosen for gain calibration has little effect on device accuracy.

If this nonlinearity is greater than ¼ bit, the output point chosen for gain calibration can determine whether or not the converter meets its accuracy specification (generally ±½ bit), since some differential nonlinearity (to be described shortly) must be presumed to exist in any converter. Because calibration at full-scale is straightforward and requires the most conservative linearity and relative-accuracy specification, Analog Devices does this as a standard practice in specifying converters, rather than choosing a "best straight line" approach.

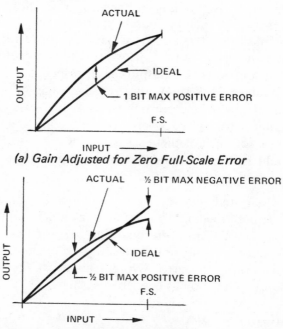

(a) Gain Adjusted for Zero Full-Scale Error

(b) Gain Adjusted to Minimize Peak Error
Figure 3. Effect of Gain Adjustment on Linearity Error for Non-Linear DAC or ADC

ZERO AND GAIN CALIBRATION

Calibration of the transfer function of a linear device requires determination of two points within the linear operating region of the device. The choice of calibration points and exact procedure depends somewhat on the nature of the particular device under test; generally, device zero is adjusted and then gain is calibrated.

UNIPOLAR DAC

The typical calibration procedure for a unipolar DAC is illustrated in Figure 4a: all bits are turned off (binary zero), and the zero control is adjusted for zero analog output. All bits are then turned on and the gain control is adjusted for correct full-scale output. (Gain could equally-well be calibrated at either 1/2 or 3/4 scale, as discussed above. Device accuracy can then be checked by turning on and off each bit in succession and comparing each bit output with its corresponding theoretical reference value. Worst-case gain error can then be found by turning on all bits having low individual outputs in relation to their respective reference values and noting the DAC output. The process is repeated for all bits having high individual bit outputs with respect to their respective reference values. The DAC output for each of these two bit combinations, which corresponds to worst-case negative and positive gain error, respectively, is then compared to the theoretical value for each of these sums. The worst-case + or − bit sum error should be less than the device error specification − generally ±½ bit at room temperature.

It should be noted that testing for worst-case calibration error in the manner described above assumes negligible nonlinearity errors. The bit combination corresponding to worst-case positive or negative gain error will not necessarily correspond to that which causes greatest nonlinearity. Nonlinearity can be checked independently of calibration as described earlier.

BIPOLAR DAC USING OFFSET BINARY OR 2'S COMPLEMENT (OB WITH COMPLEMENTED MSB)

DAC's or ADC's having offset binary coding (as distinguished from sign-magnitude coding) are generally made bipolar by summing with the unipolar output of the DAC weighting network a fixed analog output equal in magnitude, but opposite in polarity, to the first bit (MSB) analog equivalent. This shifts the DAC unipolar transfer characteristic of Fig. 4a down by half-scale, as shown in Figure 4b. With most DAC's (or ADC's), the gain control affects only the unipolar scale factor, and not that of the bipolar offset. DAC's (or ADC's) of this type are generally calibrated in the following manner: All bits are turned off (binary zero) and the bipolar offset is adjusted for correct negative full-scale reading. Bit 1 is then turned on and the gain is adjusted for zero output. All bits can then be turned on, providing a calibration check at + full scale. (Alternatively, the gain can be calibrated at + full scale, with zero analog output providing the calibration check point.) The general calibration procedure, while described for DAC's, is quite similar for ADC's (ADC calibration is discussed under ADC testing).

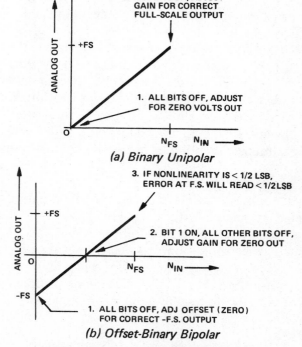

Figure 4. Typical DAC Calibration Procedure

TEMPERATURE EFFECTS

The manner in which the DAC unipolar and offset binary bipolar DAC output can shift with temperature is illustrated in Figures 5a, 5b, and 5c. In the unipolar DAC transfer curve of Figure 5a, a zero shift moves the transfer curve up or down. Since a zero shift affects all output readings by the same amount, zero temperature coefficient is expressed either directly in $\mu V/^\circ C$, or as a fraction (% or ppm) of *full-scale* per $^\circ C$. A gain shift, on the other hand, causes the slope of the transfer curve to change. This affects all output readings by the same percentage. Gain temperature coefficient is therefore generally specified as % or ppm of *reading*/$^\circ C$.

In the case of a bipolar DAC, if the temperature coefficient of the half-scale offset were exactly matched to that of the unipolar transfer curve, and there were no zero shift, the bipolar transfer curve would rotate about the zero output point with temperature, as shown in Figure 5b. In actual practice, this does not occur. The difference between the bipolar offset and unipolar gain temperature coefficients, plus the zero temperature-coefficient of the unipolar transfer characteristic will cause the bipolar transfer curve to shift up or down with temperature. The unipolar gain-temperature coefficient causes the bipolar transfer curve to rotate about the intersection of this curve with the output axis as shown in Figure 5c. Figure 5c illustrates that in the case of bipolar converters having offset binary coding, the shift in output zero with temperature is a function of both gain *and* offset shifts.

DIFFERENTIAL NONLINEARITY

Differential nonlinearity is a measure of the variation in analog value change associated with a one-bit change in the associated digital number, for either a DAC or an ADC. Ideally, a one-bit digital value change should have associated with it a constant (i.e., 1LSB) incremental change in analog signal anywhere on the input/output transfer characteristic. Differential nonlinearity can be quantified in the following manner: Assume an analog signal span E_s, and an n-bit binary converter. A normalized 1-bit increment ΔE_N can be defined, such that

$$\Delta E_N = E_S\, 2^{-n}$$

Differential linearity error, ϵ_{DL}, can then be defined by the relation:

$$\epsilon_{DL} = (\Delta E - \Delta E_N)/\Delta E_N$$

where ΔE is the actual change in analog value associated with any 1-digit change in the binary number.

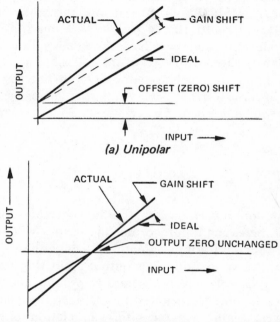

(a) Unipolar

(b) Bipolar (Offset Binary) with Offset and Gain TC Matched

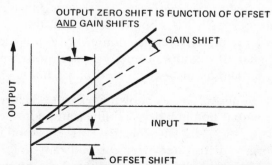

(c) Bipolar (Offset Binary) with Offset and Gain TC's Not Matched
Figure 5. Effects of Gain and Offset Shifts on DAC Output

The greatest differential nonlinearity occurs at major carry transitions of the digital number, where significant weighting network gain-factor switching occurs. To illustrate, consider a 3-bit DAC, driven by a 3-bit binary counter to sequentially generate all possible 3-bit codes corresponding to the fractions 0 to 7/8 of full-scale, as shown in Figure 6a. Ideally, this should produce a staircase output waveform having equal step heights. If the weight of the MSB (Bit 1) is ½-bit low, the output transition from code 011 (3/8) to 100 (4/8) will be ½-bit too small. All succeeding code transitions will have correct amplitude, but the output values associated with each of the codes 5/8 . . . 7/8 will be ½-bit low in terms of absolute calibration. In this case, a ½-bit differential linearity error occurs at the major carry code transition, as shown in Figure 6b.

MONOTONICITY

A monotonic output is one that either increases or remains constant, for increasing input, so that the output will always be a single-valued function of input. (Mathematically, this requires that the 1st derivative of a continuous output-input transfer function be ≥ 0; for a variable having discrete steps, the first *difference* must be ≥ 0.) Assume in the example of Figure 6a that the DAC has a bit 1 weight more than one bit low in relation to the weights of bit 2 and bit 3. In this case, the code transition from step 3 to step 4 will actually be *negative,* as shown in Figure 6c, a non-monotonic response. It should be noted that a converter specification of ±½-bit differential nonlinearity is more stringent than one of guaranteed monotonicity, since non-monotonicity implies a differential nonlinearity greater than 1 bit.

Normal device nonlinearity, as shown in Figure 3, has negligible effect on differential nonlinearity. To illustrate, consider a 10-bit converter having a ±½-bit nonlinearity. If this nonlinearity is assumed uniformly distributed over the full range of $2^{10} = 1024$ bits, the differential nonlinearity contributed at any code transition by this ±½-bit linearity error is no greater than 1/2048 bit.

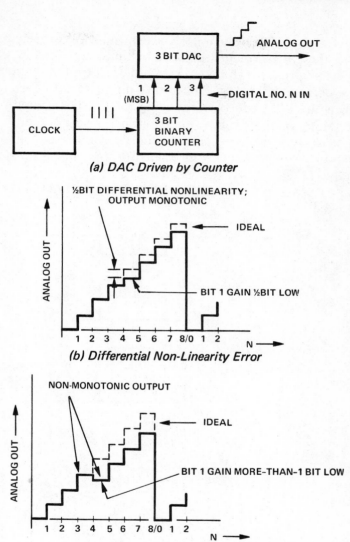

(a) DAC Driven by Counter

(b) Differential Non-Linearity Error

(c) Non-Monotonicity

Figure 6. DAC Differential Linearity and Monotonicity Errors

The effect of switch and weighting-network differential non-linearity on the digital output of a successive-approximation ADC is illustrated in Figure 7. Figure 7 shows a 3-bit successive-approximation ADC configuration using the DAC of Figure 6a as its weighting network. The analog ramp input to this converter is assumed to be slowly-varying with respect to the conversion rate, so that each point on the analog waveform is successively digitized within the ±½-bit quantization-error limits inherent in the A/D conversion process. The converter's ideal output is a sequence of codes corresponding to the binary numbers 000 through 111 (0-7), with each code corresponding to the ideal analog value. If bit 1 (MSB) of the weighting network has a weight ½ bit low with respect to those of bits 2 and 3, as in the example of Figure 6, the digital output will jump to the code 100 (4) ½-bit sooner than it should. The effect on the output is to cause a narrowing of the step width corresponding to the code 011 (3) immediately

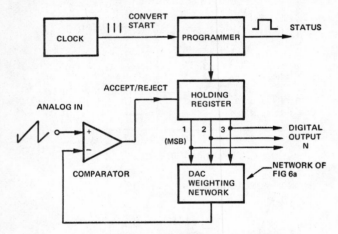

(a) Successive Approximation ADC

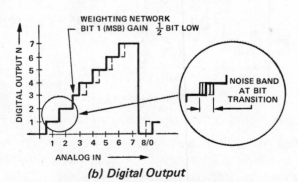

(b) Digital Output

Figure 7. Effects of Noise and Weighting Network Differential Non-Linearity on ADC Output

preceding the code 100 when bit 1 turns on and bits 2&3 turn off, as shown in Figure 7b. Conversely, if the weighting network has its bit-1 gain ½-bit high with respect to bit-2 and bit-3 gains, the width corresponding to the code 011 (3) will be ½-bit too large. In both cases, the widths corresponding to output levels 4-7 will have a correct 1-bit amplitude.

The waveform inset of Figure 7b illustrates that noise in the analog input to the converter circuit introduces an uncertainty in the analog code transition value. (The noise band associated with each code transition value can be found using an ac dither signal, as will be described in the section on ADC testing.)

If the bit 1 gain of the weighting network is more than 1 bit low, as in the DAC output waveform of Figure 6b, the code 011 will not occur and the digital output will skip from 010 (2) to 100 (4), i.e., a non-monotonic weighting network causes missing ADC output codes. A comparison of the waveforms of Figures 6b and 7b shows that a differential nonlinearity causes a variation in the output step *height* for the case of a DAC transfer function, and causes a variation in output step *width* for the case of an ADC transfer function.

DAC TESTING

A simple and effective DAC test configuration is shown in Figure 8. The digital inputs to both the device under test (DUT) and a highly-accurate reference DAC are driven in parallel from either a toggle-switch register or a dynamic programmer. Both the reference DAC and the DUT have the same output range. The output of the reference DAC is compared to that of the DUT. The difference between the two outputs is amplified in an error amplifier, which has its gain calibrated to provide a defined error output with some convenient volts-per-bit scale factor. The toggle-switch register permits selection of logic 0, logic 1, or "dynamic program" for each input bit. This permits entry of any desired code for static-accuracy tests, or dynamic programming for high-speed dynamic testing. Gain and zero adjustment can be provided in the reference DAC to effect gain normalization and zero calibration in the event the DUT has no provision for internal gain or zero calibration.

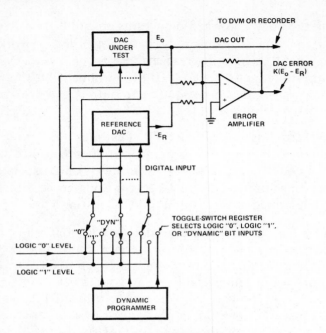

Figure 8. Basic DAC Tester

DYNAMIC PROGRAMMING

There are two dynamic programming modes that are of particular value in permitting the linearity and accuracy characteristics of the DUT to be assessed quickly; they are the *bit-scan* and *count* modes.

Bit-Scan Mode

In the "bit-scan" mode, the individual bit inputs to both the DUT and the reference DAC are time-division multiplexed, so that each bit input is turned on and off in succession. Two additional multiplexed time slots are allocated to full-scale (all bits on) and zero (all bits off) to facilitate device calibration. A bit-scan dynamic programming configuration is illustrated in Figure 9. The resulting bar graph of output error can be displayed on an oscilloscope or a high-speed strip-chart recorder (if a permanent record is desired). Figure 10a shows a typical commutator time-slot allocation for testing a 12-bit DAC in the bit-scan mode.

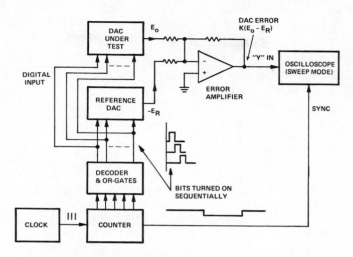

Figure 9. DAC Dynamic Test — BIT–SCAN Mode

Typical error displays resulting from this test are shown in Figures 10b, c, and d. Figure 10b illustrates an error display for a DAC having the correct binary scaling weights for all bits, but full-scale gain calibration 1-bit high. Since a 1 LSB full-scale gain error (with correct relative scaling) causes the bit 1 error to be ½-bit high, bit 2 to be ¼-bit high, bit 3 1/8-bit high, etc., the error display is exponential in shape, in this case. Figure 10c illustrates the error display for the case of a +¼-bit offset error, combined with a −1-bit full-scale gain error, assuming perfect relative weighting (i.e., differential linearity). This causes a reversal in full-scale error polarity from that shown in Figure 10b. In addition, the +¼-bit offset (zero) error shifts the complete display +¼ bit from the zero error baseline. The DUT is calibrated in the following manner, using the bit scan display: Zero is adjusted to bring the bar representing the zero error (time slot T13 in Figure 10a) to the display baseline. The gain is then adjusted to bring the bar corresponding to full-scale (time slot TO) to the baseline. Zero and full-scale of the DUT are now calibrated. (If the DUT does not have zero full-scale or full-scale adjustments, zero and full-scale of the reference DAC can be adjusted instead, to normalize the display.)

A typical "bit scan error" display after zero and full-scale of the DUT (or reference DAC) have been calibrated, is shown in Figure 10d. If the DUT is perfectly linear, the sum of all positive bit errors should equal the sum of all negative bit errors after zero and full-scale calibration; any residual error is caused by device nonlinearity.

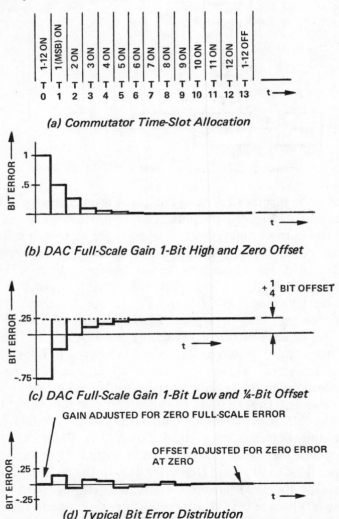

(a) Commutator Time-Slot Allocation

(b) DAC Full-Scale Gain 1-Bit High and Zero Offset

(c) DAC Full-Scale Gain 1-Bit Low and ¼-Bit Offset

(d) Typical Bit Error Distribution

Figure 10. 12-Bit DAC Dynamic Test Waveforms Bit-Scan Mode

Count Mode (Figure 11)

In the dynamic programming "count" mode, the digital inputs to both the reference DAC and DUT are driven from a counter so that all possible DAC input code combinations are sequentially generated. This produces a staircase output waveform from the DUT and the reference DAC. Zero and full-scale are most conveniently calibrated in the bit scan mode, as described above. After this calibration has been completed, the error display in the "count" mode is ideally a straight line. Using this testing technique, combined with a high-speed recording oscillograph, and a count rate of 1ms/step, all codes can be generated and a permanent error record obtained in approximately 4 seconds for a 12-bit DAC, and 64 seconds for a 16-bit DAC.

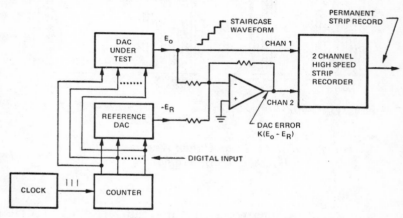

Figure11. DAC Dynamic Test – COUNT Mode

COUNT-MODE ERROR RECORD EXAMPLE

The usefulness of the error record obtained in the *count* mode as a means of quickly assessing DAC performance at various temperatures is shown by the error records in Figures 12a and 12b, obtained from an ADI Model DAC-10Z-2 10-bit ±5V bipolar D/A converter, tested at 25°C and 70°C, respectively. In these figures, the output e_o of the DUT is recorded directly on another oscillograph channel, to provide a scale reference. A line is drawn through the error-sweep waveform between zero and full-scale.

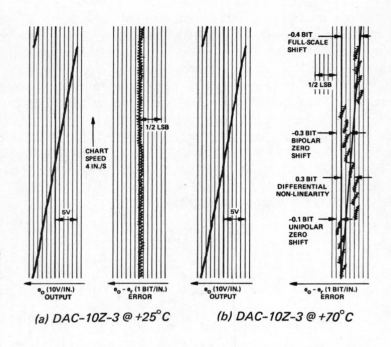

(a) DAC-10Z-3 @ +25°C   (b) DAC-10Z-3 @ +70°C

Figure 12. DAC Tester Output Waveform-COUNT Mode
Typical Chart Recording

The slope of this line represents the gain error of the DUT. Deviations from this straight line are caused by linearity and differential-linearity errors. Differential nonlinearity is measured by the peak-to-peak amplitude of the abrupt transition in the error curve occurring at the major-carry transitions of the digital-input code to the DUT. This is a measure of the difference in analog increment corresponding to a change of 1 LSB in the input digital code.

As can be seen from the error record of Figure 12a, the DUT has gain, offset, differential linearity, and linearity errors less than 0.1 bit at +25°C. The error waveform of Figure 12b shows that, at +70°C ambient temperature, full-scale and bipolar zero outputs have shifted −0.4 bit and −0.3 bit from their respective values at 25°C. At 70°C, the differential nonlinearity is 0.3 bits; the nonlinearity (deviation from the straight line joining the digital zero and full-scale analog values) is approximately half the differential nonlinearity, or 0.15 bit. Since 1 LSB, for a 10-bit DAC, is 1/1024 of FS (or 977ppm), the average gain and zero TC's in the range 25°C to 70°C are 0.4 × 977ppm/45°C = 8.7ppm/°C and 0.3 × 977ppm/45°C = 6.5ppm/°C. The unipolar zero (all bits off) has shifted −0.1 bit, while the bipolar zero (digital half scale) has shifted −0.3 bit at 70°C, corresponding to average unipolar and bipolar zero TC's of 2.2 and 6.5ppm/°C, respectively, in the temperature range 25°C to 70°C.

The error records of Figure 12 illustrate the important point that device differential nonlinearity is almost independent of the gain calibration points. That is, choosing a "best straight line" through the DAC output/input transfer curve to minimize gain or linearity error will have negligible effect on the differential linearity of the device, since the differential nonlinearity is the *peak-to-peak* error occurring at the 1–bit code changes associated with major carries in the input digital number.

DIFFERENTIAL LINEARITY TESTER

A simple scheme for testing DAC differential linearity is shown in Fig. 13a, for the case of a 4-bit DAC (for simplicity). A three-section ganged switch is wired to the DAC bit inputs so that the bit codes at either side of each carry-transition are examined by means of two out-of-phase square-waves applied to the two switch input lines. The carry transitions examined in each switch position are tabulated in Table 1 below.

Switch position	1	2	3	4
Code transition	1000	0100	0010	0001
	0111	0011	0001	0000

Table 1. 4-bit DAC Code Transitions for Differential Linearity Test

Ideally, the ac component of DAC output for each switch position is a square-wave having 1 LSB amplitude. Waveforms for several differential linearity possibilities are shown in Figure 13b. It should be noted that this test configuration tests differential linearity at major carry transitions only up to half-scale. This is generally sufficient to accurately characterize the differential linearity behavior of the device, since, unless the device is markedly nonlinear, the differential nonlinearity pattern associated with bit-2-bit-4 code transitions will repeat itself in the range from half-scale to full-scale output.

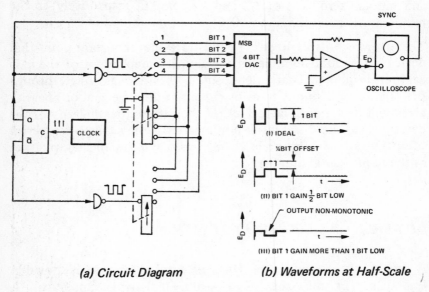

(a) Circuit Diagram   *(b) Waveforms at Half-Scale*

Figure 13. Simple DAC Differential Linearity Tester

Offset Method of Differential Nonlinearity Measurement

An alternate technique to that shown in Figure 13 for measurement of differential nonlinearity is shown in Fig. 14. The reference number, N_R, corresponding to the code of interest is applied to the DUT through the toggle-switch register. A digital subtractor subtracts 1 digit from this reference number so that $N_R - 1$ is applied to the input of a highly-accurate reference DAC.

The difference between the output of the DUT and the reference DAC is amplified and displayed on an error indicator. Ideally, this indicator should display a constant 1-bit difference for any number, N_R, applied to the input of the DUT. Differential nonlinearity at each bit code transition is tested merely by turning each individual bit switch in the toggle-switch register on and off in succession. For example, at the major carry, $N_R = 1\,0\,0\,0\,0\ldots 0$, and $N_R - 1 = 0\,1\,1\,1\,1\,1\,1\ldots 1$. Differential nonlinearity is measured as the deviation from the ideal 1-bit step.

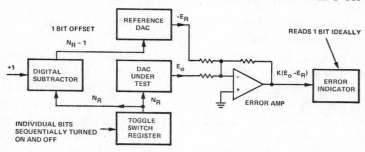

Figure 14. Offsetting Digital Input to DAC Under Test to Check Differential Linearity at Major Carry Transitions

DIGITAL DITHER GENERATOR

Frequently, the evaluation of DAC dynamic response characteristics relating to differential linearity, settling time, and switching transient (glitch) amplitude can be expedited if the DAC output can be periodically cycled through a few counts either side of each specific input code transition of interest so that the DAC output can be observed with an oscilloscope as that particular code transition is repetitively traversed from each direction. Two methods for accomplishing this are now described.

Open-Loop Digital Dither Generation

An open-loop scheme for generating a digital dither signal is shown in Figure 15. An up/down counter is preset to the reference number N_R corresponding to the code of interest. A divide-by-four binary counter and count direction control flip-flop are driven from the clock so that groups of 4 clock pulses are counted in the up and down directions alternately, so that there is no net change in the counter state at the completion of an 8-count up-down cycle. The up/down counter is preset to N_R in the middle of each burst of up and down pulses. This redundant input forces the up/down counter into the correct reference state twice per cycle, thus preventing this counter from becoming inadvertently offset from the desired reference state N_R by spurious noise pulses.

Alternatively, by incorporating independent digital high and low limit comparators, the count direction of the up/down counter can be reversed each time the high or the low limit is reached, rather than after a defined number of pulses has been counted in each direction, as in the scheme of Figure 15. This variation of the scheme permits independent control of digital dither amplitude as well as the reference code through the application of programmed high and low limits.

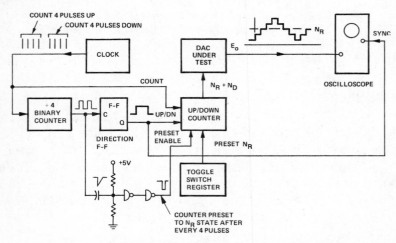

Figure 15. Digital Dither Generation for DAC Differential-Linearity Dynamic Testing

Closed-loop Dither Generation

A closed-loop digital dither generation scheme is shown in Figure 16. In this scheme, the reference number, N_R corresponding to the code of interest is applied to the digital input of a reference DAC. A digital accumulator configured as a 1-bit adder/subtractor generates the digital dither, causing the code applied to the DUT to oscillate about the reference number N_R. This is accomplished in the following manner: At each "add" time the digital number stored in the accumulator is incremented 1 bit, either up or down, depending on the state of the add/subtract *enable* line. The output of the DUT is compared to that of the reference DAC, which has N_R as its input. The difference in these two outputs is amplified and applied to the input of a Schmitt trigger. The output of this Schmitt trigger drives the add/subtract *enable* line of the digital accumulator. A cycle of operation is as follows: The analog error increases at each "add" time until the output of the error amplifier exceeds the Schmitt trigger hysteresis threshold reference level. This causes the Schmitt trigger to change state, causing the accumulator to increment in the opposite direction until the analog error exceeds the new threshold level of the Schmitt trigger, at which point the add/subtract *enable* line again changes state, causing the accumulator to increment in the original direction. Dither amplitude can be controlled by varying the gain of the error amplifier to control the number of increments required to overcome the Schmitt trigger hysteresis level. Sufficient filtering must be provided to avoid triggering the Schmitt trigger by transient spikes (glitches).

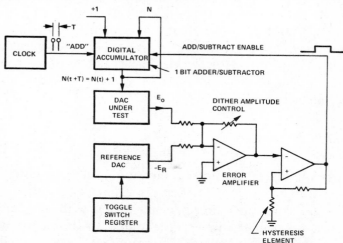

Figure 16. Closed-Loop Digital Dither Generation

DAC SETTLING-TIME MEASUREMENT

DAC settling time is a parameter of importance in high-speed applications. Settling time is defined as the time required for the output to approach a final value within the limits of a defined error band, for a step change in input. This fixed error band is generally expressed as a fraction of full scale, typically ±½-bit. If the device step response is oscillatory, so that the output swings through the defined error band before entering it for the final time, the above definition tacitly implies that settling time is measured as the time required for the output to enter the defined error band for the *final* time. The above settling time definition implies that the greater the output step change, the longer the settling time (a 1-bit output step change, for example, will be within ±½ bit of final value when this change has reached only 50% of its final value).

In addition to the usual constraints imposed on settling time by normal closed-loop linear bandwidth considerations, large output changes are generally slew-rate limited. There are two settling times of interest, depending on the application. These are *full-scale* and *bit-to-bit tracking,* depending on whether successive digital inputs are sequential or completely random in nature.

The accurate measurement of settling time for a high-resolution, high-speed DAC is fraught with practical difficulties. Measurement instrument bandwidth and thermal unbalance effects, coupled with the unavoidable presence of noise, can introduce significant measurement uncertainties when high-speed settling times to within error bands of the order of the order of 0.01% of final value are being measured.

Zero and Full-Scale

The general test configuration for measuring full-scale settling time is shown in Figure 17a. All digital input lines except that driving the LSB are connected together and driven with a square-wave having fast rise and fall times with respect to the response times being measured. The LSB DAC input line is connected to a three-position switch so that logic "0", logic "1", or "dynamic" input (consisting of the square-wave drive applied to the other bits) can be selected. When this switch is in the "dynamic" position, the DAC output is driven alternately between zero and full-scale. The DAC output is compared to a threshold reference level at the input to a high-speed comparator so that the comparator output will change state when the DAC output E_0 exceeds the threshold reference level E_R. The comparator output is displayed on an oscilloscope having its sweep start synchronized to the square-wave applied to the DAC's digital input. Choice of logic "0", logic "1", or "dynamic" for the LSB DAC digital input facilitates setting the comparator threshold reference level to within ½-LSB of the DAC full-scale output.

Full-scale settling time measurement is made in the following manner: The comparator threshold reference level is adjusted to bias the comparator output corresponding to DAC full-scale digital input into its linear operating region with the LSB set to "dynamic." This line is then switched to logic "0", reducing the full-scale DAC output level by 1 bit. This, in turn, causes the comparator output corresponding to full-scale DAC output to shift by the equivalent of 1 LSB. In the case of high-resolution DAC's having small LSB analog equivalent values, the comparator output will still remain in its linear region. This procedure establishes a calibrated 1-LSB band on the oscilloscope tube face, independent of comparator gain. Settling time is then measured from the time the digital input code changes until the time the comparator output enters a 1-bit band centered about full-scale for the final time. Typical waveforms associated with settling-time measurements made in this manner are shown in Figure 17b.

In the case of current-output DAC's, settling time can be measured by terminating the output in the inverting node of a high-speed operational amplifier, such as the ADI Model 46, connected in the inverting configuration, and making the measurement in the manner described above. Alternatively, the current output can be terminated in a resistor to convert to voltage directly. Since most current-output DAC's are output-voltage limited to approximately ±2V, the 1 LSB analog voltage equivalent is less than 1mV for

DAC's having resolution beyond 11 bits, using this technique. This reduced voltage range heightens the problem of making accurate settling-time measurements, since any noise voltage present becomes a more significant fraction of full-scale.

In general, to make accurate settling-time measurements for a current-output DAC terminated directly in a resistor, it is necessary to keep all lead lengths to an absolute minimum to reduce spurious noise pickup and ringing due to excessive lead inductance. The general tendency of high-gain comparators to oscillate can sometimes be reduced by connecting the output of the DUT to the negative, rather than the positive, comparator input, to reduce inter-wiring capacitive coupling from the comparator output to its positive input, as shown in the configuration of Figure 17.

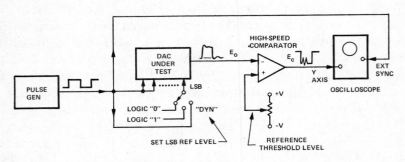

(a. Measuring Circuits)

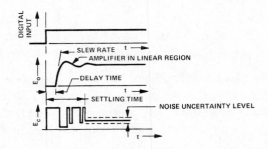

(b. Waveforms)

Figure 17. DAC Zero and Full-Scale Settling Time Measurement

Comparator Thermal Effects

High-speed comparators of the type used in the test setup of Figure 17a generally have input stages biased at a relatively large current level to maximize comparator gain-bandwidth. As a result, these comparators generally exhibit a thermal time constant of the order of several milliseconds, due to differential self-heating of the input transistor pair as the comparator output changes state. This can add a "tail" of several parts in 10,000 to the final settling time of the comparator output, attributable to the comparator, rather than the DUT. The most effective way of establishing with certainty that observed thermal settling times are due to the measurement system, rather than the DUT, is to make the settling time measurement using the technique described above twice: first with a high-speed comparator, using a square-wave frequency consistent with the anticipated settling time, then with an ultra-low-drift comparator which has been designed to minimize thermal effects (at the expense of gain-bandwidth), and a square-wave frequency below 100Hz.

Alternate Method for Zero and Full-Scale Measurement

A simpler scheme for settling-time measurement than that shown in Fig. 17a, which does not require a differential comparator is shown in Figure 18. A square-wave, synchronized to the dynamic digital input square-wave drive, but out of phase with the output of the DUT, is summed with this output. The amplitude of this reference square-wave, E_R, is adjusted to exactly equal that of the DAC output E_0 when switching transients have subsided. This produces a zero-volt steady-state error signal or "virtual ground," by analogy to the error voltage existing at the inverting node of an operational amplifier configured in the inverting mode.

Clamp diodes at the "virtual ground" point limit the voltage excursion during the switching transient period, and the subsequent oscilloscope overdrive; this reduces the oscilloscope overload recovery time. A calibrated 1-bit threshold level at either zero or full-scale DAC output can be established by switching the LSB digital input from "dynamic" to logic "1", or logic "0", respectively, as in the scheme of Figure 17a. A 1-bit band centered about the steady-state display level corresponding to full-scale, or zero, DAC output, can then be readily established on the oscilloscope tube face, and settling time to ±½ bit of final value is measured as the time for the error voltage existing at the "virtual" ground point to enter this band for the final time.

If only settling time from full-scale to zero volts is to be measured, the offset square-wave reference, E_R, and its summing resistor R can be eliminated, simplifying the measurement process, using the scheme of Figure 18.

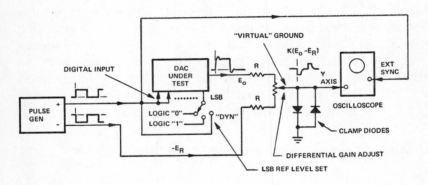

Figure 18. DAC Zero and Full-Scale Settling Time Measurement — Virtual Ground Method

Major Carry

When a DAC is operated in a tracking mode, as shown in Figure 6a, for example, the bit-to-bit, rather than full-scale settling time is of importance. The one-bit digital code transition causing the greatest switching transient, and consequently, the longest settling time at the DAC output, generally occurs at the major (½-scale) carry transition of the digital code. At this particular code transition, the digital number changes from 0111..1 to 1000..0 (or vice-versa when counting in the opposite direction), causing all bits to change state, and generally introducing the worst-case 1-LSB switching transient into the DAC output.

Figure 19 illustrates a test configuration for measuring settling time at the major-carry code transition. All bits, except the MSB, are driven in parallel by a square-wave alternating between logic "0" and logic "1" levels. This square-wave is inverted and applied to bit 1, causing this bit to be driven out-of-phase with all the other bits. The steady-state output for this input drive is a square-wave having a 1-LSB peak-to-peak amplitude at half-scale DAC output, corresponding to the major-carry input code transition being traversed from either direction. The DAC output is ac-coupled into an oscilloscope having its sweep *start* synchronized to the input square-wave. Settling time to ±½ bit of final value, in this case, is merely the time required for the 1-bit output step-change to reach 50% of its final value. (If the amplitude of the square-wave output is used to establish a 1-bit calibration reference band to expedite the measurement of tracking settling time, the differential nonlinearity occurring at the major carry should first be checked, since this generally represents the code transition causing greatest differential nonlinearity, as well as the greatest switching transient at the DAC output (as discussed under *Differential Linearity*).

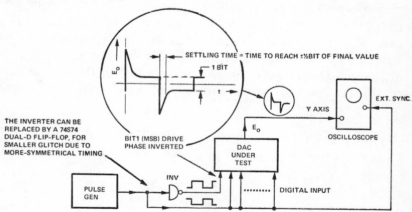

Figure 19. DAC Major-Carry Settling Time Measurement

Accurate measurement of DAC major carry transient "glitch" duration or amplitude using the scheme of Figure 19 is significantly easier than that of full-scale settling-time measurement, since the DAC analog output steady-state signal excursion in this instance is only 1 bit. As a result, amplifier or comparator overload recovery and thermal response time problems associated with large signal swings at the input to the measurement system are virtually eliminated.

ADC TESTING

Because of the fundamental ½-bit quantization uncertainty associated with analog-to-digital conversion, ADC testing is more difficult than DAC testing, owing to the need for determining both the output code and the transition point, referred to the input, rather than simply measuring an output response to a predetermined code. The effects of noise (occurring in either the signal or the converter, or picked up in the wiring) are to introduce an uncertainty in the precise determination of the analog input values at which the output code transitions take place, and to, in effect, increase the quantization band. The nature of these quantization and noise uncertainty errors is shown in Figure 20. (It should be noted, in passing, that the fundamental ±½-bit worst-case quantization uncertainty sets the requirement that the device accuracy can be no better than its resolution in the case of ADC's. This is in contrast to DAC's, which can have accuracy specifications exceeding their resolution capability. This distinction (or duality) comes about because of the inverse nature of the devices: the DAC output can, with arbitrary precision,

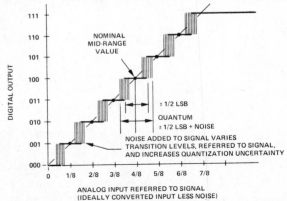

Figure 20. Quantization and Noise Uncertainty Error

locate a level which is a measure of one precise number representing either itself or the quantum determined by the digital number, while the ADC's output level is determined by any input value within the quantized range of input.)

A simplified diagram of an ADC test setup was seen in Figure 1a. The ADC calibration is established by observing correspondence between the state of the input digital toggle-switch register driving the reference DAC and the output digital display representing the state of the ADC. This simplified setup suffers from the disadvantage that the precise location of each analog calibration level within the 1-bit quantization band encompassing each of these respective values cannot be determined. As a result, calibration accuracy, linearity, and differential linearity cannot be determined to a precision greater than 1 LSB using this basic scheme.

One is generally concerned with establishing the calibration of the ADC so that the nominal analog calibration voltage is centered in the quantization band determined by the adjacent transition values. In addition, one normally is interested in checking linearity and differential linearity to a degree better than the ±½-bit quantization uncertainty imposed on accuracy.

DYNAMIC CROSSPLOT

By summing a small ac signal with the analog reference voltage applied to the input of the ADC under test, the ADC output can be dithered about each of its digital output codes of interest with a large number of analog inputs in a short time. This permits the analog values corresponding to the transitions and the center of each code quantization level to be readily determined, using a dynamic crossplot test. This in turn permits determination of device nonlinearity and differential nonlinearity to a precision greater than ±½-LSB.

The dynamic crossplot test configuration is shown in Figure 21. The digital code of interest, N_{REF}, is entered into the reference DAC via the toggle-switch register, thereby applying E_{REF}, the analog equivalent of N_{REF}, to the analog input of the DUT. Low-frequency ac dither E_{ac} and adjustable dc offset E_{os} voltages

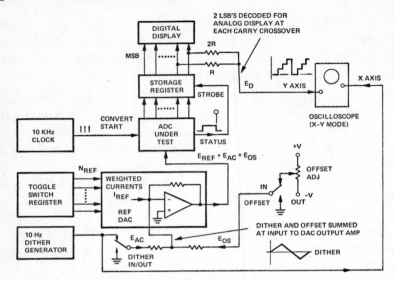

Figure 21. ADC Dynamic Cross-Plot Test

are summed with the reference DAC's output. The dither signal has a frequency that is low with respect to the conversion rate, so that the digitized output of the DUT will exactly track its analog input, within the ±½-LSB quantization limits. A digital register stores the results of each conversion. A 2-bit DAC is formed using resistors having weights of 2R and R to sum the LSB and the adjacent bit, respectively, of the stored ADC output. The decoded 4-step analog output, corresponding to the two stored-ADC least-significant-bit states, is applied to the Y axis of the oscilloscope. The ac dither signal is applied to the X axis of the oscilloscope, which is operated in the X-Y crossplot mode. A number of dynamic-crossplot waveforms, obtained using the test configuration of Figure 21, are shown in Figures 22b-22e.

The DUT is calibrated using the dynamic-crossplot display in the following way: The CRT beam is positioned in the center of the tube face, with the X-axis drive signal initially removed, to establish the Y-axis position. All bits, except the LSB of the reference DAC, are turned off; the LSB is turned on. The DUT's zero is adjusted to center the first step of the decoded output staircase waveform, corresponding to the digital code 000. . .01 on the Y-axis of the display, as shown in Figure 22b. Next, all bits,

except the LSB of the reference DAC are turned on, corresponding to the digital code 111...10, and the gain of the ADC is
adjusted to center the next-highest step of the decoded staircase
waveform on the Y axis, as shown in Figure 22c. These steps
calibrate zero and full-scale.

Using the dynamic crossplot display, differential nonlinearity and
noise at each bit code transition can be investigated. Figure 22d
illustrates the waveform that appears at the major (half-scale)-
carry code transition (0 1 1 1 . . . 1 to 1 0 0 0 . . . 0) of the digital
output code of the DUT when its bit-1 gain is ½ LSB too large
with respect to the gains of the other bits. This causes the staircase
step width corresponding to the code 0 1 1 1 . . . 1 to be ½-LSB
too wide.

Figure 22e shows the waveform at the 3/4-scale-carry code
transition, 1 0 1 1 . . . 1 to 1 1 0 0 . . . 0, when the bit-2 gain of
the DUT is ½-LSB too small with respect to the other bit gains.
This causes the staircase step width corresponding to the code
1 0 1 1 . . . 1 to be ½-bit too narrow. ADC differential nonlinearity is measured as the deviation in staircase step width from
the average step width. The waveforms in both Figures 22d and
22e, show ½-LSB differential nonlinearity.

Differential nonlinearity, non-monotonicity (missing codes), and

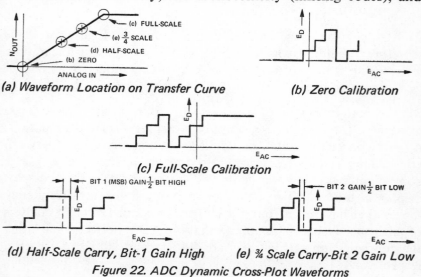

(a) Waveform Location on Transfer Curve   *(b) Zero Calibration*

(c) Full-Scale Calibration

(d) Half-Scale Carry, Bit-1 Gain High   *(e) ¾ Scale Carry-Bit 2 Gain Low*

Figure 22. ADC Dynamic Cross-Plot Waveforms

noise can be investigated at each bit code-carry transition by turning on and off each bit of the reference DAC in succession and observing the dynamic crossplot waveform in each case. Summation errors are investigated by turning on all bits, one at a time, in descending order of significance, and leaving them on. The dynamic crossplot waveform is observed as each new bit is turned on. This tests the performance of the DUT in the range from half scale to full scale.

The effects of noise and nonlinearity can also be assessed using the dynamic crossplot test. Noise is seen as a jitter in the location of each staircase-waveform step transition. Device nonlinearity will gradually displace the staircase waveform either to the left or right, as successive bits are turned on and full-scale is approached.

Several points should be noted with respect to the dynamic crossplot test configuration of Figure 21:

1) Since, for simplicity, only the two least-significant bits of the DUT's digital output are decoded, the dynamic crossplot waveform repeats every four steps. Initial DUT calibration must therefore be made statically to an error less than 2 bits before the dynamic crossplot is used, so that one can be assured that the desired code transition is being examined, and not one that is 4 LSB's away, which does not have associated with it the desired carry transitions.

2) A triangular dither waveform is shown in Figure 21. This waveform could just as well be a sine-wave, since a linear time relationship is not required in the X-Y display mode for a linear X vs Y presentation.

3) The external storage register shown in Figure 21 can be eliminated (at the expense of minor crossplot display degradation) if the conversion rate is reduced so that the time between conversions is large, compared to the conversion period, since conversion switching transients will be observed in the crossplot display in this case. Typical dither and conversion clock frequency ranges that have been found useful for dynamic crossplot analysis of high-speed successive-approximation ADC performance using the configuration of Figure 21 are 4-40Hz, and 10kHz to 100kHz, respectively.

ANOMALOUS ERRORS

The dynamic crossplot test just described is very useful in quickly detecting certain ADC performance anomalies, such as might be caused by oscillating comparators and hysteresis, for example. An oscillating comparator causes an excessive randomness in the code transition points on the displayed crossplot — more than could be attributable to random noise.

Some converters exhibit a hysteresis effect, which causes the location of the code transition points to be dependent on the direction from which the point is approached. This causes two horizontally-separated dynamic-crossplot waveforms to appear, much like a series of hysteresis loops. In addition, some converter families have been found to exhibit excessive noise at certain code transitions. The dynamic crossplot test is especially effective in facilitating discovery of such anomalies, because they are displayed quite prominently.

Single-Shot Conversion Errors

Some converters, which appear correctly calibrated when triggered at a high repetition rate, exhibit conversion errors when triggered intermittently at a low rate. Errors of this type can generally be traced to a thermally-induced offset voltage at the comparator input when this device has remained in one state for more than a few hundredths of a second. These effects are more common in older designs, which incorporate discrete-transistor comparators. Use of monolithic comparators in most contemporary converter designs has largely eliminated this problem. One-shot conversion errors are not readily detected using the dynamic-crossplot test configuration of Figure 21, since repeated conversions at a high rate are necessary to obtain a useful display, owing to the restriction on low dither rates imposed by the oscilloscope's short display persistence. Single-shot errors can be detected by removing the dither and observing the binary display as the conversion rate is reduced, while holding the analog input constant. Errors of this type will generally show up (if present) when the conversion rate is lowered to 1Hz or less.

SEMI-AUTOMATIC TESTING

A more elaborate ADC test configuration than that of Figure 21, which lends itself to semi-automatic ADC testing, is shown in Figure 23. A 3-position toggle switch permits selection of logic "0", logic "1", or "dynamic" for each reference-DAC bit input. The output E_R of the reference DAC is applied to the input of the DUT. The digital output word N_O of the DUT is transferred to a storage register at the completion of each conversion. The digital word N_R at the input of the reference DAC is subtracted from N_O, and the digital error $N_O - N_R$ is applied to a low-resolution DAC, permitting analog presentation of the error. Alternatively, this error $N_O - N_R$ can be applied to a limit comparator having preset high and low error limits, permitting go-no testing.

Dynamic testing using the configuration of Figure 22 can be done in two principal modes: *bit-scan,* and *count,* by analogy to the DAC test configuration, shown in Figures 9 and 11. The resolution of the reference DAC used in the configuration of Figure 23 should be at least two bits better than that of the ADC being tested, so that quantization of the analog input to the DUT will not limit the error readout resolution to less than that imposed by the $\pm\frac{1}{2}$-bit quantization band attributable to the DUT.

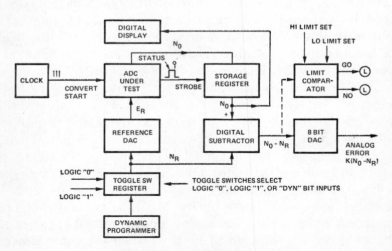

Figure 23. ADC Test Configuration

II Specifying Converters

Chapter 4

The applications for digital data-handling equipment and the products of the conversion-and-data-acquisition industry have spawned a multiplicity and diversity of companies, product lines, and products. We find it sobering (though not a little gratifying) to discover that, as a major manufacturer, with a reasonably complete line of modular products, we can deliver some 250 distinct D/A converter types, and that that line alone is growing by 75 types per year.

Thus the very large number of converter products available in the marketplace, even from a single manufacturer, can overwhelm even the most informed engineer, when faced with the problem of selecting a device, or a group of devices, for a given application.

Interpretation of the specifications adds another dimension to the task, which is further complicated by the virtual absence, to date, of standardized definitions of specifications among manufacturers.

To remedy this situation, and attempt to make the system designer's job of finding the "right" converter a little easier,* this chapter lists some of the elements of the decision and steps a user can take to help "home in" on a near-optimum selection. In this chapter are also summarized interpretations of the specifications consistent not only with the previous three chapters and with engineering practice at Analog Devices, but also – it is to be hoped – with interpretations that may become accepted as standard within the industry.

*It's possible that some of the points raised here, if previously unanticipated by the reader, may actually make the initial selection more involved, with the benefit that problems will be fewer at a later (and more expensive) stage.

A capsule selection guide is provided for the convenience of the engineer who may seek initial orientation to the various categories of devices available, in general, and to those available off-the-shelf from Analog Devices in particular. It is based on the 1972 Analog Devices catalog, which leads to the natural suggestion that the latest catalog available be consulted for specific choices. The reader is invited to request a copy from Analog Devices, either directly or via our nearest sales office.

Finally, a brief example of a data-acquisition design process, based on the suggestions in this chapter, is given.

TWO BASIC FACTORS

The two key factors in choosing the right device are:

Completely define the design objectives. Consider all known objectives and try to anticipate the unknowns that will pop up later. Include such factors as signal and noise levels, required accuracy, throughput rate, characteristics of the signal and control interfaces, environmental conditions and space factors, anticipated budgetary limitations that may force performance compromises or a different system approach.

Understand what the specs mean. It is essential to have a firm understanding of what the manufacturer means by his set of specifications. It should not be assumed (in 1972) that any two manufacturers mean the same thing when they publish identical numbers defining a given parameter. In most cases, the manufacturer has honestly attempted to provide accurate information about his product. This information must be interpreted, however, in terms meaningful to the user's requirements, which requires a knowledge of how the terms are defined. Two examples that give an insight into how differences arise are included and discussed at length in the Specifications section: *linearity* and *temperature coefficient.*

DEFINING THE OBJECTIVES – APPLICATION CHECKLISTS

General Considerations

A. Accurate description of input and output
1. Analog signal range; source or load impedance
2. Digital code needed: Binary, 2's complement, BCD, etc.
3. Logic-level compatibility: TTL, CMOS, etc., logic polarity (Unless otherwise noted, logic levels mentioned in Analog Devices publications are standard TTL, positive true)
B. Data throughput rate
C. Control interface details
D. What does the system error budget allow for each block?
E. What are the environmental conditions: temperature range, supply voltage, re-calibration interval, etc., over which the converter should operate to the desired accuracy?
F. Are there any special environmental conditions that must be coped with? High-power RF, high humidity, shock and vibration, and cramped space are a few.

In addition to the above general considerations, there are specific items to consider when choosing each block in a system.

Considerations for D/A Converters

A. What resolution is needed? How many bits (e.g., 8, 10, 12, etc.) of the incoming data word must be converted? To what degree of accuracy, linearity, etc.?

B. What logic levels and codes can be provided to the DAC? (The most popular logic system is TTL, and the most-frequently used codes are binary, 2's complement, offset binary (2's complement with a complemented MSB), as outputs of systems, and BCD, usually derived from digital voltmeters or thumbwheel switches.)

C. What kind of output signal is needed: a current or a voltage? What is the desired full-scale range? (Most DAC's are available with either current output – at very high speed – or voltage output, with the added delay of an internal operational amplifier.

Voltage-output DAC's are the more convenient to use and, with the exception of those designed specifically for high speed, will serve in all but those applications calling for μs and sub-μs settling times. Current-output DAC's are used in applications where high speed is more essential than stiff voltage output, such as circuits with comparators (e.g., A/D converters), or where fast amplification is to be provided externally (e.g., via CRT deflection amplifiers)).

D. What kind of reference is needed, fixed (internal or external) or variable (multiplying DAC)? How many quadrants are needed, and how arranged, for multiplying DAC's (1-quadrant, 4-quadrant, 2-quadrant digital, 2-quadrant analog)?

E. What are the speed requirements? What is likely to be the shortest time between data changes? After a change in the digital input data, how long can the system wait for the output signal of the DAC to settle to the desired accuracy for a full-scale change? For a 1-bit change at the major carry? Are switching transients of any consequence? Can they be filtered? Must they be suppressed (i.e., deglitched) within the DAC? What is the analog signal feedthrough requirement for multiplying DAC's at low frequencies? At high frequency?

F. Over how wide a temperature range (at the module, including its internal temperature rise) must the converter operate? Over how much of this range must the converter perform essentially within its specifications without readjustment? What deterioration of specifications is permitted (gain vs. linearity, etc.)

G. How stable are the terminal voltages of the power supplies that will power the DAC? Is the power-supply sensitivity specification adequate to hold errors from this source within reasonable limits?

Though no list can be complete, the above items will be the minimum considerations in any more-complete tabulation.

Considerations for A/D Converters

The process of selecting an A/D converter is similar to that involved in the selection of D/A converters. Some of the following considerations are analogous to those for D/A's, and others are unique to A/D's.

A. What is the analog input range, and to what resolution must the signal be measured?

B. What is the requirement for linearity error, relative accuracy, stability of calibration, etc.?

C. To what extent must the various sources of error be minimized as ambient temperature changes? Are missed codes tolerable under any conditions?

D. How much time is allowed for each complete conversion?

E. Is the reference to be fixed, adjustable, or variable (ratiometric measurement)?

F. How stable is the system power supply? How much error due to power-supply variation is tolerable in the conversion system?

G. What is the character of the input signal? Is it noisy, sampled, filtered, rapidly-varying, slowly-varying? What kind of pre-processing is to be (or can be) done that will affect the choice (and cost) of the converter? Which conversion circuit philosophies are acceptable for – or indicated by – the application? (e.g., successive-approximation, dual-slope integration, counter-&-comparator, etc. As a rule, integrating types are best for converting noisy input signals at relatively slow rates, while successive-approximation is best suited to converting sampled or filtered inputs at rates up to 1MHz. Counter-comparator types provide lowest cost but may be both slow and noise-susceptible; they are useful for peak followers and sample-holds that employ digital storage.)

Considerations for Analog Multiplexers and Sample-Holds

When a sampled-data system is to be assembled, in which one A/D Converter is time-shared among many input channels by the use of a multiplexer and sample-hold, their contribution to system performance errors must be taken into account. These accessory devices are discussed in some detail in Part 3, but they are also discussed briefly in this chapter because of their relevance to the converter selection process.

Multiplexers

A. How many input channels are needed? Single-ended or differential? High-level or low-level? What dynamic range?

B. What kind of hierarchy is used, if a great many channels are involved? What is the addressing scheme?

C. How much time is needed for settling to desired accuracy when switching from one channel to another? Maximum switching rate?

D. How much ac crosstalk error between channels is allowable? At what frequencies?

E. What error is produced by the leakage current flowing through the source resistance?

F. What will be the multiplexer "transfer" error, produced by the voltage divider formed by the *on* resistance of the multiplexer and the input resistance of the sample-hold. Is the multiplexer active or passive (i.e., does it have an output amplifier?)

G. Is the channel-switching rate to be fixed or flexible? Continuous or interruptible? Should it be capable of stopping on one channel for test purposes?

H. Is there danger of damage to active signal sources when the power is turned off? (MOSFET multiplexers are inherently "safe," since the switches open when power is removed. JFET multiplexer switches can conduct when power is removed, making it possible to interconnect, and therefore damage active signal sources.

Sample-Holds

A. What is the input signal range?

B. Considering the slewing rate of the signal and the multiplexer's channel-switching rate, what is the sample-hold's allowable acquisition time to within the desired error band?

C. What accuracy is needed (gain, linearity, and offset errors)?

D. What aperture delay and jitter are allowable, going into *hold*? (The delay component of aperture time is considered to be correctible, since the switching operation can be advanced to compensate. The uncertainty (jitter) cannot be compensated, and a random jitter of 5ns applied to a signal slewing at, say, $1V/\mu s$ produces an uncertainty of 5mV. In sampled-data systems, operating at a constant sampling rate, with data that is not correlated to the sampling rate, delay is of no importance, but jitter modulates the sampling rate.

E. How much droop is allowable in *hold*?

F. What are the effects of time, temperature, and power supply variation?

G. What offset error is caused by the flow of the sample-hold's input bias current through the series resistance of the multiplex switch and the signal source?

DEFINING THE SPECIFICATIONS

Figures 1 and 2 depict the specifications of typical D/A and A/D converters. Though the specs probably mean "what you think they mean," it is important that their meaning and implications be spelled out. The following list, in alphabetical order, should prove helpful.

Absolute Accuracy. When a converter's full-scale point is adjusted, it will be set with respect to a reference voltage which, in turn can be traced to a recognized voltage standard. The *absolute accuracy* error of the converter is the tolerance of the full-scale set point referred to the *absolute* voltage standard.

Acquisition Time. The acquisition time of a sample-hold circuit is the time it takes to acquire the input signal to within the stated accuracy. When conservatively specified, as in Analog Devices' specifications, it includes the *settling time* of the output amplifier. Since it is possible, in some cases, for a signal to be fully acquired (and the circuit switched into *hold*) before the output has settled, one should be sure of what a manufacturer means by this term, since the output of the sample-hold is not meaningful until it has settled. (See the chapter on Sample-Holds.)

Common-Mode Range. Common-mode rejection usually varies with the magnitude of the range through which the input signal can swing, determined by the sum of the common-mode and the differential voltage. *Common-mode range* is that range of *total* input voltage over which specified common-mode rejection is maintained. For example, if the common-mode signal is ±5V and the differential signal is ±5V, the common-mode range is ±10V.

Common-Mode Rejection. The ability of a device to reject the effect of voltage applied to both input terminals simultaneously. It is usually expressed either as a ratio (CMRR = 10^6) or as $20 \log_{10}$

of the ratio (CMR = 120dB). A CMRR of 10^6 means that a 10V common-mode voltage is processed by the device as though it were an additive differential input signal of $10\mu V$ magnitude.

Common–Mode Voltage. A voltage that appears in common at both input terminals of a device, with respect to its output reference (usually "ground"). For inputs V_1 and V_2, with respect to ground, $CMV = \frac{1}{2}(V_1 + V_2)$. *Common–mode error* is any error at the output due to the common–mode input voltage.

DAC-QM AND DAC-QS		Digital-to-Analog Converters
SPECIFICATIONS (Typical @ +25°C unless otherwise noted)		
MODEL	DAC-QM	DAC-QS
RESOLUTION	- 8QM 8-bits -10QM 10-bits -12QM 12-bits	- 8QS 8-bits -10QS 10-bits -12QS 12-bits
DIGITAL INPUTS	"0" E < +0.8V @ −3.2mA "1" +2 < E < +6V @ +80µA TTL Compatible	* * *
STROBE	Data transfers from inputs to register on "0" to "1" change. Width at least 50ns, "0–1" transition at least 100ns after data change	No Strobe
INPUT CODES	Binary, 2's Compl., BCD, and their Complements	Complementary Binary only
OUTPUT RANGES (User programs with jumpers)	0 to +5V @ 10mA 0 to +10V @ 10mA ±2.5V, ±5V, ±10V @ 10mA	* * *
OUTPUT IMPEDANCE	0.02Ω	*
CONVERSION SPEED Slewing Rate	5µs to 0.01% 20V/µs	* *
LINEARITY	±½LSB	*
ACCURACY ABSOLUTE	±½LSB	*
TEMP. COEFFICIENT Gain Zero	 ±7ppm/°C max ±15µV/°C max	 * *
TEMP. RANGE Standard Optional	 0°C to +70°C −55°C to +125°C[1]	 * *
POWER REQUIRED	+15VDC @ +25mA −15VDC @ −30mA +5VDC @ +150mA	* * +5VDC @ +35mA
POWER SUPPLY SENSITIVITY	0.002%/% supply ΔE (±15VDC supplies only)	*
ADJUSTMENTS (User Provides) Gain Adj. Zero Adj.	 100Ω rheostat 20kΩ pot	 20kΩ pot *

Figure 1. Typical D/A Converter Specifications

ADC−QU ANALOG-TO-DIGITAL CONVERTERS

SPECIFICATIONS (typical @ +25°C and nominal supply voltages, unless otherwise noted)

MODEL	ADC−QU
RESOLUTION	
ADC−8QU	8-bits
10QU	10-bits
12QU	12-bits
ACCURACY	
Relative	±½LSB
Quantization	±½LSB
Monotonicity	Monotonic from 0°C to +70°C
DIFFERENTIAL LINEARITY	<±½LSB
DIFFERENTIAL LINEARITY TC	±3ppm/°C, max (ADC−12QU)
TEMPERATURE COEFFICIENT	
Gain	±5ppm/°C of Range
Zero	±50µV/°C
Long Term Stability of Linearity	±½LSB typ
CONVERSION TIME	
ADC−8QU	6.4µs max (from trailing edge of convert
10QU	8µs max command to "1−0" change of
12QU	15µs max status signal)
INPUT VOLTAGE RANGES	±5V, ±10V, 0 to +10V, 0 to +5V, ±2.5V
INPUT IMPEDANCE	
Buffer	100 Megohms, min
Direct	
0 to +10V, or ±5V	5kΩ
0 to +5V, or ±2.5V	2.5kΩ
±10V	10kΩ
INPUT TRIGGER	Positive pulse, 100ns wide, min
(Convert Command)	Leading edge ("0" to "1") resets previous data
(see Figure 1)	Trailing edge ("1" to "0") initiates conversion
	TTL/DTL Compatible, 1 TTL/DTL Load
OUTPUT SIGNALS	Parallel, TTL/DTL Compatible; 4 TTL/DTL
(see Figure 1)	Loads/Bit
	Serial, RZ, TTL/DTL Compatible, 1 TTL/DTL Load
OUTPUT CODES	
Unipolar	Binary, BCD (Positive True)
Bipolar	Offset-Binary, 2's Complement (Positive True)
OUTPUT LEVELS	
"0"	<+0.4V
"1"	>+2.4V TTL/DTL Compatible
STATUS (see Figure 1)	"1" during conversion, 10 TTL/DTL Loads
STATUS COMPLEMENT	"0" during conversion, 4 TTL/DTL Loads
POWER SUPPLY REQUIREMENTS	+15V ±3% @ +25mA
(Separate Analog & Digital Grounds)	−15V ±3% @ −50mA Analog
	+5V ±5% @ 300mA Digital
POWER SUPPLY SENSITIVITY	±0.002%/%ΔV$_S$ (±15V only)
TEMPERATURE RANGE	
Operating	0°C to +70°C*
Storage	−55°C to +125°C
ADJUSTMENTS	
(External Potentiometers Required)	
Zero:	100k pot across ±15 with 3 Meg in series w/slider to pin 20
Gain:	100k pot across ±15 with 30k in series w/slider to pin 1
DIMENSIONS	2″ x 4″ x 0.4″ Module, Nominal

*Extended operating temperature versions available on special order.

Figure 2. Typical A/D Converter Specifications

Conversion Time. The time required for a complete measurement by an analog-to-digital converter. In successive-approximation converters, it ranges typically from 0.8µs (ADC-8F) to 400µs (ADC-16Q). Popular 12-bit general-purpose A/D converters, such as the ADC-12QM, have conversion time of about 25µs.

Crosstalk. Leakage of signals between circuits or channels of a multi-channel system or device, such as a multiplexer. Crosstalk is usually determined by the impedance parameters of the physical circuit, and actual values are frequency-dependent.

Deglitcher (See *Glitch*). A device that removes or reduces the effects of time-skew pulses in D/A conversion. It normally consists of a sample-hold circuit, which holds the DAC output constant until the switches reach equilibrium. Since the phenomena involved can be extremely fast, the *deglitcher* is usually a portion of the circuit, rather than a specific general-purpose modular device.

Differential Nonlinearity. In a converter, differential linearity error describes the variation in the analog value of transitions between adjacent pairs of digital numbers, over the full range of the digital input or output. If each transition is equal to its neighbors (i.e., 1LSB), the *differential nonlinearity* is zero. If a transition differs from one of its neighbors by more than 1LSB (e.g., if, at the transition 011. .11 to 100. . .00, the MSB is low by 1.1LSB), a D/A converter can be *non-monotonic,* or an A/D converter using it may miss one or more codes. A specified maximum differential nonlinearity of ±½LSB at 25°C ensures that monotonic behavior will exist over a tangible range of temperature, or each step is (1 ± ½)LSB.

Differential-Nonlinearity Temperature Coefficient. Since bit weightings vary to some degree with temperature, a converter having acceptable differential nonlinearity at 25° may have > 1LSB error at some other temperature. The temperature coefficient describes the maximum variation of differential linearity error with temperature over the specified range. Often, instead of a temperature coefficient, this specification may appear as a range of temperature for which behavior is monotonic.

Droop Rate. When a sample-hold circuit using a capacitor for storage is in *hold,* it will not hold the information forever. Droop rate is the rate at which the output voltage changes, and hence gives up information. As a rule, when using a SHA (sample-hold amplifier) ahead of an ADC, the SHA should not droop more than 0.1 LSB during the conversion time of the ADC.

Dual-Slope Converter. An integrating A/D converter in which the unknown signal is converted to a proportional time interval, which is then measured digitally. This is done by integrating the unknown for a length of time determined by a counter. Then a reference input is switched to the integrator, which integrates "down" from the level determined by the unknown until a "zero" level is reached. The time for the second integration process is proportional to the average of the unknown signal level over the predetermined integrating period. The same counter and clock are used for this measurement, and thus the output is immune to long-term variations of the integrator's characteristic time and the clock frequency. The counter provides the digital readout.

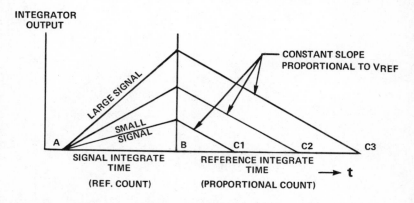

Figure 3. Voltage-Time Relationships in Dual-Slope Conversion

Feedthrough. A term referring to that characteristic of a circuit or device manifested by undesirable signal leakage around switches or other devices that are supposed to be turned off or provide isolation. Both digital and analog signals can cause analog feedthrough errors.

Four-Quadrant. In a *four-quadrant* multiplying DAC, if both the reference signal and the number represented by the input may be bipolar, the output can be either positive or negative, obeying the rules of multiplication as to algebraic sign in all four quadrants.

"Gain" Adjustment. The "gain" of a converter is that analog scale factor setting that establishes the nominal conversion relationship, e.g., 10V full scale. It is adjusted either by setting the feedback resistor of a DAC, the input resistor in a current-comparing ADC, or the reference (voltage or current).

"Glitch" If one applies the output of a counter to the input of a DAC to develop a "staircase" voltage, the number of bits involved in a code change establish "major" and "minor" transitions. The most major transition is at ½-scale, when the D/A switches all bits, i.e. from 011...111 to 1000...00. If the switches are faster to switch *off* than *on,* this means that, for a short time, the DAC will have zero output, and then return to the required 1 LSB above the previous reading. This large transient spike is commonly known as a "glitch." The better-matched the switching times, and the faster the switches, the smaller will be the energy contained in the glitch. (See also *Deglitcher*)

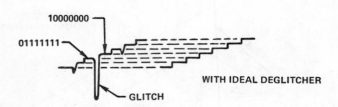

Figure 4. Glitch at a Major Carry

Least-Significant Bit (LSB). In a system in which a numerical magnitude is represented by a series of binary (i.e. two-valued) digits, the *least-significant bit* is that digit (or "bit") that carries the smallest value or weight. For example, in the natural binary number 1101 (decimal 13, or $(1 \times 2^3) + (1 \times 2^2) + (0 \times 2^1) + (1 \times 2^0)$), the rightmost "1" is the LSB. The weight of 1 LSB, in relation to full scale, is the *resolution* implied by the digital number.

Linearity. The conventional definition for nonlinearity of a device is the deviation from a "best straight line." This means that, to determine whether a device meets the stated linearity specification, the "shape" of the nonlinearity and the magnitude have to be known so that the end points (e.g., the zero and full scale points for a unipolar converter) can be offset by a "best" amount to minimize linearity error. Since this definition is totally impractical for *users* of converters, Analog Devices defines nonlinearity as follows: the nonlinearity of a converter is the deviation from a straight line drawn between the end points, as calibrated by a normal adjustment procedure. As shown in Figure 5, this definition is more conservative than the "best straight line" since, if all errors are of the same polarity, they may only be half as great.

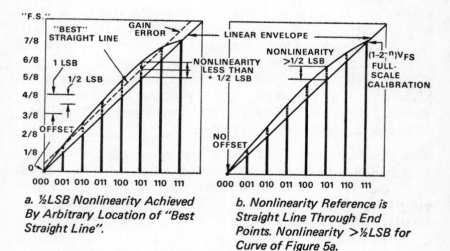

a. ½LSB Nonlinearity Achieved
By Arbitrary Location of "Best
Straight Line".

b. Nonlinearity Reference is
Straight Line Through End
Points. Nonlinearity >½LSB for
Curve of Figure 5a.

Figure 5. Comparison of Linearity Criteria for 3-Bit D/A Converter.
Straight Line Through End Points is Easier to Measure, Gives More-
Conservative Specification.

The user of the converter now needs only to set the two end points to measure the nonlinearity. The normal limit that is used for a good converter is ±½LSB, including the *differential nonlinearity.* This means that the sum of the positive errors or the sum of the negative errors of the individual bits must not exceed ½LSB, which means further that the errors of the bits themselves must be considerably less than ½LSB. For the higher-resolution converters (14 and 16 bits) from Analog Devices, the nonlinearity of *each and every code* is computed and plotted, to check performance before shipment. Linearity determines *relative accuracy* of converters. Once the converter has been adjusted and calibrated, deviations from linearity become absolute errors. While differential-linearity errors are cyclic, other linearity errors, such as might be caused by amplifier nonlinearity, tend to follow the usual nonlinearity patterns of other analog devices.

Monotonicity. The output of a monotonic D/A or A/D converter, in response to a continuously-increasing input signal (A/D) or count (D/A) should not, at any point, decrease or skip one or more codes. Monotonic behavior requires that the *differential* `nonlinearity` be < 1LSB. Integrating converters tend to be inherently monotonic. The higher-speed types that use D/A converters can be easily trimmed to be monotonic over a narrow temperature range, but for high resolutions over wide temperature ranges, switches and resistors must track very closely. Until the recent introduction of monolithic quad switches and film resistor networks (e.g., the μDAC's) such converters had not been commonly available at reasonable cost.

Most Significant Bit (MSB). In a system in which a numerical magnitude is represented by a series of binary (i.e., two-valued) digits, the *most-significant bit* is that digit (or "bit") that carries the greatest value or weight. For example, in the natural binary number 1101 (decimal 13, or $(1 \times 2^3) + (1 \times 2^2) + (0 \times 2^1) + (1 \times 2^0)$), the leftmost "1" is the MSB, with a weight of ½ nominal peak-to-peak full scale. In bipolar devices, the sign bit is the MSB. In A/D converters having overrange bits, the MSB is the most-significant "overrange" bit.

Multiplying DAC. A multiplying DAC differs from the conventional fixed-reference DAC in being designed to operate with reference signals that vary, often at high speeds. The output signal of such a DAC is proportional to the product of the reference voltage and the fractional equivalent of the digital input number. In addition to the usual DAC specifications, the multiplying DAC is specified as to analog signal *feedthrough* at low and high frequencies, and number of quadrants (1, 2-digital, 2-analog, or 4).

Noise. In high-resolution DAC's, such as the DAC-16QM, noise can be an important consideration, since the resolution is not confidently assignable when the peak noise exceeds the LSB value over a reasonable bandwidth. For an ADC, noise, either in the input signal, the input circuitry, or the conversion device itself, effectively increases the size of the quantization band, and may thus impart statistical properties to the output numbers, which may then require additional processing for successful interpretation.

Noise: RMS vs. Peak-to-Peak. For all but integrating converters, peak noise must be considered carefully, especially where small numbers of readings and limited processing capacity are available. An rms noise specification over a given bandwidth allows peak-to-peak predictions for gaussian noise (peak-to-peak values greater than 7x rms will probably occur less than 0.1% of the time). However, both peak-to-peak and rms noise specs should be looked at, since large spikes could be present on the output of a chopper-stabilized amplifier, or could be coupled into the analog portion of the system. These spikes, if narrow, will contribute little to driving the rms noise out of spec, but could nevertheless be considerably greater than 7x rms. If a DAC having spike noise on its output were used in a display system, the noise would cause distortion of the pattern, and loss of useful resolution.

Offset. For the great majority of bipolar converters (e.g., ±10V output range), to obtain negative outputs corresponding to negative numbers, a unipolar device is used, offset by ½ the full-scale range (instead of generating a set of negative values independently). For best results, this offset voltage or current is usually derived from the same reference supply that determines the scale factor of the converter, to make the zero-output point (of a D/A converter) independent of the thermal drift of the reference. The reason is that the ½-scale offset completely cancels the weight of the MSB at zero, independently of the amplitude.

Power-Supply Sensitivity. The sensitivity of a converter to changes in the power supplies is normally expressed in terms of percent change in analog value (D/A output, A/D input) for a 1% change in power supply, e.g., $0.05\%/\%\Delta V_s$. As a rule, the fractional change in scale factor should be well below the equivalent of $\pm\frac{1}{2}$LSB for a 3% change in power-supply voltage. There should be no adverse effects on linearity or offset. When power-supply voltage changes affect conversion accuracy excessively, the key culprit is often a marginal "constant-current-circuit" for the reference diode.

Quantizing Uncertainty (or "Error"). The analog continuum is partitioned into 2^n discrete ranges for n-bit conversion. All analog values within a given quantum are represented by the same digital code, usually assigned to the nominal midrange value. There is, therefore, an inherent quantization uncertainty of $\pm\frac{1}{2}$LSB, associated with the *resolution,* in addition to the actual conversion errors. This uncertainty is a property of the *system* resolution.

Relative Accuracy. Relative accuracy error is the difference between the nominal and actual ratios to full scale of the analog value corresponding to a given digital input, independently of the full-scale calibration. This error is a function of the linearity of the converter, and is usually specified at less than $\pm\frac{1}{2}$LSB.

Resolution. Nominal Resolution is the relative value of the LSB, or 2^{-n} for binary devices, for n-bit converters. It may be expressed as 1 part in 2^n, as a percentage, in parts-per-million, or simply by *"n* bits." *Useful resolution* (not usually specified explicitly) is the smallest uniquely-distinguishable bit for all conditions of required operation (time, temperature, etc.) For example, a "12-bit" converter may have a useful resolution, over its temperature range, of only 10 bits. Useful resolution of DAC's and devices using them (including ADC's) is limited by the *relative accuracy,* but resolution need not limit accuracy. For example, a 4-bit D/A converter used in a programmable power supply has 16 levels, but it could have a required accuracy within 0.01% (absolute and/or relative. Note that low-cost completely-monolithic 8-bit DAC's would not necessarily have sufficient accuracy for such an application, although their resolution is more than adequate.

Settling Time. This is the time it takes for a DAC to settle for a full-scale code change, usually to within $\pm\frac{1}{2}$LSB. For some applications, e.g., in staircase waveform generation, a more important specification is the settling time for a single LSB change (at the major carry).

Slew(ing) Rate. The maximum rate at which an output voltage can change, in response to a full-scale-output demand. It is usually imposed by the availability of only limited current to charge a capacitor, either internally, or at the output, or by the tailoring of frequency response for some purpose such as dynamic stability. The output slewing speed of a modern digital-to-voltage converter is usually limited by the slew rate of the amplifier used at its output. Slew rate magnitude is usually a guide (but by no means infallible) to settling time.

Stability. In a well-designed intelligently-applied converter, *dynamic stability* is never a serious question. The term *stability* usually connotes the insensitivity of a converter's characteristics to time, temperature, etc. All measurements of instability are difficult and time-consuming (especially in high-resolution devices), but instabilities vs. temperature are sufficiently critical in most applications to warrant universal inclusion in tables of specifications (see *temperature coefficient*).

Successive Approximations. A method of comparing an unknown against a group of weighted references (usually binary), capable of high speed. The process of successive approximations in an A/D converter is generally similar to the orderly weighing of an unknown quantity on a precision chemical balance, using a set of weights, such as: 1 gram, ½ gram, ¼ gram, etc.

Switching Time. In a D/A Converter, the switching time is the time taken for an analog switch to change distinguishably to a new state from the previous one. It includes delay time, and rise time from 10% to 90%, but does not include settling time.

Temperature Coefficient (See also *Differential-Nonlinearity Temperature Coefficient*). Temperature coefficients of gain and offset are defined in terms of the "average" deviation over a range of temperature variation, i.e. $(\epsilon_{T_1} - \epsilon_{T_2})/(T_1 - T_2)$. For specified temperature ranges that extend from below room temperature to above room temperature, the device is zeroed and calibrated at room temperature, and the temperature coefficient for the "high" range $(T_H - T_R)$ and for the "low" range $(T_R - T_L)$ are both compared with the specification; both must be better than specified.

   a. Gain TC This is affected by the reference zener ($<$ 5ppm/°C for a good diode) and the reference circuitry, including the reference amplifier and switches. The total gain (or scale factor) change is specified in ppm/°C.

   b. Zero TC (unipolar converters) The zero stability of a unipolar DAC is almost entirely governed by the output amplifier's zero stability. Since output amplifiers are usually employed essentially as current-to-voltage converters, they operate at low values of closed-loop gain, and the zero TC is not greatly affected by the choice of programmable gain setting (i.e., 0-5V or 0-10V). Zero TC is usually expressed in $\mu V/°C$. Zero TC in ADC's is generally dependent only on the zero stability of the input buffer amplifier (if included) and the comparator, and is expressed in $\mu V/°C$, referred to the input.

   c. Zero TC (bipolar converters) Converters that use offset-binary coding are "zero" set at the all-bits-off point, and their scale factor is set at either all-bits-on, or (for more precise zero) at the MSB transition. However, the zero TC is measured at the MSB transition (analog zero). It is affected by the reference TC, the tracking of the offset reference, and the tracking of the bipolar-offset and gain-setting resistors. For such precision DAC types as DAC-12QM, which use the same reference for both the scale factor and the MSB offset, and monolithic resistor networks (with their excellent tracking), the zero-TC specification is the same for both the unipolar and bipolar connections.

Zero Setting. The zero level of a unipolar DAC is set to zero volts at the code corresponding to 0V. The LSB transition of an ADC is offset by ½ LSB, so that all subsequent transitions ideally occur midway between the nominal code values. (See also *offset* and *zero TC.*)

SYSTEM-COMPONENT SELECTION PROCESS

The most natural process for selection of appropriate off-the-shelf components to meet a system requirement involves a method of "successive approximations:" Choose the least costly device that meets the most significant requirements, and perform an error analysis to check its adequacy.

If its performance seems far in excess of that needed (at possibly excessive cost), or inadequate in some respects, inspect the discrepancies for possible design tradeoffs, make a new choice (if necessary) and repeat the analysis. Remember, though, that in a maturing industry, costs can be expected to decline. *It is often less costly, in the long run, to go for better performance (rather than lowest possible cost) in the initial stages of a design.* Also, efforts aimed at reducing the cost of any element of a system should bear in mind the relationship of its cost relative to that of the entire project.

TYPICAL CONVERTER CLASSIFICATIONS

Once the problem is defined, and the key specifications have been determined, one is still faced with the question of narrowing the choice to devices likely to "fill the bill", as rapidly as possible, so as to conserve the time needed for actual evaluation. The "Capsule Selection Table" is a useful tool for accomplishing this objective of making a provisional selection. Tables 1, 2, and 3 illustrate examples of DAC, ADC, and sample-hold selection guides, as listed in the 1972 Analog Devices catalog. They contain a listing of products likely to fill a large fraction of conversion needs as of Spring 1972.* Their use is self-explanatory.

---

*Readers of this book are invited to communicate with ADI or our representatives for more recent listings, or to receive additional product suggestions for a given application.

Product Classification		General Purpose — Low Cost			General Purpose — High Performance			Fast Display		Resolution		Multiplying		MIL Grade I.C.	
Model Series		DAC-QZ	DAC-Z	MDA-Z	DAC-QS	DAC-QM	DAC-Q	DAC-DF[1]	MDA-F[2]	DAC-QG	DAC-16QM	MDA-11MF[3]	DAC-M[4]	MDA-QD[5]	AD560
Resolution Bits	8				●	●	●		●	●			●	●	●
	10		●	●	●	●	●	●	●	●		●			●
	12	●			●	●	●			●		●		●	
	14									●	●				
	16									●	●				
Input Codes	BIN	●	●	●	●	●	●	●	●	●	●	●	●	●	●
	BCD	●			●	●	●			●	●				
	Compl.	●			●			●		●			●	●	●
	Other					●	●			●					
Input Register	Yes					●		●							
	No	●	●	●	●				●			●	●	●	●
	Opt						●			●					
Output Signal	Current			●					●			●	●		
	Voltage		●				●	●		●					
	Both	●			●	●					●				
Output Range	Fixed		●	●				●	●	●		●	●	●	●
	Selectable	●			●	●					●				
Settling Speed	<200ns							●	●			●			
	200ns –5µs	●	●	●	●	●	●							●	●
	>5µs									●	●		●		
Tempco Gain in ppm/°C	<10				●	●	●			●	●			●	
	10–25												●		●
	25–50	●	●	●				●	●			●			
Package	Module	●	●	●	●				●	●		●	●	●	
	Card						●	●		●					
	Style	C-1	C-1	C-1	C-1	C-3	C-8	C-8	C-3	C-8	C-3	C-8	C-3	C-7	I.C.[6]
Replaces		MDA-H DAC-H MDA-U MDA-L			DAC-T			DAC-10D		DAC-R					
Details on Page		74			76			78		80		82		84	

[1] 200ns settling to 0.05% LSB changes.
[2] Settles to 0.05% in 40ns.
[3] One or two quadrant, for use with very fast ramp reference; has 11-bit resolution.
[4] Four quadrant, low frequency.
[5] Very small hermetic package.
[6] Ceramic DIL, 16 pins.

From *Analog Devices, Inc.,*
Product Guide, 1972

Table 1. Capsule Selection Table: Digital-to-Analog Converters

Product Classification		Low Cost General Purpose			High Performance General Purpose			Fast	High Resolution		Low Power
Model Series		ADC-Z	ADC-H	ADC-S	ADC-QU	ADC-QM	ADC-Q	ADC-F	ADC-16Q	ADC-I	ADC-QL
Resolution Bits	8		•	•	•	•	•	•			
	10	•	•		•	•	•	•			
	12				•	•	•				•
	16								•		
	17									•	
Convert Time Highest Resolution Version	Note								2	3	
	<1μs							•			
	1–10μs										
	10–50μs	•	•		•	•	•				
	>50μs			•[1]					•	•	•
Range	Fixed		•				•	•			•
	Selectable	•		•	•	•			•	•	
Output	Serial								•		
	Parallel			•			•	•		•	
	Both	•	•		•		•		•		•
Codes Available	BIN	•	•		•		•	•	•	•	•
	BCD		•	•	•	•	•			•	
	Other		•		•	•	•		•		
Tempco ppm/°C Highest Resolution Version	<10				•	•	•		•	•	
	10–25										•
	25–50	•	•					•			
	>50			•							
Package	Card						•	•	•		•
	Module	•	•	•	•	•				•	
	Style	C-3	C-3	C-2	C-3	C-3	C-8	C-6	C-8	C-5	C-8
Replaces					ADC-T, ADC-U						
Details on Page		86			88			94	90		92

[1] Convert time 1ms FS.
[2] 400μs without buffer.
[3] Dual slope integrator; 40ms.

From *Analog Devices, Inc., Product Guide, 1972*

Table 2. Capsule Selection Table: Analog-to-Digital Converters

APPLICATIONS	General Purpose SHA–1A	Fast SHA–2A	Low Droop Slow Settle SHA–3	Low Droop Fast Settle SHA–4	Low Cost SHA–5
Data Acquisition					
1–15µs/sample	•	•			
15–80µs/sample					
80–250µs/sample					•
>250µs/sample			•	•	
Suggested for Use With These A/D Converters					
ADC-F		•			
ADC-H	•				•
ADC-I			•	•	
ADC-Q	•				
ADC-QM	•				
ADC-QU	•	•			
ADC-S				•	•
ADC-Z	•				
Data Distribution*					
Fast (20ms between updates)	•				
Slow (100ms between updates)			•	•	•
Suitable for Systems With Following Limit of Linearity Errors:					
0.05%		•			•
0.01%	•		•	•	
Details on Page	96	96	96	96	96

*For Data Distribution, use any DAC of appropriate resolution. Those with internal registers (DAC-QM) may be most convenient. From *Analog Devices, Inc., Product Guide, 1972*

Table 3. Capsule Selection Table: Sample and Hold Amplifiers

AN EXAMPLE OF THE SELECTION AND VERIFICATION PROCESS*

A computer data-acquisition system is to be assembled to process data from a number of strain gages. Signal-conditioning hardware, to be purchased with the gages, delivers ±10V full-scale signals with 10-ohm source impedance. The signal channels must be sequentially scanned in no more than 50 microseconds per channel. Maximum allowable error of the system is about 0.1% of full scale. System logic is to be TTL, and hardware may work in either binary or 2's complement code. Parallel data readout will be used.

*For maximum tutorial benefit, to avoid clutter, and to fit the available space, some of the less-salient sources of error have been intentionally omitted. If there are any that you're concerned about for your application but don't see here, we invite you to communicate with our Applications Engineers.

Probable temperature range in the equipment cabinets (including equipment temperature rise) is +25°C to +55°C. Sufficient power at both ±15V and +5V is available, but the regulation of the ±15V supply is 150mV.

The objective: specify a set of conversion components having appropriate accuracy and speed.

FIRST APPROXIMATION

A useful rule of thumb that usually provides satisfactory results is this: For the critical specs of a multi-component system, choose each component to perform roughly 10 times better than the overall desired performance. Thus, for a system that needs 0.1%-grade performance, use a 0.01% converter (12 bits) with compatible multiplexer and sample-hold.

Reviewing the available A-D converters, we find the ADC-12Q and ADC-12QM to be possible choices. If the entire system is to be built on a single card, the ADC-12QM, a 2" x 4" x 0.4" encapsulated module would be a convenient choice.

The ADC-12QM completes a conversion in 25μs. For sample-hold, the compatible SHA-1A is chosen, adding 5μs of settling time. Thus, the combination appears to be amply capable of meeting the 50μs/channel scanning requirement. Since the multiplexer will scan sequentially, its settling time is inconsequential. The multiplexer can be switched to the next address as soon as the SHA goes into *hold* on data from the current address. Thus it has at least 25μs to settle before a measurement is called for. For convenience, one may use the MPX-8A; the small 2" x 2" x 0.4" module fits into the packaging concept, and the built-in complete binary-address decoding makes it easy to work with.

ERROR ANALYSIS

It's clear that the MPX-8A, the SHA-1A, and the ADC-12QM generally meet the problem's requirements for speed and resolution. Now we must look further into the details of errors, to determine if the worst-case situation is within the allowable 0.1% system error.

Multiplexer

The switches of the MPX-8A, being MOSFET's, with variable-resistance channels, are not subject to voltage offset errors. Errors here will be due to two factors:

1. Leakage current into the *on* channel from the *off* channels develops an offset voltage across the source impedance.

   Leakage current @ 25°C   10nA
   Source impedance   10Ω
   Error voltage = 10 x 10 x 10^{-9} = 10^{-7} V (negligible)

2. Transfer error due to voltage division across the MOSFET *on* resistance and input impedance of the SHA-1A:

   ON resistance   1000Ω maximum
   SHA-1A R_{in} 10^{12}Ω
   Divider ratio attenuation error: 10^{-9} (negligible)

Sample-Hold

1. Nonlinearity is 2mV over the 20V range, or 0.01%
2. Gain error of 0.05% maximum (and other similarly small initial gain errors in the system) may be compensated for overall when calibrating the system by setting the scale constant of the ADC. It is not considered as part of the error budget.
3. Input bias current of 10na (max) causes an offset error voltage in the source resistance.

   Source resistance = 10Ω (source) + 1kΩ(MPX switch)
   Offset error = 10^3 X 10^{-8} = 10μV (negligible)

4. Offset vs. temperature = 25μV/°C

Since the temperature inside the housing may change by as much as 30°C, the total change over the range will be

$$25 \times 30 = 750\mu\text{V, or 75 ppm of } \pm 10\text{V}$$

An offset adjustment is provided for initial trimming.

5. Offset vs power supply = 100μV/%ΔV_s

Since the supply may vary by 150mV or 1% of 15V, the error contribution is 100μV, or 0.001% of full scale.

By an analysis comparable to the above, we would normally also prepare a system timing diagram, and assign operate-and settling-time allowances. However, the components selected for this example have more than adequate settling time, even for 0.01% operation; consequently, we can overlook the need for a formal timing analysis to determine whether settling times are adequate.

Converter

1. Specified linearity error (relative accuracy) ½LSB, or 0.0125%.
2. Quantizing uncertainty: ½LSB, or 0.0125%. This is a resolution limitation, not normally considered in the error budget.
3. Temperature errors
   a. Gain temperature coefficient: 5ppm/°C for 30°C
      5 x 30 = 150 ppm, or 0.015%
   b. Zero temperature coefficient: 5ppm/°C for 30°C
      5 x 30 = 150 ppm, or 0.015%
4. Power supply sensitivity error: 0.002%/%ΔV_s
For a 1% shift, the error is 20ppm
5. Differential nonlinearity temperature coefficient, 3ppm/°C. For 30°C temperature change, error is 90ppm, less than ½LSB. Therefore, 12-bit monotonicity can be maintained, with no missing codes.

CONCLUSION

In this example, the worst-case arithmetic sum of these errors is 0.07%, and the rms sum is 0.03%. Since these values are reasonably conservative for a system with specified error of 0.1%, the designer may either rest with these choices and go on to the more-difficult hardware, software, interface, and wiring problems, or − if absolute-minimum cost of conversion hardware is an important objective − seek to reduce cost by considering a more marginal design.

In this chapter, we have sought to help the designer in his process of choosing a converter by providing checklists of relevant questions in making a choice, definitions of specifications and related features, a capsule selection guide, and an example of selection and evaluation. We now go on to some considerations for what must be done to make the system work as expected.

II Applying Converters

In Chapter 4, it was pointed out that, considering the many different types of converters on the market, the complex manner in which converter specifications relate to a specific system application, and the fact that prices of converters range from less than $10 to several thousands of dollars, selecting the most economical converter for an application is not a simple task. To make the most appropriate converter choice requires that the user consider a number of questions: What are the real objectives of the conversion process, and how do they relate to the converter's specifications? How may the system be configured to relax the converter's performance (and price) requirements, and at what overall cost? How will the other system components limit and degrade the converter's performance? What tradeoffs are available in the system error budget? Is it more economical to make a long-term choice of one "general-purpose" converter, which will meet the needs of a large number of system designs, or to go through an optimum selection process for each individual application?

In this chapter, we will discuss system aspects of selecting converters, a continuation of the discussion in the last chapter.

After selecting the appropriate converter, the user should be fully aware that the thorough preliminary analysis and economic component choice usually involved is not by itself sufficient to ensure that the system performance needs will be met. The system designer must take into account the physical surroundings, interconnections, grounding and power supplies, protection circuitry, and all the other details that constitute good engineering practice.

While these few pages cannot (and are not intended to) be a primer on engineering practice, it is useful for the converter user to become aware of those elements of practice that are of particular relevance to converter-system design.

MAKING THE PROPER SYSTEM CHOICES

A general rule of thumb used by some designers may be expressed as follows: "As the converter performance requirements approach state-of-the-art converter capabilities in *both speed and accuracy,* the price of the converter will increase exponentially." The user may expect substantial cost savings if he can relax either of these parameters.

Data-Acquisition Systems

An example will serve to illustrate the process of elimination and winnowing that can be profitably employed to determine a converter's minimum performance requirements. Figure 1 shows, in the simplest terms, a block diagram of an analog data-acquisition system, the primary application for which A/D converters are used.

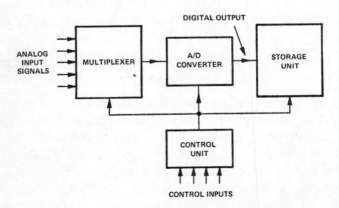

Figure 1. Data-Acquisition System

The data-acquisition system, under the direction of the control unit, selects the multiplexer input points, one at a time, and directs the signal appearing on each point to the analog input of the A/D converter via the associated multiplex channel. The signal level is encoded by the converter and outputted to storage. The storage unit retains each piece of data in a predetermined format, and holds it for further processing.

Three Classes of Converter Specifications

In attacking the problem of determining the converter performance requirements, it is useful to divide the converter specifications into three classes: Those that determine accuracy under optimum conditions, those that are dependent on time (or speed of response), and those that are substantially affected by the environment.

In the first class are included resolution, relative accuracy, differential linearity, noise, quantization uncertainty, monotonicity, and differential-linearity temperature coefficient. The reason this last term is included, though it would appear to be an environmental specification, may be somewhat unexpected: Although the ambient temperature may be in the steady state, it can be elevated (e.g., 25°C above normal room temperature) by virtue of enclosure in a cabinet. Although calibration *in situ* can correct for errors produced by variation of gain and offset with temperature, no correction can normally be effected for errors characterized by the differential-linearity T.C., due to individual bit variations with temperature. For this reason, the differential-linearity error at 25°C is augmented by the product of the steady-state temperature rise and the differential-nonlinearity temperature coefficient.

Speed-dependent specifications in the second category include conversion time, bandwidth, settling time of the input circuitry, etc. Environment-related specifications in the third category include gain (i.e., scale-factor) T.C., offset T.C., limits of the operating temperature range, etc.

Approaches to Relaxing the Specifications

Relaxation of the specifications in the first class may be effected through the use of signal conditioners. Choice of the specific form signal-conditioning may take is based on our knowledge of the input signals to be encoded and the information to be extracted from the encoded data. Known or unwanted signal components may be extracted from the input signals, and the peak-to-peak variation of the remaining signals may be scaled to equal the input voltage range of the A/D converter with an analog subtractor having adjustable gain. For example, if the signal conditioner is a differential instrumentation amplifier, such as the Model 604, it may be used to reject common-mode signals, to bias out dc offsets, and to scale the input appropriately. (Figure 2)

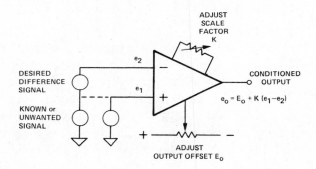

Figure 2. Differential Instrumentation Amplifier as a Signal Conditioner for Data Acquisition

The level-shifting-and-scaling operation can be used to obtain efficient use of the converter's input range. By scaling, voltage increments in the original signals that were less than 1 LSB of the converter's input voltage range may be measured.

Logarithmic Compression

In applications calling for wide dynamic signal range but capable of tolerating constant fractional error (e.g., 1% of actual value), rather dramatic efficiency can be realized through the use of logarithmic amplifiers for data compression, as shown in Figure 3. Here, a logarithmic amplifier allows encoding of signals, that would ordinarily require a minimum of 20-bit conversion to handle the dynamic range, with a far-less-costly 12-bit converter. Modest accuracy in a fixed ratio to (e.g., % of) actual value is substituted for extreme accuracy in relation to the entire full-scale range, at considerably less cost. For many applications this is an ideal performance mode, except for those applications in which extremely small errors are required at all points in the range (e.g., measuring long-term stability of voltage sources). The logarithmic data can be dealt with easily if the data is to be processed digitally; or it can be recovered in linear analog form (if it is simply to be stored or transmitted digitally) by the use of another log amplifier, in the antilog connection, with a D/A converter.

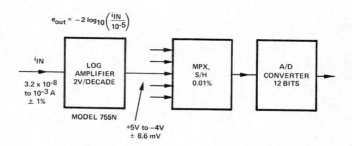

Figure 3. Using a Log Amplifier for Range Compression in a Data-Acquisition System

Filtering

Another commonly-used signal-conditioning unit is the filter. Low-pass filters are used to extract carrier, signal, and noise components, above the frequencies of interest, from the input signals. These components appear as noise if the converter is unable to follow them. A/D converters often incorporate follower circuits for impedance buffering. With a modicum of external wiring, they can be connected as active low-pass filters. (Figure 4)

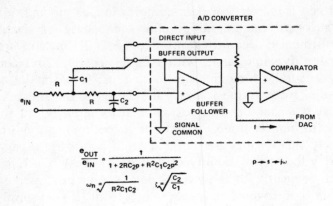

**Figure 4. Input Buffer of an A/D Converter Connected
as an Active Low-Pass Filter**

Sample-Hold

A relaxation of the second class of specifications can also be effected by adding a sample-hold amplifier to the system configuration, as depicted in Figure 5.

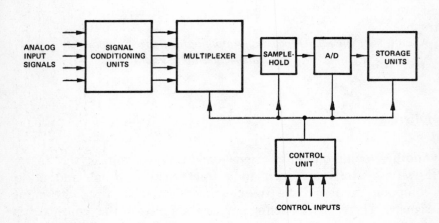

**Figure 5. Data-Acquisition System with Sample-Hold
and Input Pre-Conditioning**

The use of a sample-hold amplifier can increase the system throughput rate and increase the highest-frequency signal, of a given amplitude, that may be encoded within the resolution of the converter. The system throughput rate, without the sample-hold, is determined primarily by the multiplexer's settling time, plus the A/D converter's conversion time.

The multiplexer settling time is the time required for an analog signal to settle to within its share of the system error budget, as measured at the input to the converter, after selection by the multiplexer. For a 12-bit conversion system, with a ±10V range, multiplexers typically settle within $1\mu s$, and typical conversion times are $20\mu s$. The sample-hold can be used to hold the last channel's signal level for conversion, while the next channel is selected and settles. Since sample-hold amplifiers with acquisition times of less than $5\mu s$ to within 0.01% are readily available, the throughput time can be reduced to approach the conversion time. Pairs of sample-holds and A/D converters can be used for alternate conversions to increase throughput rate even further, though at considerable increase in cost.

The following example indicates the improvement possible with a sample-hold: If the input is a full-scale sine wave, $E_{FS}\sin(2\pi ft)$, the maximum rate-of-change is at zero, and (as can be found by differentiating with respect to t) equal to $2\pi f\, E_{FS}$. If the change is to be less than 1 LSB in the conversion time, the highest frequency that can be applied is

$$f_{max} = \frac{\Delta E}{E_{FS}} \frac{1}{2\pi\, \Delta t}$$

For a 12-bit converter with a $20\mu s$ conversion time, $f_{max} \simeq 2Hz$! Using a sample-hold, one can reduce the uncertainty in the time of measurement from the ADC's conversion time to the aperture time of the sample-hold, thus effecting an improvement in f_{max} by the ratio of the conversion time to the aperture-time uncertainty.

Since 20ns or better is routinely available in sample-holds designed for operation with 12-bit converters, an improvement of 1000:1 is quite feasible, assuming that the S/H has adequate bandwidth.

If the speed of A/D conversion is significantly limited by the settling time of the input buffer-follower, the sample-hold may be connected to bypass it, providing an even greater increase in throughput rate.

Relaxation of the third class of errors, those due to environment-related specifications, may be abetted by allotting one multiplexer channel to carry a ground-level signal, and another to carry a precision reference-voltage level that is near-full-scale. Data obtained from these channels may be used by a processor to correct gain and offset variations common to all channels, generated in the sample-hold, the A/D converter, and the associated wiring.

Contributions to Error

The decision to seek means of relaxing the required specifications is based on the availability and cost of devices that meet the original specifications, as compared to the cost of alternatives, and any additional problems engendered by departing from a straightforward approach. To evaluate the performance tradeoffs, an error budget is a useful tool.

Three classes of errors should be considered:
Errors due to the non-ideal nature of each component
Errors due to the physical interconnections of the system components
Errors due to the interaction of system components.

The first group of errors can be determined from the spec sheets for the system components. The second group result from parasitic interactions that are a function of the way the interconnections are managed, e.g., grounding, shielding, contact resistance, etc. The third group result from specific interactions between components in the system; though they are not specifically called out in spec sheets, they can be predicted from careful reading of the specifications of the individual devices, or from the user's knowledge of how they are designed. An example of this class of error sources might be the offsets created by series impedances in the signal path (signal-source impedance, multiplexer-switch *on* impedance) and the bias and leakage currents of the stages following these impedances, to which they are connected. A second example might be disturbances caused at the signal source as the multiplexer switches to its terminal.

By showing where the important contributions to error lie, the error budget is used as a tool for establishing tradeoffs to set the final performance requirements for the system. The error budget can be used as a tool in predicting the overall expected error, whether by worst-case summation, by root-sum-of-the-squares summation, or by combinations of the above using specific knowledge of possible compensations and common sense.

INSTALLATION AND GROUNDING

The current popularity of modularized converters makes it worthwhile to consider some elements of their design.

For one thing, many types are "customer-programmable." This means that the customer may select one of several possible signal voltage ranges by choosing the appropriate jumper-wiring configuration at the module's terminals. It goes without saying that all terminals used to determine the signal voltage range involve analog signals; to protect their low resolution levels, they should be kept away from circuit-card etch runs that carry logic signals.

Customer-programmable inputs also permit modification by the connection of external resistors, in addition to the jumpering mentioned above. Care should be exercised in doing this, for the reasons mentioned above. In addition, it should be noted that the excellent gain and offset T.C.'s of these devices are achieved by depending, not on perfect stability with temperature, but rather on the close tracking with temperature of key resistors within the module. Therefore, even if 0ppm/°C TCR resistors are used externally, the overall gain and offset performance vs. temperature may be appreciably degraded. Since there may be ways of avoiding excessive errors, the manufacturer should be consulted before external resistors are "frozen" into the design. It may also be helpful to read about resistor tracking in actual designs, as covered in the "Designing Converters" chapter.

In the design of the converter module, great care is taken to separate the analog and digital signal lines. This procedure should also be followed with the external layout of the board on which the converter is mounted. Etch runs of digital signal lines should not run parallel in close proximity with etch runs of analog signal lines. If these lines must cross, they should do so at right angles. Particular care should be taken with low-level high-gain points, e.g., the comparator input on A/D converters and the summing junction of the output amplifier on D/A converters. Etch runs to these points should be as short as possible and should not create loops. Analog-ground guard runs may also help reduce interference.

Grounding

Converter modules (actually, most data-acquisition components) have a number of ground terminals, which are not connected together within the module. These "grounds" are usually referred to as the Logic Power Return, Analog Common (Analog Power Return), and Analog Signal Ground (or Sense). These grounds must be tied together at one point, the system "mecca," usually at the system power-supply ground. Ideally, a single solid ground would be desirable. However, since current flows through the ground wires and etch stripes of the circuit cards, and since these paths have resistance and inductance, hundreds of millivolts could be generated between the system mecca point and the ground terminal of the module. Separate ground returns are provided to minimize the current flow in the path from sensitive points to the system mecca point. In this way, supply currents do not flow in the same return path with analog signals, and logic-gate return currents are not summed into the return from a precision reference-zener diode. (Figure 6)

In any event, the connections between the system mecca point and the ground terminals should be as short as possible and should have the lowest feasible impedance.

Each of the module's supply terminals should be capacitively decoupled as close to the module as possible. A large-value capacitor with a high resonant frequency should be used. A 15μF solid-tantalum capacitor is usually sufficient. Analog supplies are bypassed to the module's analog power return terminal, and the logic-supply terminal is bypassed to the logic power return terminal.

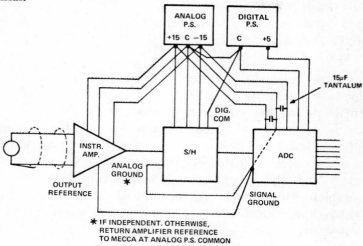

Figure 6. Basic Grounding Practice

When gain and offset adjustments are available and are intended to be used, the potentiometers with which they are performed should be mounted (with short leads) in such a position that they will be accessible when the mounting board is installed in the system.

The same care should be taken to locate a converter properly within a system, as is taken to mount a module on its circuit board. A converter should never be located near a transformer or fan blower motor. Using mu-metal shielding to protect against electromagnetic and RFI pickup is an expensive and not-always-successful proposition. D/A converters should be located at their loads. This may require long cable runs for the digital control signals; however, the reduction in noise pickup and ground-potential differences between the D/A's output and the load can easily justify the expense. Similarly, A/D converters should be located near the signal source when possible. Since this is not always possible, one suggestion is to use a differential amplifier to receive the signal at the end of a long cable run before presenting it to the A/D converter. When laying out the system, unshielded analog signal lines should never run in channels with either digital signal lines or power lines.

Reducing Common-Mode Errors

As we have indicated, a differential amplifier may be used to eliminate ground-potential differences in various parts of the system in which the converter is used. In Figure 7, the signal source is a remotely-located transducer, and the differential amplifier is located near the A/D converter. The common-mode signal is the potential difference between the ground signal at the converter and the ground signal at the transducer, plus any undesirable common-mode signal produced by the transducer, and any voltages developed across the unbalanced impedances of the two lines.

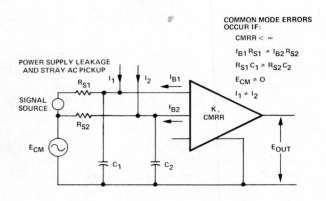

Figure 7. Common-Mode and the Difference Signals Due to Line Unbalance

If the signal source is the output of the system's D/A converter, the differential amplifier would be located near the remote load. The common-mode signal is developed by the differences in ground potential at the two locations.

The amount of dc common-mode offset that is rejected depends on the CMRR of the amplifier. However, bias currents flowing through the signal source leads can cause offsets if either the bias currents or the source impedances are unbalanced. DC CMRR specifications generally include a specified amount of source unbalance (e.g., 1kΩ). Such specifications also indicate a top frequency for which the dc spec is valid, usually the line frequency (50-60Hz), but sometimes 100Hz. At higher frequencies, unbalanced RC time constants (balanced or unbalanced series resistance and shunt capacitance to common, plus the amplifier's internal unbalances) reduce the common-mode rejection, by producing a quadrature normal-mode signal. This source of error can be greatly reduced by proper use of a guard shield, as shown in Figure 8.

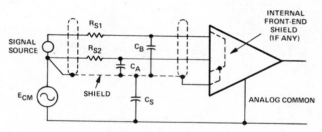

Figure 8. Use of Guard Shield to Improve Common-Mode Rejection at Higher Frequencies

Here, no part of the common-mode signal appears across the capacitors C_A and C_B, since the shield is driven by the source of the common-mode signal. The shield also provides electrostatic shielding to minimize coupling to other signal lines in close proximity to the input leads.

When installing a guard shield, it is important that the guard shield connect only at one point to the source of the common-mode signal and that the shield be continuous, i.e., through multiplexers, connectors, patch panels, etc. Since the shield is carrying a common-mode signal, it should be properly insulated to prevent it from shorting to other shields or the earth ground. A final precaution that should be taken is to make sure that a conductive return path exists for the bias and leakage currents of the differential amplifier (unless it has transformer or optically-isolated, floating inputs).

It is helpful, in reducing noise and improving common-mode rejection, to connect the largest tolerable capacitance *between* the input leads. It will provide some filtering, and will reduce the capacitive unbalance by more than its ratio to the stray capacitance. (Figure 9)

In portions of a system where differential amplifiers are not used, sufficient precautions should be taken to insure that voltages are not induced in ground return leads to the single-point ground, and that the system is free from ground loops.

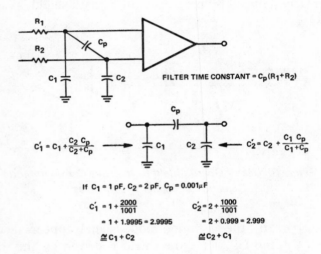

Figure 9. Capacitance Between the Input Leads to Reduce Unbalance and Provide Filtering

Operational Amplifiers

The operational amplifier, so named for its early association with precision computing networks to simulate various mathematical *operations*, is truly a workhorse in A-D conversion and interface circuits, as well as in general Electronics. Its applications include scaling and input conditioning, sample-hold, precision comparisons, current-to-voltage conversion and voltage-to-current conversion, active filters, etc.

For a broad understanding of the operational amplifier and a panoramic view of its possibilities, the reader is referred to any of the (many) papers, handbooks, and textbooks now in print. The objective of this chapter is to assist the reader in selecting the best operational amplifier for the job. But we start with a brief discussion of "op amp" principles, followed by a guide to definitions and specifications.

UNDERSTANDING OPERATIONAL AMPLIFIERS

While there is no single commercially-available op amp that can meet the requirements of every application (the *ideal op amp*), the concept of an ideal operational amplifier is helpful in the initial analysis of a given configuration, and for synthesizing basic circuit configurations to perform given mathematically-described tasks. In short, the ideal device is useful for deriving closed-loop relationships that can be directly applied to real circuits, with little error in many cases. When the desired circuit configuration has thus been established, it is not difficult to analyze error in terms of *statics* (dc offset errors) and dynamics (gain, common-mode errors, and response to rapidly-changing inputs), to determine the required amplifier parameters.

The Ideal Op Amp

The accepted symbol* for an operational amplifier is shown in Figure 1. The triangle points in the direction of causal signal flow. Considering the amplifier as a four-terminal network, the output, e_o, is related to the inputs ($e_A - e_B$) as shown graphically in Figure 1. For changes in e_A that are positive with respect to e_B, the output moves in the same sense (or phase), and the terminal at e_A is therefore marked "+" for *non-inverting*, or *reference* input. Since corresponding variations in e_B cause the output to move in the opposite sense (or 180° out-of-phase), this terminal is marked "−" for *inverting* input. The "−" input is frequently called the *summing point*, for reasons that should shortly become clear.

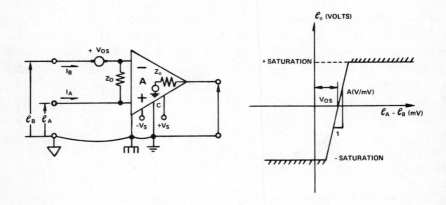

Figure 1. Operational Amplifier − Block Diagram and Response

---

*Some use a triangle with a curved back, the vestige of a practice sporadically employed in the analog computing field to distinguish open-loop amplifiers from committed amplifiers. However, since the first major publication devoted to operational amplifiers as circuit elements, the "GAP/R Applications Manual," appeared in 1956, the straight-backed triangle has been the symbol of choice.

Although the negative input is conventionally drawn above the positive input, it is often convenient, when sketching circuits, to interchange their locations. This is permissible, if they are appropriately, clearly, and unambiguously marked (and the circuit is drawn correctly).

The idealized properties generally assumed for deriving the ideal performance of circuits employing the amplifier of Figure 1 are:

Open-loop gain	$A \to \infty$ dc to high frequencies	typical value: 100kV/V
Voltage offset	$V_{os} = 0$ volts	typical value: ± 1mV @ 25°C
Bias currents	$I_A = I_B \equiv I_b = 0$ amperes	typical values: 10^{-14} to 10^{-6} A
Input impedance	$Z_D \to \infty \Omega$	typical values: $10^5\Omega$, $10^{11}\Omega$
Output impedance	$Z_0 = 0$ ohms	typical values: 1 to 10Ω
Common-mode rejection	CMRR * $\to \infty$	typical values: 60dB to 120dB

From the ideal considerations noted above, it is evident that the op amp will act much like a two-level high-gain comparator if used open-loop. If fact, comparators are essentially op amps in which open-loop speed has been optimized at the expense of closed-loop stability. To achieve the many benefits of operational circuitry, though, it is necessary to employ negative feedback. With negative feedback, the operational-amplifier circuit is in effect a control loop dedicated to maintaining the "error" voltage between the inputs equal to zero. In fact, if the output voltage is to be within its linear range, $e_A - e_B$ must approach zero.

$$e_A - e_B = \frac{e_o}{A} \tag{1}$$

As

$$A \to \infty, \; e_A - e_B \to 0$$

or,

$$e_A \cong e_B \tag{2}$$

Dynamic summing-point error is often written as

$$e_A - e_B = \frac{e_o}{A} + \frac{e_A}{CMRR}$$

or the instantaneous (or vector) sum of differential gain error and common-mode error. Although common-mode voltage would be conventionally defined as $(e_A + e_B)/2$, difficulties stemming from the use of e_A alone tend to be negligible, because e_A and e_B are usually very-nearly equal.

For example, in order for $e_o = 8V$, if $A = 100,000$, $e_A - e_B = 80\mu V$.

The simplest feedback circuit that one might devise is the ideal unity-gain follower of Figure 2, in which 100% of the output voltage is fed back to the negative input. The input signal source is connected directly to the non-inverting input, and the output follows precisely. Summing voltage around the loop,

$$e_1 + (e_B - e_A) - e_o = 0 \qquad (3)$$

since

$$e_B - e_A \rightarrow 0, e_o = e_1 \qquad (4)$$

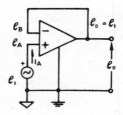

Figure 2. Unity-Gain Follower

The gain is precisely unity. The input impedance is infinite, and the output impedance is zero, because we are considering an ideal amplifier. For practical applications, the major factors limiting performance of this circuit are the common-mode voltage range and error, as well as bias current (if source impedance is high). Changes of bias current with common-mode level may also be important, since many manufacturers specify it at zero common-mode voltage only.

Non-Inverting Amplifier

In Figure 3, instead of feeding back the entire output voltage, it is divided down through a simple attenuator, to reduce the feedback voltage. Thus,

$$e_1 + (e_B - e_A) - \frac{R_1}{R_1 + R_2} \, e_o = 0 \tag{5}$$

and

$$e_o = \left[\frac{R_2}{R_1} + 1 \right] e_1 \tag{6}$$

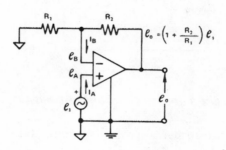

Figure 3. Non Inverting Amplifier

The gain is ideally determined solely by the passive components used, is positive, and must be equal to or greater than unity. Note that the voltage follower is simply the special case for $R_2 = 0$. Again, input impedance is infinite for $I_A = 0$, and output impedance is zero. However, $R_2 + R_1$ are now part of the load on the op amp output. The same basic limitations as for the follower apply, except that the magnitude of the common-mode problem is generally reduced as the required gain is increased, since the maximum non-saturating input is determined by the ratio of maximum output to maximum input.

Inverting Amplifier

The basic circuit for the inverting amplifier is shown in Figure 4. In this case, the non-inverting, or reference input is connected directly to signal/power ground, and the input signal is connected at R1, which forms part of the negative-feedback network. Unlike the non-inverting case, where e_B follows the input signal e_A

through a common-mode range, e_B (still following e_A) is constrained to zero, within the gain error of the amplifier (i.e., e_o/A). That is, e_B will behave as a *virtual ground.*

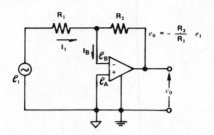

Figure 4. Inverting Amplifier–Attenuator

The analysis is quite straightforward: summing currents at B,

$$\frac{e_1 - e_B}{R_1} + \frac{e_o - e_B}{R_2} - I_B = 0 \tag{7}$$

Since

$$e_B = e_A = 0, \text{ and } I_B = 0,$$

$$\frac{e_1}{R_1} + \frac{e_o}{R_2} = 0 \tag{8}$$

and

$$e_o = -\frac{R_2}{R_1} e_1 \tag{9}$$

Again, the gain is determined solely by the passive components used to set the amount of feedback, but this time the output is an inverted version of the input. Input impedance seen by the signal source is now R_1, while output impedance remains zero.

There are a number of useful properties inherent in this circuit:

    1. *Virtual ground.* Voltage e_B is essentially at ground potential.

    2. *Voltage-to-current transconductance.* The current through $R_2 (= e_o/R_2)$ is determined by e_1/R_1, independently of R_2. e_o becomes whatever voltage is necessary (within limits) to maintain

the current e_1/R_1. This is true irrespective of the nature of the element labeled R_2, which may be nonlinear (e.g., a diode), or contain storage (e.g., be a capacitor, in which case $e_o = -(1/RC) \int e_1 dt$), or be an *n*-terminal network (e.g., an attenuator).

3. *Current-to-voltage transresistance.* If a current source *i* is connected at B, the current will flow through R_2 to the output, and develop an output voltage $-iR_2$, which depends only on the values of *i* and R_2. The virtual ground at B is an ideal load for a current source. Output resistance is reduced by the *loop gain* (p. III-8).

4. *Summation.* Since the terminal B must be maintained at virtual ground, any number of currents developed by current sources, voltages-and-resistors, etc., may be independently applied, and their algebraic sum will flow through R_2, developing an output voltage $-e_o = \Sigma\, i_{IN}R_2$ (Figure 5).

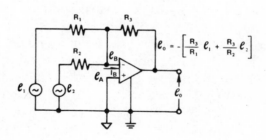

Figure 5. Inverting Summing Amplifier

There are a few additional comments that may be made about this circuit, since misunderstandings often develop:

1. The summing point (B) behaves as a virtual ground, or current sink *only while the amplifier's behavior is linear.* If the amplifier's output voltage or rate-of-change of output is in limits, it is no longer amplifying and must be treated in terms of an equivalent circuit appropriate to its new mode of operation.

2. In normal operation, since there is little voltage difference across the differential input, the impedance, Z_D, has negligible effect on the circuit behavior. R_1 is the input impedance

presented to e_1. For computations, R_1 includes the input signal's source impedance.

3. If the amplifier is used in a charge mode (e.g., with R_1 or R_2, or both, replaced by capacitance, to form a differentiator, integrator, or charge amplifier) it is often desirable to maintain resistance in series with the amplifier's input terminal to protect it against transient charging currents, especially in high-voltage charge-amplifier applications.

Gain, Errors, and Stability

There are five kinds of "gain" defined for operational-amplifier circuits:

Open-loop gain (A) is the relationship, previously defined, between the output voltage* and the differential input voltage.

Feedback ratio (β) is the net amount of voltage fed back from the output to the amplifier's input. It is a function of the entire circuit from output back to input, including both designed and stray circuit elements and the input-impedance characteristics of the amplifier. Its inverse ($1/\beta$) is often called the *closed-loop gain,* or "noise" gain; in fact, it is the *ideal* closed-loop gain.

Loop gain ($A\beta$) is the fraction of open-loop gain that is available for error-correction. Its magnitude is a figure-of-merit for a particular circuit configuration. Its magnitude/phase relationship can be used to predict circuit stability.

Closed-loop gain is the gain for signals in series with the positive input (or, with opposite polarity, for a signal directly in series with the negative input). Closed-loop gain is

$$\frac{1}{\beta} \cdot \left[\frac{1}{1 + \dfrac{1}{A\beta}} \right] \tag{10}$$

---

*with a specified value of load resistance. Lighter loading usually results in somewhat higher open-loop gain, depending on the output impedance. It is generally preferable, as well as realistic, to specify loaded gain rather than unloaded gain (with an output-resistance calculation), since load can be more-easily increased (if necessary) than decreased.

Since offset voltage, drift, and noise voltage are specified as "referred to the input," they are amplified by this term. For this reason, it is also called the "noise" gain. For $A\beta \gg 1$, closed-loop gain is $1/\beta$.

Signal gain is the closed-loop transfer relationship between the output and any signal-input to an operational-amplifier circuit. For example, if the amplifier is connected as an inverting summing amplifier with gains of 1 and 3 for the two inputs being summed, $\beta = 1/5$; closed-loop gain is approximately 5; $A\beta$ (for $A = 100,000$) is 20,000; and a $100\mu V$ offset, referred to the amplifier's input, becomes 0.5mV at the output. Referred to the *actual* signal inputs, the offset is 0.5mV (gain-of-1), and $167\mu V$ (gain of 3).

Difference Amplifier

There is no universally-applicable approach to analyzing op amps connected differentially. However, the equivalent circuit of Figure 6 probably represents one of the most useful configurations.

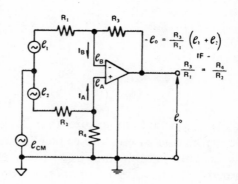

Figure 6. Difference Amplifier Configuration

If e_{CM} is zero, the circuit is the familiar subtractor, while, for e_1 or e_2 zero, the circuit reduces to a simple bridge or differential amplifier, with or without the common-mode voltage e_{CM}. Using the known results derived earlier for the non-inverting and inverting cases, and the theorem of superposition, and with the usual assumptions for ideal behavior,

$$e_o = -e_1 \frac{R_3}{R_1} + e_A \left[1 + \frac{R_3}{R_1} \right] - e_{CM} \frac{R_3}{R_1} \qquad (11)$$

Since

$$e_A = e_2 \frac{R_4}{R_2 + R_4} + e_{CM} \frac{R_4}{R_2 + R_4}$$

$$= e_2 \frac{R_4}{R_2} \left[\frac{1}{1 + \frac{R_4}{R_2}} \right] + e_{CM} \left[\frac{R_4}{R_2} \frac{1}{1 + \frac{R_4}{R_2}} \right] \qquad (12)$$

$$e_o = -e_1 \frac{R_3}{R_1} + e_2 \frac{R_4}{R_2} \left[\frac{\frac{R_3}{R_1} + 1}{\frac{R_4}{R_2} + 1} \right] + e_{CM} \left[\frac{R_4}{R_2} \cdot \frac{\frac{R_3}{R_1} + 1}{\frac{R_4}{R_2} + 1} \right] - \frac{R_3}{R_1} \qquad (13)$$

If

$$\frac{R_4}{R_2} = \frac{R_3}{R_1}$$

then

$$e_o = (e_2 - e_1) \frac{R_3}{R_1} \qquad (14)$$

It is (obviously) important to ensure that $R_3/R_1 = R_4/R_2$, if common-mode errors due to e_{CM} are to be eliminated. R_1 and R_2 should include the internal impedances of the sources e_1 and e_2. The source impedance of e_{CM} is of importance only to determine the actual amount of common-mode signal level at e_A. The actual common-mode signal seen by the *amplifier* is e_A, not e_{CM}.

Any common-mode error in the above expression is due to resistance-ratio mismatch. The common-mode response of the amplifier itself will increase or decrease that number. If the circuit is linear, the introduction of a small mismatch in resistor ratio may be used to compensate for the amplifier's common-mode error, in many cases.

Inside-Out Follower

As mentioned earlier, the op amp is a 4-terminal device, although one or more terminals may be restricted in use (e.g., the chopper-stabilized amplifier). To achieve follower operation with a single-ended chopper-stabilized amplifier, it is usually necessary to "float" the power supply, as shown in Figure 7. Negative feedback is derived from power common to the non-inverting input; then, $e_o = e_1$.

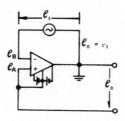

Figure 7. "Inside–Out" Follower

One benefit of this circuit (also applicable to bipolar differential amplifiers) is its ultra-high input impedance, since the common-mode impedance is now bootstrapped by the power-supply isolation impedance. However, cost is not trivial, since the amplifier requires a separate supply.

Summary of "Understanding Operational Amplifiers"

Each of the circuits described in this section has been developed with resistive feedback elements. In general, any complex linear or nonlinear feedback element, passive or active, may be used (if the configuration is stable) with appropriate modifications of the analysis to include the reactive or nonlinear relationships.

Typical applications include voltage-to-current and current-to-voltage conversion, sums and differences, scaling, rectifying, filtering, modulating, demodulating, classifying, peak-following, log(arithm)ing, multiplying/dividing/rooting, integrating, differentiating, oscillating, phase shifting, bridging, push-pulling, etc. The number of possible useful circuits using op amps staggers the imagination.

In sum, the power of the feedback technique resides in the gain that is so high that performance of the circuit depends, not on the open-loop gain of the amplifier, but on the external components and the configuration in which they are connected.

The equation that determines viability of a given circuit from the dynamic point of view is

$$e_o = \frac{\text{Ideal Relationship } f(e_1, e_2, \ldots e_n)}{1 + \dfrac{1}{A \cdot \beta}} \tag{15}$$

The magnitude of $A\beta$ determines functional fidelity, and its phase relationship, following the requirements of Nyquist and Bode, the circuit's stability (the total phase shift must be less than $180°$ at the highest frequency at which $|A\beta| \geqslant 1$.)

Static Errors of Op Amps

In deriving the idealized (yet practical) circuits described above, it was assumed that the amplifier possessed ideal properties. It is of course the departures from the ideal that determine the specifications of the amplifier and its properties in a given application. We have already touched on some dynamic specifications (gain and CMRR), and hinted at those that affect response and stability. In this section, we shall touch on those that affect steady-state precision.

In Figure 8, there appear an equivalent voltage offset V_{os} (which could be in series with either input) and bias-current errors, I_A and I_B at each input, respectively. Since other input impedances may contribute non-negligible error, they are lumped in with R_3 and R_4. Summing input currents at B,

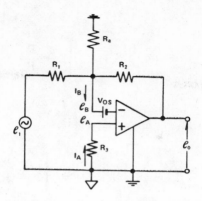

Figure 8. Voltage and Current Offset Errors

$$0 = \frac{e_1 - e_B}{R_1} + \frac{e_o - e_B}{R_2} - \frac{e_B}{R_4} - I_B \qquad (16)$$

or

$$e_o = -e_1 \frac{R_2}{R_1} + \underbrace{e_B \left[1 + \frac{R_2}{R_1} + \frac{R_2}{R_4}\right] + I_B R_2}_{\epsilon_{RTO}} \qquad (17)$$

$$\epsilon_{RTO} = (e_B + I_B R)\left[1 + \frac{R_2}{R_1} + \frac{R_2}{R_4}\right]$$

where

$$\frac{1}{R} = \frac{1}{R_1} + \frac{1}{R_2} + \frac{1}{R_4} \qquad (18)$$

Now,

$$e_B = e_A + V_{os} = -I_A R_3 + V_{os} \qquad (19)$$

Thus,

$$\epsilon_{RTO} = (V_{os} + I_B R - I_A R_3)\left[1 + \frac{R_2}{R_1} + \frac{R_2}{R_4}\right] \qquad (20)$$

If $R_3 = 0$,

$$\epsilon_{RTO} = (V_{os} + I_B R) \left[1 + \frac{R_2}{R_1} + \frac{R_2}{R_4} \right] \tag{21}$$

If $R_3 = R$, (i.e., $\frac{1}{R_3} = \frac{1}{R_1} + \frac{1}{R_2} + \frac{1}{R_4}$)

$$\epsilon_{RTO} = (V_{os} + \{I_B - I_A\} R) \left[1 + \frac{R_2}{R_1} + \frac{R_2}{R_4} \right] \tag{22}$$

From equations (21) and (22), it is evident that errors attributable to bias currents I_A and I_B can be equated to an equivalent offset voltage at the summing point $(I_A R_3 - I_B R)$. If $I_A = I_B$, then by selecting a resistor R_3, equal to R, bias-current error can be reduced to that of offset or difference current, $(I_B - I_A)R$. This technique is often useful, but it is important to note that it can be downright detrimental with some amplifier configurations. It works best with bipolar transistor input designs, as offset is generally an order of magnitude smaller than bias currents, and bias current errors generally are large enough so that "any" change is an improvement. However, R_3 is less effective, and questionable, with FET-input op amps, where offset current can equal bias current, and it is harmful with chopper-stabilized or varactor-bridge designs. Also, it is ineffective or impractical in circuits having complicated circuitry in which resistances (e.g., potentiometer settings) can change, circuits are switched, or capacitors play a major role (e.g., integrators), since any changes on one side must be imaged on the other.

CHOOSING AN OP AMP

Selecting the best amplifier for a particular application has become almost an art when you consider the overwhelming proliferation of both integrated-circuit and modular devices. On the other hand, the choice has become somewhat easier at Analog Devices, because both IC and modular devices are available, including some that are unique in the industry. Having a wide repertoire available, our applications engineers (and customers) benefit by the possibility of a truly disinterested choice, based not on what one has to sell, but on the needs that must be fulfilled.

The following sections are intended to guide the user to the best choice for his application, whether he be expert or newcomer. Familiarity with amplifier types and specifications naturally tend to facilitate the choice.

First there will be a discussion of the classification of amplifiers, with a table illustrating the specifications of representative devices in the various classes. Then there is a listing of the definitions of specifications. For an excellent and thorough (but too lengthy to include in this volume) discussion of selection principles for operational amplifiers, we strongly urge the reader to consult the *Analog Devices Product Guide, 1972,* or, if out of print, its successor publications.

CLASSIFICATION OF AMPLIFIERS

Table 1, which appears on the next two pages, is a capsule selection guide, outlining the key parameters of a wide range of both IC and modular devices. They are divided into seven major classes, based on key application features:

Key Feature	Application	Amplifier Classification
Low drift and noise, long term stability	Medical and industrial, transducers, amplifiers, preamps	{ Low drift chopper Low drift differential
Low bias current	High source impedance, integrators, charge amplifiers	{ General purpose FET Electrometer
Wideband and fast settling	D/A, A/D converters, sample and holds, comparators	Wide bandwidth fast settling
Economy, moderate performance	Function generators, general designs, active filters	{ General purpose bipolar General purpose FET
Voltage and/or current booster	Audio and servos, power regulators, galvanometers, current source	High output capability

Table 1.   *Capsule Selection Table:*

Description	Model	Open Loop Gain V/V	Rated Output V	Rated Output mA
General Purpose — Bipolar				
Moderate Performance Op Amps				
Good Performance Economy	118 A/K	250k	±10	±5
Low Cost, 20mA Output	119 A/K	500k	±10	±20
Slew Rate, High Gain, IC	AD507 J/K	80k	±10	±10
Economy, Speed, IC	AD201A	50k	±10	±5
Lowest Cost, General Purpose, IC	AD741 K/L	50k	±10	±5
Super Beta-Low 2nA I$_{bias}$, IC	AD208/A	50k/80k	±13	±1.3
General Purpose FET —				
Low Bias Current, High Z$_{in}$ Op Amps				
Lowest Cost Discrete	40 J/K	50k	±10	±5
Guaranteed CMR – Low Bias	43J	50k	±10	±5
Lowest Bias – High CMR	41 J/K/L	100k	±10	±5
Lowest Drift – 20mA Output	146 J/K	100k	±10	±20
Best Choice – Economy IC	AD503 J/K	20k/50k	±10	±5
Hybrid – Lowest Offset & Bias, IC	AD511 A/B	25k	±10	±5
High GBW, Slew Rate, IC	AD513 J/K	20k/50k	±10	±5
Wide Bandwidth —				
Fast Settling Op Amps				
1000V/μs Slew, 100ns Settling, 100mA	46 J/K	25k	±10	±100
125V/μs, 250ns Settling to 0.1%	48 J/K	100k	±10	±20
Lowest Cost –1μs Settling to 0.01%	45 J/K	50k	±10	±20
0.01% Buffer, 1μs to 0.01%	44 J/K	100k	±10	±20
100MHz GBW, Lowest Drift	120 A/B	500k	±10	±25
Wideband, 130V/μs, IC	AD505 J/K	100k/250k	±10	±5
Low Voltage Drift —				
Chopper Stabilized Op Amps				
0.1μV/°C Drift – Lowest Noise	234 J/K/L	10M	±10	±5
Lowest Cost – General Purpose	233 J/K/L	10M	±10	±5
Low Cost, Non-Inverting, High Z$_{in}$	260 J/K	5M	±10	±5
General Purpose – 25mA Output	231 J/K	10M	±10	±25
High Bandwidth – 20mA Output	210/211	100M	±10	±20
Low Voltage Drift —				
Differential Input, High CMR Op Amps				
Lowest Cost – 0.25μV/°C	184 J/K/L	300k	±10	±5
Battery Powered – Gen. Purpose	153 J/K	50k	±1.0	±1.0
Lowest Bias, 4nA, 0.5μV/°C	180 J/K	300k	±10	±2.5
Super Beta, 1μV/°C, 20nA, IC	AD508 J/K/L	250k/500k/1M	±10	±5
Highest CMR, Low Offset and Drift, IC	AD504 J/K/L	250k/500k/1M	±10	±5
Electrometers —				
Ultra Low Bias Current				
Varactor, Inverting	310 J/K	100k	±10	±5
Varactor, Non-Inverting	311 J/K	100k	±10	±5
Lowest Cost – High Gain FET	42 J/K/L	300k	±10	±5
High CMR, Wideband	41 J/K/L	100k	±10	±5
FET, Input, IC	AD523 J/K/L	75k	±10	±5
High Output Voltage or Current Op Amps				
100mA Booster – Lowest Cost	B100	0.85	±10	±100
20V, 20mA Output – High CMR	163 A/K	500k	±20	±20
20μV, 5mA Output – Economy	165 A/K	250k	±20	±5
100mA Output – 10MHz fp – Diff Input	46 J/K	25k	±10	±100
Guaranteed 10mA vs. Temp, IC	AD512 K/S	50k	±12/±10	±12/±10

Based on *Analog Devices, Inc. Product Guide — 1972*

Operational Amplifiers

| Frequency Response | | | Offset Voltage vs. Temperature | Input Bias Current | |
| | | | | @25°C | vs. Temperature |
Unity Gain MHz	Full Power kHz	Slew Rate V/μs	μV/°C max	pA	pA/°C
1.5	100	6.0	±20/±5	0,+35nA	±0.6/±0.5nA/°C
1.5	100	6.0	±20/±5	0,+35nA	±0.6/±0.5nA/°C
35	320	20	±15/±15 max	±25nA	—
1.0	10	0.5	±15	±75nA	—
1.0	10	0.5	±15/±5	±75nA	—
1.0	10	0.3	±15/±5	±2.0nA	—
4.0	100	6.0	±50/±20	0,-50/-20	2x/10°C
4.0	100	6.0	±30	0,-10	2x/10°C
1.0	50	3.0	±25/±10/±25	0,-0.5/-0.25/-0.15	2x/10°C
5.0	150	10	±7/±2	0,-30/-20	2x/10°C
1.0	—	6.0	±75/±25	0,-15/-10	2x/10°C
1.0	70	5.0	±75/±25	0,-25/-10	2x/10°C
1.0	—	20	±75/±25	0,-30/-20	2x/10°C
40	10MHz	1000	±75/±25	0,-100	2x/10°C
15	1.5MHz(inv.)	125 (inv.)	±50/±15	0,-50/-25	2x/10°C
10	1MHz	75	±50/±15	0,-50/-25	2x/10°C
10	1MHz	75	±50/±15	0,-50/-25	2x/10°C
10-100	4MHz	250	±15/±8	0,+55nA	0.9/0.7nA/°C
10	2MHz	120	±15/±8 typ	±75/±25nA	—
2.5	500	30	±1.0/±0.3/±0.1	±100	±4/±2/±2
0.5	4.0	0.25	±1.0/±0.3/±0.1	±50	±2/±1/±0.5
100Hz	2-50Hz	100V/sec	±0.3/±0.1	±300	±10
0.5	3.0	0.2	±0.25/±0.1	±100/±50	±1/±0.5
20	500	100	±0.5/±1.0	±100/±150	±1/±3
1.0	5.0	0.3	±1.5/±0.5/±0.25	0,+25nA	±0.25nA/°C
0.15	5.0	0.02	±5.0/±2.0	±3nA	±0.1nA/°C
1.0	10	0.6	±1.5/±0.5	±4nA	±0.1/±0.05nA/°C
0.3	1.5	0.12	±5.0/±3.0/±1.0	±50/±20/±20	—
0.3	1.5	0.12	±5.0/±3.0/±1.0	±200/±100/±80	—
2kHz	7Hz	0.4V/ms	±30/±10	±10fA	±1fA/°C
2kHz	7Hz	0.4V/ms	±30/±10	±10fA	±1fA/°C
1.0	4.0	0.25	±75/±25/±75	0,-0.5/-0.25/-0.15	4(0 to +70°C)
1.0	50	3.0	±25/±10/±25	0,-0.5/-0.25/-0.15	4(0 to +70°C)
0.5	70	5.0	±90/±30/±60	-1.0/-0.5/-0.25	2x/10°C
—	1MHz	—	±1.0mV/°C	±500μA	—
1.5	50	6.0	±20/±5	0,+35nA	±0.6/±0.5nA/°C
1.5	50	6.0	±20/±5	0,+35nA	±0.6/±0.5nA/°C
40	10MHz	1000	±75/±25	0,-100	2x/10°C
1.0	10	0.5	±20/±25	±200nA	—

(Specifications typical @ +25°C and rated power supply unless otherwise noted.)

Data for the table has been distilled from the *Analog Devices Product Guide — 1972.* It is suggested that the reader consult the latest *Product Guide* or supplement for information on the most-current product line. Copies of the *Guide,* as well as individual product data sheets, are available from Analog Devices or the nearest field office or representative.

In settling on the seven major classes, we have established what appears to be a near-optimum point of departure for proper amplifier selection. In some exceptional cases, an amplifier has been included in more than one category because of its outstanding versatility. But in most instances, one single attribute or key parameter is focussed on in each group. For example, the chopper-stabilized group naturally features low drift; however, it includes several models which could qualify for high output capability or wide bandwidth.

To ease the task of designers seeking the best device for a given job, based purely on its technical qualifications, both modules and IC's are listed together in each category. However, for the benefit of the many users who prefer IC's because of their low cost, small size, and hermetically-sealed package, we have clearly identified the IC members of each family as such under "Description."

OPERATIONAL AMPLIFIER CLASSIFICATIONS

1. General Purpose — Moderate Performance

Amplifiers in this group include Analog's lowest cost devices. They are best suited for general purpose designs with moderate drift requirements in the range from 5 to $40\mu V/^\circ C$, unity gain-bandwidths to 1MHz, and full-power response to 100kHz. Typical applications include summing, inverting, impedance buffering (followers) and active filtering. They are also useful for developing nonlinear transfer functions.

2. General Purpose FET — Low Bias Current, High Z_{IN}

These models should meet most design requirements, especially those which cannot be satisfied by bipolar input designs because of excessive bias currents or too-low input impedance. The lower bias currents (0.15 to 100pA) and higher input impedances (10^{11} ohms) of FET's make them a natural choice when resistance values exceed $100k\Omega$ and it is necessary to minimize input loading and current-offset errors to improve accuracy. Significant applications include integrators, sample and hold amplifiers, current to voltage converters and low-bias-current log circuits.

3. Wide Bandwidth — Fast Settling

Amplifiers in this group feature both differential FET and bipolar input stages, which afford a wide choice of drift and bias current specifications. They emphasize exceptionally fast response and wide bandwidths (to 40MHz, 100ns settling) for applications in data-acquisition and pulse-data transmission systems. Critical specifications are step response settling time, full power response and current output.

These amplifiers are useful for sample and hold circuits, A/D converters, and as high-speed buffers and integrators. Offering high output current capability, they should be considered for video or line driver circuits, D/A output amplifiers or as deflection coil amplifiers.

4. *Low Voltage Drift — Chopper Stabilized*

These amplifiers are widely accepted as the best choice when it is essential to maintain low voltage offsets and bias currents with time and temperature or whenever external offset adjustments are not practical in the application. Using carrier modulation techniques, these designs achieve bandwidths to 20MHz, drifts to $0.1\mu V/°C$ and long term stability of $2\mu V$/month. Typical applications include error-summing amplifiers for servo loops, precision regulators, or as input amplifiers for laboratory grade metering instruments and test equipment.

5. *Low Voltage Drift — Differential Input, High CMRR*

"Chopperless" low drift designs with differential inputs should be considered for high-accuracy instrumentation, low-level transducer bridge circuits, precision voltage comparators and for impedance buffer designs. In general, they should be selected over single ended choppers where a differential input is required or whenever possible chopper modulation spikes are objectionable in the circuit design.

Amplifiers in this group feature differential bipolar transistor input stages achieving input drifts as low as 0.25 $\mu V/°C$, offset voltages to $100\mu V$ and exceptionally stable long term drifts of $3\mu V$/month. These devices offer differential performance with input noise of $1\mu V$ p-p, a CMV of 10V and 100dB of CMR. For comparison, chopper-amplifier stability approaches $1\mu V$/month, but they are useful as single-ended amplifiers only.

6. *Electrometer — Ultra Low Bias Current*

Amplifiers with bias currents less than 1pA are classified as suitable for electrometer use. Frequency response and voltage drift are usually secondary requirements. Both varactor bridge and FET-input designs are employed to achieve low bias currents, ranging from one picoamp (10^{-12}A) to ten femtoamps (10^{-14}A). These amplifiers are used as current-to-voltage converters with high impedance transducers such as photomultiplier tubes, flame detectors, pH cells and radiation detectors.

7. *High Output — Voltage/Current*

Amplifiers offered here have bipolar or FET inputs with output voltage swings of ±20 volts or output current to ±100mA. Also included is model B100, a 100mA wideband booster for op amps. Typical applications include audio amplifiers, voltage or current regulators and driver stages for sonar transducers, galvanometers and deflection coils.

DEFINITIONS OF OP AMP SPECIFICATIONS

Absolute Maximum Differential

Under most operating conditions, feedback maintains the error voltage between inputs very close to zero volts. However, in some applications, such as voltage comparators, the voltage between inputs can become large. E_d defines the maximum voltage which can be applied between inputs without causing permanent damage to the amplifier.

Common Mode Rejection

An ideal operational amplifier responds only to the difference voltage between inputs (e+ minus e−) and produces no output for a common mode voltage, that is, when both inputs are at the same potential. However, due to slightly different gains between the plus and minus inputs, common mode input voltages are not entirely subtracted at the output. If the output error voltage is referred to the input (dividing by closed loop gain) it reflects the common mode error voltage between the inputs. Common mode rejection ratio (CMRR) is defined as the ratio of common mode voltage to common mode error voltage. CMRR is sometimes expressed in dB.

$$CMR = 20 \log_{10} (CMRR)$$

Precisely specifying CMRR is complicated by the fact that common mode voltage error, e_{ecm}, can be a highly non-linear function of common mode voltage, and it also varies with temperature. This is particularly true for FET-input amplifiers. As a consequence, CMRR data published by Analog Devices are average figures assuming an end point measurement at the common mode voltage specified. The incremental CMRR about some large common mode voltage may be less than the average CMRR which is specified, but much greater at lower voltages. Published CMRR specifications apply only to DC input signals. CMRR decreases with increasing frequency.

Drift vs. Supply

Offset voltage, bias current and difference current change with time as components age. It is important to realize that the published time drift for amplifiers does not accumulate linearly. For example, voltage drift for a chopper stabilized amplifier (which is by far the best amplifier type .for long term stability) might be quoted as $1\mu V$/day whereas cummulative drift over 30 days would not exceed $5\mu V$ nor $15\mu V$ in a year. In general the drift accumulation may be extrapolated by multiplying the specified drift/day by the square root of the number of days. Since our catalog specifies drift/month, divide by $\sqrt{30}$ or 5.5 to obtain drift/day.

Full–Power Response

The large signal and small signal response characteristics of operational amplifiers differ substantially. An amplifier will not respond to large signal changes as fast as the small-signal-band-width characteristics would predict, primarily because of slew-rate limiting in the output stages. We specify full power response in two ways: Full linear response and full peak response.

Full linear response, f_p, is the maximum frequency at unity closed loop gain, for which a sinusoidal input signal will produce full output at rated load without exceeding a pre-determined distortion level. Note that this specification does not relate to "response" in the sense of gain reduction with frequency but refers only to distortion in the output signal. There is no industry-wide accepted value for the distortion level which determines the full linear response limitation, but we use 3% as a maximum acceptable limit. One subtle point here is that in many applications the distortion which is caused by exceeding the full linear response can be comfortably ignored. But a far more serious effect, often overlooked, is that a DC offset voltage can be generated when the full linear response is exceeded. This is due to rectification of the asymmetrical feedback waveform or overloading the input stage with large distortion signals at the summing junction.

Certain amplifiers designed to optimize high-frequency performance will provide full output swing substantially beyond the full linear response (3% distortion) limit described above. Since linear waveshape is not generally a consideration in the use of these devices, they are specified for the maximum frequency at which they will produce full output swing. This is termed "full peak response" and is indicated as such on the specification charts by the word "peak" in the row marked "Full Power Response."

Initial Bias Current

Bias current, i_b, is defined as the current required at either input from an infinite source impedance to drive the output to zero (assuming zero common mode voltage). For differential amplifiers, bias current is present at both the negative and positive inputs. All Analog Devices specifications pertain to the worse of the two (not average or mean). For single ended amplifiers, bias current refers to the current at the active input only.

Initial bias current, I_b, is the bias current at either input measured at +25°C, rated supply voltages and zero common mode voltage. The designation $(0, +)$ or $(0, -)$ indicates that no internal compensation has been used to reduce initial bias current and hence the polarity is always known. The sign indicates the power supply polarity to which an external compensating resistor should be connected to zero the initial bias current. The designation $(\pm)$ indicates that internal compensation has been used to reduce initial bias current, and that the residual bias current may be of either polarity. In general, compensating initial bias current has little effect on the bias-current temperature coefficient. One should note that the bias current of FET amplifiers increases by a factor of 2 for each 10°C rise in temperature.

Initial Difference Current

Difference current, i_d, is defined as the difference between the bias currents of a differential amplifier. The input circuitry of differential amplifiers is generally symmetrical, so that bias currents at both inputs tend to be equal and tend to track with changes in temperature and supply voltage. Therefore, difference current is about 10% of the bias current at either input, assuming that initial bias current has not been compensated.

Input Impedance

Differential input impedance, R_d, is defined as the impedance between the two input terminals, measured at +25°C, assuming that the error voltage e_e is nulled or very near zero volts. To a first approximation, dynamic impedance can be represented by a capacitor, C_d, in parallel with R_d.

Common-mode impedance, R_{cm}, is defined as the impedance between each input and ground (or power supply common) and is specified at +25°C. For most circuits, common-mode impedance at the negative input R_{cm-}, has little significance, except for the capacitance which it adds at the summing junction. However, common-mode impedance on the plus input, R_{cm+}, sets the upper limit on closed-loop input impedance for the non-inverting configuration. Dynamic impedance can be represented by a capacitor, C_{cm}, in parallel with R_{cm}; it usually ranges from 5 to 25pF on the plus input.

Common-mode impedance is a non-linear function of both temperature and common-mode voltage. For FET-input amplifiers, common mode impedance is reduced by a factor of two for each 10°C temperature rise.

As a function of a common mode voltage, R_{cm} is defined as average impedance for a common mode voltage change from zero to $\pm E_{cm}$, that is, maximum common mode voltage. Incremental R_{cm} about some large common mode voltage may be considerably less than the specified average R_{cm}, especially for FET input amplifiers.

Initial Offset Voltage

Offset voltage, e_{os}, is defined as the voltage required in series with the input from a zero source impedance to drive the output to zero. Initial offset voltage, E_{os}, defines the offset voltage at +25°C and rated supply voltages. In most amplifiers, provisions are made to adjust initial offset to zero with an external trim potentiometer.

Input Noise

Input voltage and current noise characteristics can be specified and analyzed very much like offset voltage and bias current characteristics. In fact, drift can be considered to be noise which occurs at very low frequencies. The primary difference in measuring and specifying noise as opposed to DC drift is that bandwidth must be considered. At low frequencies, 100Hz or less, 1/f noise prevails, which means that the noise per root cycle increases inversely with the square root of frequency. At the mid-band frequencies noise per root cycle is constant or "white."

For this reason two noise specifications are given. Low-frequency random noise in a pass band of 0.01 to 1Hz is specified as peak-to-peak with a 6.6 rms uncertainty, signifying that 99.9% of the observed peak-to-peak excursions will fall within the specified limits. Wideband noise in a bandpass of 5Hz to 50kHz is specified as rms.

Maximum Common–Mode Voltage

For differential-input amplifiers, the voltage at both inputs can have values above or below ground potential. Common mode voltage, is defined as the voltage (above or below ground) when both inputs are at the same voltage. E_{cm} is defined as the maximum peak common mode voltage which will produce less than a 1% error at the output. E_{cm} establishes the maximum input voltage for the voltage follower connection.

Open–Loop Gain

Open loop gain, A, is defined as the ratio of a change of output voltage to the error voltage applied between the amplifier inputs to produce the change. Gain is usually specified only at $DC(A_o)$, but in many applications the frequency-dependence of gain is also important. For this reason, the typical open-loop gain response is published for each amplifier.

Overload Recovery

Overload recovery defines the time required for the output voltage to recover to the rated output voltage E_o from a saturated condition. In some amplifiers the overload recovery will increase for large impedances (greater than $50k\Omega$) in the input circuit. Published specifications apply for low impedances and assume that overload recovery is not degraded by stray capacitance in the feedback network. Overload recovery is defined for 50% overdrive.

Rated Output

Rated output voltage is the minimum peak output voltage which can be obtained at rated output current before clipping or excessive non-linearity occurs. Rated output current is the minimum guaranteed value of current supplied at the rated output voltage. Load impedance less than E_o/I_o can be used but E_o will decrease, distortion may increase and open loop gain will be reduced. (All models are short-circuit protected to ground.)

Settling Time

Settling time is the time required, after a demand for an output step change (such as a step input to a unity-gain follower), for the output to reach and remain at the final value, within a band of specified magnitude. This period includes an initial delay, a period of "slewing" at maximum speed, a period of recovery during which an overshoot or "ringing" may occur, and final relaxation to within the defined error band (sometimes with a long "tail.") For small error bands, such as 0.01%, settling time is difficult to measure. One approach, used for measuring converter settling time, is discussed in the chapter "Testing Converters." Other means have been discussed in the literature.*

Slewing Rate

Slewing rate, S, usually in volts/μsec, defines the maximum rate of change of output voltage for a large input step change. $S = 2\pi f_p E_o$

Temperature Drift

Offset voltage, bias current and difference current all change or "drift" from their initial values with temperature. This is by far the most important source of error in most applications. The temperature coefficients of these parameters, $\Delta e_{os}/\Delta T$, $\Delta i_b/\Delta T$, and $\Delta i_d/\Delta T$ are all defined as the average slope over a specified temperature range. In general, however, drift is a non-linear function of temperature and the slopes are greater at the extremes of temperature than around normal (+25°C) ambient which generally means that for small temperature excursions, the specification is conservative.

For example, a rather popular method of specifying this extremely important parameter consists of: a) arithmetically subtracting the measured offset values at the upper and lower temperature extremes and b) dividing this difference by the temperature excursion. This can yield an extremely misleading result, particularly where offset drifts in the same direction at the two extremes. It is obviously possible to have no difference in the two end-point measurements, yet severe slopes may exist between the two as illustrated in Figure 9. In this case the apparent (specified) drift would be zero $\mu V/°C$.

Analog Devices employs two methods of drift specification – a "true butterfly" curve characteristic for the high performance/low drift models, and a "modified butterfly" for the lower cost amplifiers. Both overcome the deficiencies described above. A

---

*For example, *Analog Dialogue,* Vol. 4, No. 1, "Settling Time of Operational Amplifiers"

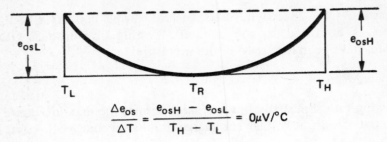

$$\frac{\Delta e_{os}}{\Delta T} = \frac{e_{osH} - e_{osL}}{T_H - T_L} = 0\mu V/°C$$

Figure 9. Two-point method of computing Offset Temperature Coefficient

comparison of these methods is shown with definitive equations in Figure 10. Essentially, the butterfly characteristic insures that if the amplifier is adjusted to zero at room temperature (T_r), the offset at any temperature would, in no case, exceed the value predicted by multiplying the specified drift rate (in $\mu V/°C$) by the temperature excursion.

BUTTERFLY CHARACTERISTICS

True Butterfly Spec   Modified Butterfly Spec

$$\frac{\Delta e_{os}}{\Delta T} \le \frac{e_{osH}}{T_H - T_R} \text{ or } \frac{e_{osL}}{T_L - T_R}$$ $$\frac{\Delta e_{os}}{\Delta T} = \frac{|e_{osH}| + |e_{osL}|}{T_H - T_L}$$

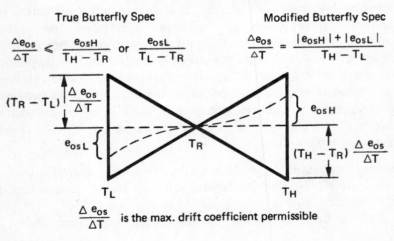

$\dfrac{\Delta e_{os}}{\Delta T}$ is the max. drift coefficient permissible

Figure 10. 3-point ("Butterfly") Definition of Offset Temperature Coefficient

Unity–Gain Signal Response

Unity-gain small-signal response, f_t, is the frequency at which the open loop gain becomes unity or zero dB. "Small signal" indicates that in general it is not possible to obtain large output voltage swing at high frequencies because of distortion due to slew rate limiting or signal rectification. For amplifiers with symmetrical response on both inputs, f_t may be obtained by either the inverting or non-inverting configurations. Some wideband amplifiers with feed forward design have fast response only on the negative input, which restricts high-speed use to the inverting circuit.

SELECTION PRINCIPLES

In selecting the right device(s) for a specific application, the designer should have clearly in mind the design objectives, a firm understanding of what the published specifications mean, and the significant features affecting the application.

1. *A complete definition of the design objectives* includes signal levels, desired accuracy and bandwidth, circuit impedances, environmental conditions, etc.

2. *Firm understanding of what the manufacturer means by the numbers published for the parameters.* Often, two manufacturers may have comparable published specifications, which may have been arrived at using differing measurement techniques,* creating a pitfall for the designer.

---

*An excellent contemporary case in point is the room-temperature bias-current spec for FET-input I.C. op amps. When bias current is measured on automated high-speed test equipment, the chip doesn't have sufficient time to warm up, which means that the reading will be low, often by a factor of 4, because of the doubling per 10°C temperature rise. At this writing, Analog Devices is one of the few IC manufacturers to take this into account and specify the current actually encountered by the user under equilibrium conditions rather than a useless "test" spec. Also, maximum bias current is specified by Analog Devices as the worse of the two input currents, rather than their average. With the "average" spec, e.g., $(0.1 + 1.9)/2 = 1.0$ "Murphy's Law" decrees that the larger current will appear at the active terminal.

3. *A checklist of essential characteristics of the design*

    A. Character of the application: differential or single-ended, follower or inverter, linear or nonlinear

    B. Accurate description of the input signals: voltage or current source, range of amplitudes, source impedance, time/frequency characteristics

    C. Environmental conditions: maximum ranges of temperature, time, and supply voltage over which the circuits must operate (to the required accuracy) without readjustment

    D. Accuracy desired, as a function of bandwidth, static and dynamic parameters, loading

SELECTION PROCESS

In general, the objective of amplifier selection should be to choose the least-expensive device that will meet the physical, electrical, and environmental requirements imposed by the application. This implies that a "general purpose" amplifier will be the best choice in all applications where the desired performance requirements can be met. Where this is not possible, the limitations are usually imposed by either bandwidth requirements or offset and drift parameters. As mentioned earlier, an extended discussion of these factors appears in the *Analog Devices Product Guide — 1972* and (if out of print) its successor publications, available upon request.

III

Instrumentation Amplifiers

Chapter 2

As we have noted in the chapter on Data Acquisition, and elsewhere, it is often necessary to retrieve millivolts of analog data from volts of common-mode interference. In some cases, it is also necessary to galvanically isolate the amplifier's input from its output and the power source, either to protect the amplifier from high voltage, to protect the device being measured (viz., a hospital patient) from stray leakage current, or simply to obtain better common-mode rejection.

The instrumentalities for achieving these objectives are called *instrumentation amplifiers,* and they include a special subclass of *isolation amplifiers.* Although amplifiers of this class often contain operational amplifiers, they are distinguished from op amps in being *committed* devices with a definite (set of) output-input relationship(s) and an essentially fixed configuration. They are designed to meet the specific objectives of high CMRR, low noise and drift, moderate bandwidth, and a limited range of gains (usually 1 to 1000, programmable by a single resistor).

Although there are a wide variety of frills and added-cost "extras" in the $250+ range on the market, ranging from digitally-programmed gain to autoranging (primarily for use in low-level-multiplexed systems), simple instrumentation amplifiers are becoming available at such low cost* that they seem destined to encourage the growth of per-channel amplification in instrument applications. For example, as this is written, the AD520 Monolithic

---

*both from manufacturers, such as Analog Devices, and built in-house using low-cost IC op amps

Instrumentation Amplifier has just been introduced (Spring, 1972) at an initial price of $12 in 100's.†

Accordingly, this chapter will focus on the properties, specification, and application of simple instrumentation and isolation amplifiers, while recognizing that more-complex devices exist and do have a role (albeit somewhat limited) in A/D conversion systems.

INSTRUMENTATION AMPLIFIERS

The instrumentation amplifier is a committed-gain amplifier with internal high-precision feedback networks. Its excellent drift, linearity, and noise-rejection capability make it a natural choice for extracting and amplifying low-level signals in the presence of high common-mode-noise voltages.

These devices are commonly used as transducer amplifiers for thermocouples, strain-gage bridges, current shunts, and biological probes. As preamplifiers, they are capable of extracting small differential signals superimposed on large common-mode voltages. Wideband designs are also available for data-acquisition systems.

Design

Figure 1 shows a number of commonly-used circuit-design approaches. All require that only one resistor be adjusted to control the gain. Most commercially-available types have feedback *sense* and *reference* terminals for lead compensation, current-output sensing, and adjustable offset reference voltage. A few uses of these terminals are discussed under Applications.

The simple subtractor (1a), uses only one operational amplifier. It has the disadvantage of poor source unbalance characteristics, because of its low input impedance, for normal values of R_1 (CMR

---

†The AD520J, in a 14-pin hermetically-sealed DIL package (small size, environmentally protected), is *not* an op amp but a true-differential instrumentation amplifier, with $2 \times 10^9 \, \Omega$ Z_{in}, 90dB minimum CMRR at gain of 100 (0-100Hz, 1kΩ source unbalance), 50kHz full-power bandwidth, single-resistor gain adjustment.

depends critically on resistance matching). If a FET-input amplifier is used with very large values of resistance, noise and bandwidth characteristics will suffer.

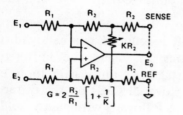

$$G = 2\frac{R_2}{R_1}\left[1 + \frac{1}{K}\right]$$

a. Simple Subtractor

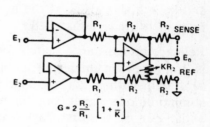

$$G = 2\frac{R_2}{R_1}\left[1 + \frac{1}{K}\right]$$

b. Buffered Subtractor

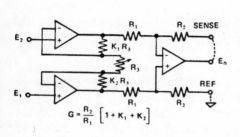

$$G = \frac{R_2}{R_1}\left[1 + K_1 + K_2\right]$$

c. Buffered Subtractor With Gain

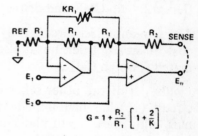

$$G = 1 + \frac{R_2}{R_1}\left[1 + \frac{2}{K}\right]$$

d. High-Input-Impedance Image of Subtractor

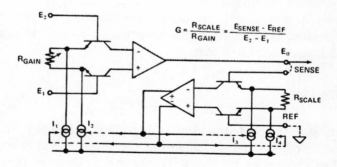

$$G = \frac{R_{SCALE}}{R_{GAIN}} = \frac{E_{SENSE} - E_{REF}}{E_2 - E_1}$$

e. Current-Feedback Type (AD520)

Figure 1. Instrumentation-Amplifier Designs

III-33

The buffered subtractor (1b) gets around the problem, at the cost of two additional op amps. Bipolar types are ordinarily adequate, but FET-input types would be used with signal inputs having high source impedance. Matched input-followers will provide low drift and keep high CMRR, if the main amplifier's drift is low and the resistances are well-matched.

Reliance on resistance match for CMR is reduced, and bandwidth is improved in high-gain applications by using the buffered subtractor-with-gain (1c). The first stage has unity gain for the common-mode signal, thus increasing overall CMR by the differential gain of the first stage. (Separate followers-with-gain would not be capable of this improvement, because they would amplify differential and common-mode signals equally.) Matched amplifiers will help CMR and drift-stability.

The two-amplifier circuit (1d) has high input impedance, saves the cost of an amplifier, but it also increases dependence on resistance match for high CMR.

Unlike all of the other schemes, the differential current-feedback circuit (1e) has high-impedance *sense* and *reference* input terminals, allowing them to play a more important part in a wider range of applications. (It will be noted, in all of the other circuits, that resistance in series with either of those terminals, unless matched at the other, will cause common-mode errors.) The scheme also has a simple relationship between the gain and the resistance used to adjust it. The ability to match transistors and current-sources, and the close spacing on the monolithic chip, tend to make this approach feasible at low cost.

Applications

In data systems, instrumentation amplifiers are used primarily for pre-amplification and for adapting the input signal range to the usually-fixed range of the A/D converter. Because they ideally respond only to the difference between two voltages, they can be used in both balanced and unbalanced systems. *Balanced* implies that the output of the signal source appears on two lines, both having essentially equal source resistances and output voltages in relation to either ground or the local common-mode level, e.g., bridge outputs (Figure 2a); *unbalanced* means that inherent symmetry is not a property of the configuration — in fact, a major application of instrumentation amplifiers is in eliminating the effects of ground-potential differences in non-ideal single-ended systems (Figure 2b).

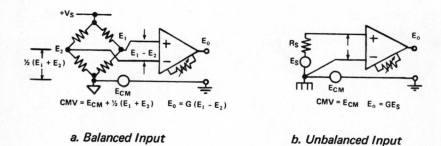

| a. Balanced Input | b. Unbalanced Input |

Figure 2. Balanced and Unbalanced Inputs

Because instrumentation amplifiers can measure voltage differences at any level within their specified range, they are useful in current measurement. Typically, they will measure and amplify the voltage appearing across a low-resistance shunt, often in the "high" line (Figure 3).

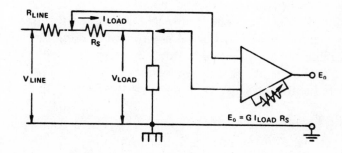

Figure 3. Current Measurement

If the *reference* terminal is available, it may be used for biasing the location of the pen in chart-recorder applications; it may be used to bias out dc normal-mode voltages, e.g., contact potentials; or it may be used to bias relay or comparator trip points. The reference terminal may be driven by the output of an operational amplifier with either constant or variable voltage; in addition, if the amplifier has high input impedance at the reference terminal, it may be driven passively by a voltage divider or a potentiometer.

In normal applications, the *sense* and *reference* terminals are connected to the specific points at which the output is to be accurately maintained; the circuit will then ignore voltage drops in the output signal or ground lines.

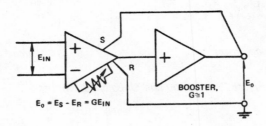

Figure 4. Maintaining Accuracy With an External Current Booster

The *sense* terminal is especially useful in circuits employing current-booster followers, since the booster may then be included within the feedback loop, and its offsets, drifts, and gain errors nullified (Figure 4). The sense and reference terminals, if high enough in impedance to avoid significant loading, are also useful for driving current to either floating or grounded loads. (In the circuit of Figure 5, for floating load, the reference is grounded, for grounded load, the sense terminal is connected to the output.)

For circuits employing the sense and reference terminals in other than "straight" differential amplification, it is essential to consider the possibility of and, if necessary, to take proper precautions to avoid dynamic instabilities: overshoots, ringing, or oscillation.

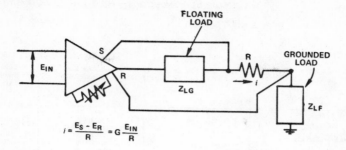

$$i = \frac{E_S - E_R}{R} = G\frac{E_{IN}}{R}$$

Figure 5. Current Drive to Floating or Grounded Load

Specifications

The table on the following page indicates specifications for typical instrumentation amplifiers. In many respects they appear similar to those for operational amplifiers. Differences include:

Gain An open-loop gain specification is unnecessary; However, gain nonlinearity and instability are specified.

Offset Offset drift specifications are given, referred to the *input*, at the two extremes, 1 and 1000. To determine the corresponding specification at any arbitrary value of gain, referred to the *output*, the following formula is used, to an excellent approximation:

$$\text{Drift}|_G \cong \frac{1000 \cdot \text{Drift(rti)}|_{1000} - \text{Drift}|_1}{1000} \cdot G + \text{Drift}|_1$$

Other specifications are listed at specific values of gain. Intermediate values may usually be interpolated. Unless noted otherwise, specifications not associated with a gain value are essentially independent of gain.

An Example

Since errors from all sources, though not individually significant, can add up to a substantial amount, it is important to perform an

Table 1.   *Capsule Specifications – Instrumentation Amplifiers*

Model	High CMR, Low Drift 0.005% Linearity 605 J	K	L	Wideband, Low Drift 25µs Settling to 0.01% 604 J	K	L	Economy Monolithic AD520 J
Gain							
Range	1 to 1000			1 to 1000			1 to 1000
Formula	$G = 1 + (200k/Rg)$			$G = (3 \times 10^5)/Rg$			$G = 10^5/Rg$
Deviation From Formula, max	±0.1%			±0.1%			±0.05%
vs. Temp, max	±15ppm/°C			±15ppm/°C(±5ppm/°C typ)			—
vs. Time	±0.0003%/mo.			±0.0003%/mo.			—
Nonlinearity, max	±0.005%			±0.01% (0.005% typ)			±0.02% typ
Rated Output, min	±10V@5mA			±10V@10mA			±10V@5mA
Frequency Response							
Unity Gain, Small Signal, (-3dB)							
G = 1	300kHz			50kHz			300kHz
G = 1000	300Hz			50kHz			35kHz
Full Power Response, min	1.5kHz typ			50kHz[1] typ			60kHz typ
Slew Rate	0.1V/µs			3V/µs[2]			3.5V/µs typ
Unity Gain Settling Time to 0.1%	130µs(0.01%, G = 1)			25µs (to 0.01%)[1]			—
Offsets Referred to Input							
Initial Offset Voltage	Adjust to 0			Adjust to 0			Adjust to 0
vs. Temp, max G = 1	±150µV/°C			±3	±1	±0.5mV/°C	±1.0mV/°C typ
G = 1000	±3	±1.0	±0.5µV/°C	±3	±1	±0.5µV/°C	±5.0µV/°C typ
vs. Supply G = 1	±0.2mV/%			±2mV/% max			—
G = 1000	±4µV/%			±0.2 µV/% max			±300µV/% typ
Input Bias Current							
Initial, 25°C	0, +100nA			0, +100nA			±100nA
vs. Temp	-1nA/°C max			0, -1.0nA/°C max			±1nA/°C
Input Difference Current							
Initial, 25°C	±100nA max			±10nA max			±25nA
vs. Temp.	±1nA/°C max			±100pA/°C max			0.25nA/°C
Input Impedance							
Differential	$10^9\ \Omega$			$(10^{11}\ \Omega/G)//10pF$			$2 \times 10^9\ \Omega$
Common Mode	$10^9\ \Omega$			$10^{11}\ \Omega//10pF$			—
Noise Referred to Input							
Voltage Noise, 0.01 to 1Hz, p-p							
G = 1	15µV(0.1 to 10Hz)			100µV (0.1 to 10Hz)			1.0mV (0.1 to 10Hz)
G = 1000	1.5µV(0.1 to 10Hz)			1µV (0.1 to 10Hz)			
Voltage Noise, 10Hz to 10kHz, rms							
G = 1	5.0µV			100µV (1.5µV, G = 1000)			—
Input Voltage Range							
Linear Differential Input	±10V			±10V			±12V
Max Differential Input	±20V			±20V			—
Max Common Mode	$\pm V_s$			±10V			±10V
CMR @ ±10V, DC to 60Hz							
(1kΩImbalance) G = 1	70dB[3]			60dB[3]			70dB
G = 1000	94dB(120dB typ)DC to 5Hz[3]			120dB DC to 5Hz[3]			106dB
Reference Terminal							
R_{in}	$10^4\ \Omega$			$5 \times 10^9\ \Omega$			$10^7\ \Omega$
Output Offset Range	±10V			±10V			±10V
Gain Offset Range	+1.00			+1.00			1.000
Bias Current	200nA			200nA			4µA
Power Supply Range, ±V_s(VDC)	±(12 to 18)V			±(12 to 18)V			±(12 to 18)V
Operating, Rated Specifications (VDC)	±15V@7mA			±15V@7mA			±15V@4mA
Temperature Range							
Operating, Rated Specifications	0 to +70°C			0 to +50°C			0 to +70°C
Package Outline	FA–5			C–15			TO–116
Case Dimensions	1.5" x 1.5" x 0.4"			2" x 3" x 0.4"			—

(Specifications typical @ +25°C and ±15VDC power supply unless otherwise noted.)

(1) ±0.1% amplitude accuracy to 1kHz min.
(2) Constant with gains from 3V/V to 1000V/V.
(3) Minimum CMR with 1kΩ imbalance.

error-budget analysis to find (and if possible reduce) the most significant terms. An example of a circuit application is given in Figure 6.

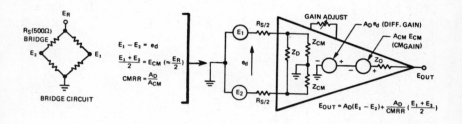

Figure 6. Instrumentation Amplifier-Equivalent Model When Used as a Bridge Amplifier

These are the given operating conditions and hypothetical amplifier specifications to be used in the example:

Operating Conditions		*Amplifier Specifications*	
e_{IN}	= ±5mV	e_{OS} Drift 11mV/°C (G = 1000) at output	
e_{OUT}	= ±5V	Gain Drift = ±0.01% (G = 1000)	
E_{CM}	= +5V	I_B	= 20nA
ΔT	= ±20°C	Z_d	= 300MΩ
T_A	= +25°C(ambient)	Z_{CM}	= 1000MΩ
R_L	= 10kΩ	CMRR (A_D/A_{CM}) = 10^5 (100dB CMR)	
R_{BRIDGE}	= 500Ω	Gain = 1000	
		Nonlinearity = ±0.01%	
		R_o = 10Ω	

The error budget is computed as follows:

Error Source	Calculation	Value	%F.S.(5V)
Gain Drift (+5° to 45°C)	$0.01\%/°C \times \Delta T \times E_{OUT}$	± 10mV	0.2%
Offset Drift (+5° to 45°C)	$11mV/°C \times \Delta T$	±220mV	4.4%
Total Drift Error		230mV	4.6%
Linearity Error	0.01% @ 10V	± 10mV	0.2%
	(independent of output)		
Common-Mode Error	$E_{CM} \times A_D/CMRR$	± 50mV	1.0%
Offset Error	(adjust to zero)	negligible	
Input Loading Error	R_{BRIDGE}/R_D	negligible	
Output Loading Error	$(R_o/R_L) \times e_{OUT}$	5mV	0.1%
Total Error at 25°C		± 65mV	1.3%
Total Error (+5°C to +45°C)		±295mV	5.9%

For the given example, the error is 5.9%. Its largest components are offset drift (4.4%) and CME (1%).

If an amplifier having output drift of $2mV/°C$ at G = 1000 were used, the offset drift error would be reduced to ±40mV (0.8%). If the common-mode voltage is relatively constant (this is the case for a bridge circuit), then a simple offset adjustment can reduce the common-mode error virtually to zero, a 50mV, or 1% improvement. The total error will then be approximately ±55mV (1.1%).

This error-budget analysis demonstrates the importance of analyzing the problem and applying major error-reduction effort to the most-important sources of error.

ISOLATION AMPLIFIERS

There are certain classes of application conditions that require actual galvanic isolation of the amplifier's input circuit from its output and the power supply.

1. Very-high common-mode voltage, well beyond 500V, between input and output.
2. Safety requirements for medical-electronics equipment
3. Two-wire input, with no ground return for bias current
4. High CMRR required, with appreciable source unbalance

The two most promising approaches to obtaining isolation at the present time appear to be transformer and optical coupling. While optical coupling appears to be quite effective at isolation, since it uses a portion of the electromagnetic spectrum that completely abandons voltage, current, charge, and magnetic flux for energy transmission, the components and techniques applicable to low-cost high-performance linear circuits are still relatively primitive (but developing rapidly).

Recognizing these realities, as well as the present urgent needs, Analog Devices has developed, for sale at low cost, a series of isolation amplifiers, employing transformer coupling, that offers total galvanic isolation, low capacitance ($<$ 10pF between input and output ground circuits), high CMR (115dB at 60Hz), and high common-mode voltage ratings (to 5kV). Capable of transmitting millivolt signals in the presence of up to 1000 volts common-mode, with unity gain, or with adjustable gain, these devices (the

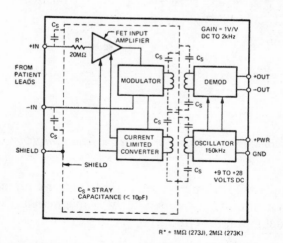

R* = 1MΩ (273J), 2MΩ (273K)

Figure 7. Block Diagram of Unity Gain Isolation Amplifiers

272, 273, 274 class) are ideal for medical applications (where an ECG waveform is the input signal to the data system), where it is mandatory to isolate hospital patients from potentially-lethal ground-fault currents, and for industrial applications, to interrupt ground loops between transducers and output-conditioning circuits.

Like instrumentation amplifiers, amplifiers of this type have committed gain circuits with internal feedback networks. All models operate from dc to 2kHz. They are designed in two parts: an isolated front-end amplifier section, and a grounded output section (Figure 7). The front end includes the fixed-gain op amp, a modulator, and a dc regulator circuit, all enclosed in a floating guard-shield. The output section contains a demodulator, filter, and power-supply oscillator circuit, operating from a single

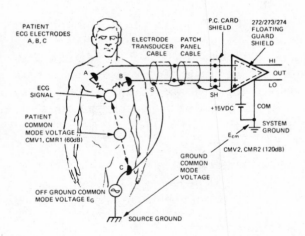

Figure 8. Patient-Amplifier Interconnection Diagram

+15Vdc supply. Operating power is transformer-coupled into the shielded input circuits and capacitively or magnetically coupled to the output demodulator circuit.

A typical connection in a medical-electronics data-acquisition system front end is shown in Figure 8.

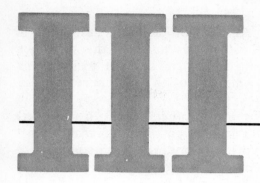

Multiplexers

Chapter 3

MULTIPLEXING AND MULTIPLEXERS

When more than one quantity has to undergo analog-to-digital conversion, it is necessary either to time-division multiplex the analog inputs to a single A/D converter, or to provide an A/D converter for each input and combine the converter outputs by digital multiplexing.

Until recently, analog multiplexing was the universally-favored technique for achieving lowest system cost, but the rapidly-decreasing cost of A/D converters and the availability, at low cost, of digital integrated circuits specifically designed for multiplexing provide a viable alternative with many advantages.

A decision on the correct technique to use for a given system will have to make tradeoffs between the following factors:

1. Resolution of measurement. The cost of A/D converters rises very steeply as the resolution increases, due mainly to the cost of precision elements used in the converter. At the 6-8 bit level, the per-channel cost of an analog multiplexer ("MUX") is likely to be a considerable proportion of the cost of a converter, and at lower resolutions it may actually exceed the converter cost. At higher resolutions, above 12 bits, the reverse is at present (but decreasingly) true and analog multiplexing has tended to be most economical.

2. Number of channels. This controls the size of the multi-plexer required and the amount of wiring and interconnections that will be needed. Digital multiplexing onto a common data bus

cuts wiring to a minimum. Analog multiplexing is best-suited to handling 8-256 channels; beyond this number, the technique becomes unwieldy and analog errors are difficult to minimize. Analog and digital multiplexing can often be combined advantageously in very-large systems.

3. Speed of measurement, or *throughput rate*. High-speed A/D converters carry a considerable cost premium. If analog time-division multiplexing will demand a very high speed converter to achieve the desired sample rate, a slower converter-per-channel with digital multiplexing may be a better choice.

4. Signal level and conditioning. Wide dynamic ranges between channels are difficult to handle with analog multiplexing. Small signals less than 1V will generally require differential low-level analog multiplexing (which is expensive), and programmable-gain amplifiers may well be required after the MUX. The alternative is fixed-gain converters on each channel, with signal-conditioning specifically designed for the channel requirement, again combined with digital multiplexing.

5. Physical location of measurement points. Analog multiplexing is best suited to making measurements at distances no farther than a few hundred feet (100m) from the converter. Analog lines are inherently prone to losses, transmission-line reflections, and interference. Satisfactory lines range from simple twisted wire-pairs to multiconductor shielded cable, depending on the signal level, distance, and noise environment. Digital multiplexing is a viable technique from zero distance to thousands (perhaps millions) of miles, with suitable transmission equipment. Digital transmission systems generally possess useful noise-rejection characteristics, which are essential for long-distance transmission.

MULTIPLEXER FUNCTIONAL REQUIREMENTS

The most important single requirement for a multiplexer is that it operate without introducing unacceptable error at a speed consistent with the sample-rate requirements. For a digital MUX, it is relatively straightforward to determine speed from propagation-delay parameters and the time required to achieve an adequately-settled output on the data bus. Considerable information exists on calculating the performance of logic families, and it is not proposed to consider the problem here.

Analog multiplexers are much more difficult to characterize, as their speed is a function, not only of their internal parameters, but also of such external parameters as channel source impedance, stray capacitance (i.e., due to layout and following amplifier characteristics), and also the number of channels and the circuit organization. The user must be aware of the limiting parameters in his system to gauge their effect on performance. These are detailed in succeeding sections.

Because of their non-ideal transmission and open-circuit characteristics, analog multiplexers introduce static and dynamic errors into the selected signal path. These include leakage through switches, coupling of control signals into the analog path, and interaction with both sources and following amplifiers. Poor circuit layout and cabling can compound these effects and further degrade performance.

As analog multiplexers are usually connected directly to sources (which may be delicate, have little overload capacity or poor settling after an overload), practical requirements dictate that the switches have an inherent break-before-make action to preclude any possibility of shorting channels together. Some commercially-available multiplexers can be deficient in this respect. Frequently it is necessary to avoid shorted channels when power is removed from the multiplexer and an "all channels off with power down" characteristic is desirable in a general-purpose MUX. Again, many commercial devices do not embrace this feature.

Besides the channel-addressing lines, which are usually binary-coded, it is useful to have one or more *inhibit* or *enable* lines to turn all switches off regardless of the channel being addressed. This greatly economizes on external logic required to cascade multiplexers and is also useful in certain types of channel addressing.

A final requirement for both analog and digital multiplexers is adequate tolerance of likely line transients and overload conditions, and the ability to absorb transient energy without damage.

MULTIPLEXER SWITCHING ELEMENTS

Analog Elements

Many alternative types of analog switches are available in electromechanical and solid-state (discrete and integrated) forms.

Electromechanical types include relays, stepper switches, cross bar and reed (mercury-wetted and dry) relay switches. The best switching speed can be realized with reed relays, < 1 ms. All mechanical switches provide high dc isolation resistance, low contact resistance, and the capacity to handle high voltages directly (typically up to 1kV), and they are usually inexpensive. Multiplexers employing mechanical switches are suited to low-speed applications and also those having high resolution requirements, and they interface well with the slower types of A/D converters, e.g., integrating dual-slope. All mechanical switches have a finite life, usually expressed in number of operations. A good reed relay may well have a life of 10^9 operations, which, for instance, would amount to a life of 3 years at 10 operations/second continuously.

Solid-state switches are capable of high-speed operation (< 30ns), and have a life likely to exceed most equipment requirements. Field-effect transistors (FET's) are universally used in multiplexers and have superseded bipolar transistors (which can introduce large voltage offsets when used as analog switches).

The FET is a majority-carrier device, and, depending on whether the majority carriers are holes or electrons, the FET is termed P or N-channel, respectively. Due to the greater mobility of electrons, a given FET geometry has a lower *on* resistance if it is an N-channel structure, rather than P; and for a given *on* resistance, N-channel structures have lower capacitance and superior parameters to those of P-channel devices. Consequently, for use in MUX, N-channel junction FET's are preferred to P-channel devices of comparable cost. Metal-oxide silicon (insulated gate, or MOS) transistors have only recently become available at competitive cost in N-channel structures; the P-channel device has been available for several years and is in common usage in multiplexers.

N-channel junction and MOS devices suitable for use in multi-plexers typically provide *on* resistances in the 10-100-ohm region (extended limits from 2 to 1000 ohms), and P-channel devices fall in a higher band, typically 100 to 1000 ohms.

Junction FET's operate in the depletion mode and are turned on fully with zero gate-source voltage ($V_{GS} = 0$). MOS FET's are available in both depletion and enhancement mode (enhancement-mode devices are off with $V_{GS} = 0$, and once the gate voltage exceeds a threshold level V_{th}, the *on* resistance falls as the gate voltage increases). The characteristics of these devices are shown in Figure 1.

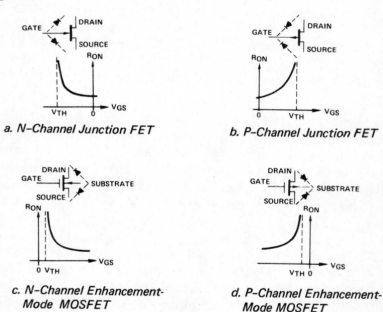

a. *N–Channel Junction FET*

b. *P-Channel Junction FET*

c. *N–Channel Enhancement-Mode MOSFET*

d. *P-Channel Enhancement-Mode MOSFET*

Figure 1. Junction FET's and Enhancement–Mode MOS FET's

Circuit arrangements in multiplexers usually ensure that the gate voltage of a conducting junction-FET tracks the drain-source voltage to maintain $V_{GS} = 0$. Thus, the *on* resistance of a switch is constant and is not a function of the signal level being multi-plexed. This is not true of MOS FET multiplexers, where the insulated gate is driven to a fixed potential in the *on* condition, so that V_{GS} and the *on* resistance vary with the level of the applied signal. This variation can be considerable: a typical P-channel device operating on ±15V supplies may have $R_{ON} = 200\Omega$ with the channel at +10V, and $R_{ON} = 1000\Omega$ with the channel at −10V, the gate being switched to −15V.

All FET devices suffer from leakage from drain to source in the *off* state and leakage from gate or substrate to drain and source in both the *on* and the *off* states. Gate leakage in MOS devices is negligible compared to other sources of leakage, unless the device has a Zener-diode-protected gate, in which case an additional leakage path exists between gate and source. Generally, the leakage characteristics of junction FET's are superior to those of MOS FET's. Junction FET's with drain-source leakages of 100pA at 25°C are commonplace, but MOSFET's are typically in the range 1-5nA. As leakages double every 8-10°C, junction FET's are superior at the higher temperatures, where leakage becomes a severe problem.

Enhancement-mode MOSFET's have the theoretical advantage that the switch turns off when power is removed from the MUX, as $V_{GS} = 0$. In fact, the advantage may be lost unless the drive circuit around the FET is correctly designed. The circuit shown in Figure 2 allows positive input voltages to be short-circuited to ground when the power is removed (the +15V line falls to ground potential, and conduction takes place through the drain-substrate isolation diode). Additional components are required to ensure that the switch remains off under all conditions of input with the power shut down. Figure 3 shows the necessary modification: negative input voltages are blocked by the drain-substrate diode of the MOSFET Q1, and positive voltages are blocked by D1 and the collector-base diode of Q2, while R ensures that the gate-substrate voltage of Q1 remains zero, keeping it turned off. Even with this modification, leakage is likely to be several nA greater with power down than with power on. As an inherent matter of their processing, most integrated-circuit MOS multiplexers do not incorporate this feature, and it is up to the user to provide protection, both for the multiplexer and the signal sources. (As a final note, junction-FET multiplexers *always* turn on with the power down, so it is necessary to maintain supply voltage to maintain channel isolation.)

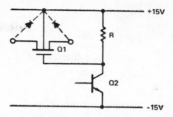

Figure 2. MOSFET Power-Off Short-Circuit Mode

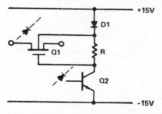

Figure 3. Circuit to Maintain Power-Off Open Circuit

A more recent development is the CMOS (COSMOS) complementary MOS switch, which has the great advantage of being able to multiplex voltage up to and including the MUX supply voltages, i.e., a ±10V signal can be handled with a ±10V supply to the MUX. A P-channel device can only switch signals between +V_s and a voltage slightly greater than $-(V_s - V_{th})$, and an N-channel device can only switch signals between a voltage slightly less than $(V_s - V_{th})$ and $-V_s$. In both cases, there is considerable variation of *on* resistance with signal level. By combining an N- and a P-channel device in parallel, each makes up for the deficiencies of the other, and it is possible to switch signals between ±V_s (Figure 4). Since the *on* resistances of the switches are in parallel, device geometries and thresholds can be adjusted so that the parallel sum of the *on* resistances varies little over the signal range (Figure 5). Note that $2V_s > (V_{thP} + V_{thN})$, or a conduction deadband will exist in the switch. With most types of CMOS processing, this is a problem only when $2V_s < 5V$. The switches require complementary gate drive, which is usually derived from an inverter, resulting in an integrated structure similar to that shown in Figure 4.

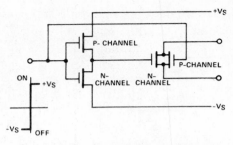

Figure 4. Complementary MOS Switch

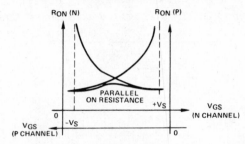

Figure 5. On-Resistance of CMOS Switch vs. Input Voltage

Digital Elements

For small numbers of channels, medium-scale integrated digital multiplexers are available in TTL and MOS logic families. The SN74151 is a typical example, as shown in Figure 6. Eight such integrated circuits could be used to multiplex 8 A/D converters of 8-bit resolution onto a common output bus.

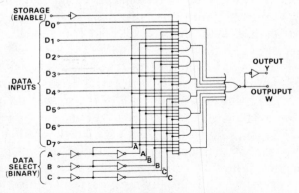

Figure 6. Typical Digital Multiplexer SN74151

This type of digital multiplexing offers little advantage in wiring economy, but it is low in cost, and, through its very high switching speed, operation is possible at sampling rates far in excess of those obtainable with analog multiplexers. Also, the multiple A/D converters used are required only to keep up with the channel sample rate, and not with the commutating rate of the MUX.

Where larger numbers of A/D converters are to be multiplexed, the data-bus technique shown in Figure 7 provides great economies in system interconnection and organization. This alone may in many cases justify multiple A/D converters. Data can be bussed onto the lines in bit-parallel or bit-serial format (many converters have both serial and parallel outputs to allow this choice to be made readily). A wide variety of devices exist to drive the bus, from open-collector and tri-state TTL gates, special line drivers and opto-electronic isolators, giving a wide range of common-mode and noise-margin performance to suit the most rigorous requirements. Channel-selection decoders can be built up from 1-of-16 decoders to any required size. This system also contains some redundancy, in that a failure of one A/D, or overload of one source, will not affect the other channels.

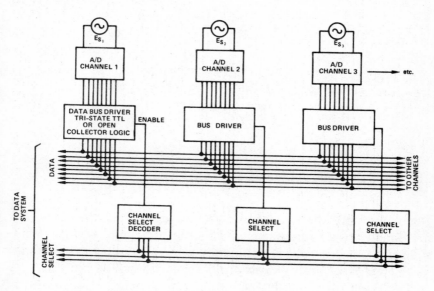

Figure 7. Digital Multiplexing on to a Common Data Bus

BASIC ANALOG MULTIPLEXER CONFIGURATIONS

High-Level Multiplexers

High-level multiplexers are designed to handle input signal voltages greater than 1V without introducing significant error. The most-common type consists of a bank of switches connected to a common output bus, as shown in Figure 8. The bus output may be buffered by a non-inverting operational amplifier, as shown. This configuration is simple, and, when used with an output amplifier, offers high input impedance.

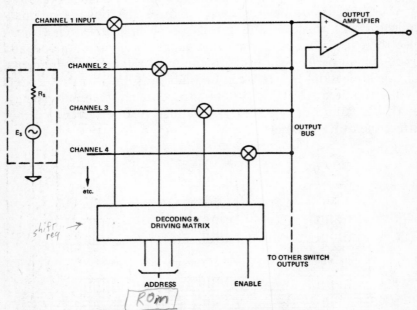

Figure 8. High-Level Voltage Multiplexer

Depending on the choice of switching device, this type of multiplexer can operate over a wide range of input voltage. With solid-state devices, input-voltage excursion is usually limited to ±20V, and most multiplexers are designed to handle the standard analog range of ±10V; but some devices that use high-threshold switches are suitable for only ±5V operation.

When it is desired to switch high voltages (up to several hundred volts) with the speed of solid-state switching, the inverting current-switching MUX should be used (Figure 9). Since all switching takes place at the summing junction, with protective diodes to ground, the switches are never exposed to high voltage. This type of MUX is characterized by high immunity to transient voltages, constant but low input resistance (equal to the channel input resistor) while conducting and is inherently safe when power is removed from the MUX. Each channel can be adjusted to an appropriate gain to suit the input. If R_c is large, so that switch R_{on} temperature variations are small in comparison, the transfer ratio for the circuit

$$-\frac{R_f}{R_c + R_s}$$

can be set to a high degree of accuracy, provided R_s is constant. No common-mode voltage is applied to the amplifier, so no common-mode error can be generated.

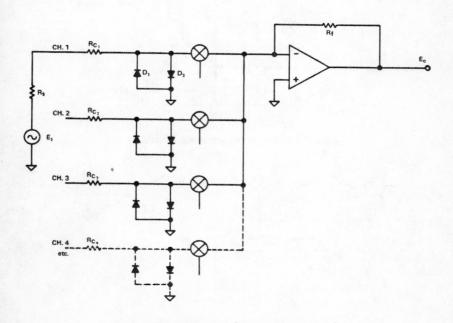

Figure 9. Inverting (Current) Multiplexer

This type of multiplexer is very robust and is particularly suited to industrial system control and interfacing with the older type of ±100V analog computers.

Two modifications are popular: The diodes D1, D2, etc., can be replaced by FET's driven in complementary fashion to the transmission switch to ensure that the input resistor R_c is always terminated in a real or virtual ground, so that the input resistance is nearly-constant, whether the channel is selected or not (Figure 10). This avoids settling problems at the transducer during switching, due to change of loading (the diode resistance is a function of the current through them). In a second modification, R_c can be removed (i.e., set equal to zero) to render the circuit suitable for multiplexing current-output transducers (Figure 11). If current output switching is used, then transfer accuracy is unaffected by variations in line- and interconnection resistances.

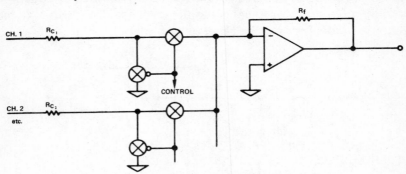

Figure 10. Constant-Impedance Multiplexer

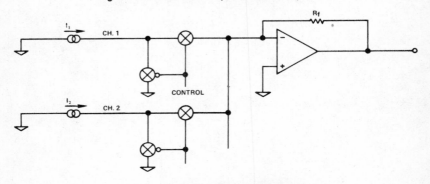

Figure 11. Current Multiplexing

Low-Level Multiplexing

For multiplexing small voltages in the millivolt range, up to 1V, more-sophisticated multiplexers are required. Problems most frequently arise at low levels due to interference and thermal effects, so lines are run in pairs, and differential techniques are used to remove any interference that is induced as a common-mode signal. Where very-high common-mode voltages are present, guarding techniques also improve performance, and 3-wire multiplexers are required with shielded input pairs.

A simple 2-wire differential MUX is constructed using pairs of switches, as shown in Figure 12. The output amplifier usually consists of a data or instrument amplifier designed to have very high common-mode rejection (generally > 100dB). Such high rejection can only be achieved if the input lines are identical. This requires twisted pairs for cabling and great attention to matching the dc and the ac parameters of the channels and switches in the MUX. Integrated structures and dual-FET switches are superior in achieving the matching required. Also, switch leakage and thermal EMF's can introduce serious errors in low-level inputs, and drift can also be a problem. The amplifier configuration shown indicates how operational amplifiers are classically used to form a differential high-gain amplifier. Modular and integrated-circuit instrumentation amplifiers, specifically-designed for the purpose,

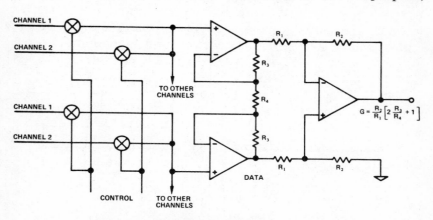

Figure 12. Differential Multiplexer and Amplifier

are, of course, available; they require much less effort to use, and − in IC form (e.g., the AD520) − they are not at all costly.

To reduce the effects of unbalance in the input cabling, cables can be made up as shielded pairs, and the shield driven by common-mode voltage, either by the source or a mid-position tap on R4 in the data amplifier (or a mid-position tap between the input terminals, unloaded by a unity-gain follower). This shielding, or "guarding" is commonly used in high-resolution data-acquisition systems, where common-mode interference levels are frequently very high.

Another type of low-level multiplexer that provides considerable immunity against common-mode interference is the flying-capacitor multiplexer. Essentially, this is a two-wire sample-hold (Figure 13). Switches A and A′ are turned on (with B & B′ off) to acquire the input signal. When capacitor C is fully charged, all switches are momentarily turned off; then B & B′ are turned on to transfer the signal to the output amplifier. Since no common-mode voltage is transferred across the switches, the output amplifier can be a simple single-ended-input non-inverting amplifier. This is an effective method of eliminating common-mode voltage; but it is a poor choice if normal-mode interference is present as well, since much-better rejection of both normal mode and common mode could be obtained with a "straight-through" multiplexer and a floating-input integrating converter. (An integrating converter used with a flying-capacitor multiplexer will integrate the *sample* of the input rather than the input, and the sample will include variations due to normal-mode interference.)

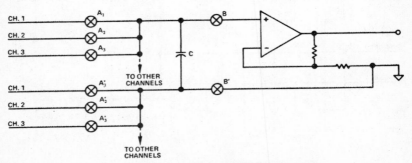

Figure 13. Flying–Capacitor Multiplexer

ERRORS IN HIGH-LEVEL MULTIPLEXERS

Multiplexing introduces static (i.e., dc) and dynamic errors into the signal. If these errors are large in relation to the resolution of measurement, they will produce undesirable variations in system performance. It is therefore necessary to determine the errors and compare them against the system requirements.

Broadly, errors arise from two sources. Static errors originate from switch leakage, offset in output buffer amplifiers, and gain errors due to switch *on* resistance, source resistance, amplifier input resistance, and amplifier-gain non-linearity. Dynamic errors arise from charge injection of the switch control voltages, settling times of the common bus and input sources due to circuit time constants, crosstalk between channels, and output-amplifier settling characteristics. Dynamic errors are greatly affected by multiplexer organization and system layout, and can prove difficult to calculate to any degree of accuracy. A rough estimate of their magnitude is, however, usually adequate for design purposes. Other errors may arise through characteristics peculiar to the multiplexer components, e.g., reed relays may generate thermal EMF's up to $40\mu V/°C$. These require additional consideration.

Static Errors

Gain or Transfer Ratio

The circuit resistances controlling transfer accuracy are shown in Figure 14. R_s is the internal resistance of the source; it will generally vary from channel to channel, and it is likely to be temperature-dependent. $R_{leakage}$ is distributed along the input cabling and output bus and is controlled by circuit insulation. It should always be several orders of magnitude greater than R_s; use Teflon-insulated wiring, if necessary, to achieve this. $R_{leakage}$ can then be safely neglected. Good wiring practice and board layout are also helpful in minimizing $R_{leakage}$ and are essential in high-humidity environments.

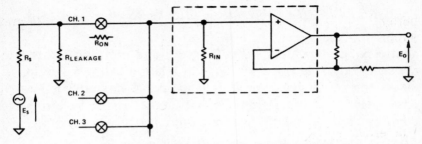

Figure 14. Resistances Affecting Gain Error of MUX

R_{on}, the switch *on* resistance, is a function of the switch design. Mechanical switches have the lowest initial contact resistance but can develop enormous variations of resistance under dry-circuit conditions and towards the end of switch life. Solid-state switches have reproducible *on* resistance, with R_{on} of FET switches ranging from a few ohms to a few thousand ohms. The very-low *on*-resistance large-geometry FET's give excellent static performance at the expense of dynamic performance, as they are handicapped by very large gate capacity and drain-source capacitance. The *on* resistance of FET's is a function of temperature, increasing with temperature at roughly ½ to 1%/°C.

The input resistance, R_{in}, of the amplifier is a function of its differential and common-mode input resistances and loop gain

$$R_{in} = \frac{1}{\dfrac{A_c}{A_o R_d} + \dfrac{1}{R_{cm}}}$$

where

    A_c Closed-loop gain of the amplifier circuit
    A_o Open-loop gain of the amplifier
    R_d Differential input resistance of the amplifier
    R_{cm} Common-mode input resistance of the amplifier

Since open-loop gain and input resistance are functions of temperature, input voltage, and supply voltage, a worst-case figure for R_{in} should be calculated (or estimated). It is easy to achieve an input resistance of 100MΩ for a unity-gain follower with low-cost monolithic IC amplifiers; higher input resistance may require the better amplifier parameters obtainable with FET-input IC and modular amplifiers.

If $R_{leakage}$ is neglected, the dc transfer ratio is clearly

$$\frac{E_o}{E_s} = \frac{A_c R_{in}}{R_s + R_{in} + R_{on}}$$

The effect of A_c, R_s, R_{in}, R_{on}, and their variations may be calculated. Constant errors in the transfer ratio, due, for example, to a constant-but-high source resistance, may not be serious, as they will introduce systematic errors that can be allowed for. The variations in transfer ratio due to temperature and voltage generally require careful consideration, as they cannot easily be compensated.

Gain nonlinearity of the amplifier is likely if the loop gain is inadequate. In general, it is easy to achieve 80dB of loop gain with low-cost amplifiers used as followers.

$$A_c = \frac{(ideal\ gain)}{1 + \dfrac{1}{(loop\ gain)}}$$

Loop gain = $A_o\beta$, where β is the fraction of output fed back. Nonlinear CMR at extreme values of CMV is a more-important source of error in followers.

Leakage Errors

FET switches have finite *off* resistance and consequently are afflicted by drain-to-source leakage currents. In addition, junction FET's and Zener-diode-protected MOSFET's have leakage paths between gate and channel. Unprotected insulated-gate MOSFET's generally have negligible gate leakage (while they last).

The leakage currents of all the switches in a multiplexer return to ground via the input source resistance and the input resistance of the amplifier. Leakage on the input side of non-conducting channels is usually of little interest, as it does not affect the signal path; but leakage of all the output sides of the channels and the conducting channel into the signal path causes a voltage error (Figure 15).

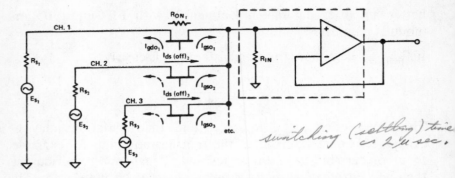

Figure 15. Sources of Current Error in Multiplexer

If the gate-to-drain leakage of the conducting channel is neglected in comparison to the sum of the leakages of all the other channels, an error voltage is developed:

$$V_{e(CH1)} = \frac{(R_{on1} + R_{s1})(R_{in})}{(R_{on1} + R_{s1} + R_{in})} \left\{ I_{gso1} + \sum_{j=2}^{N} (I_{gsoj} + I_{ds(off)j}) \right\}$$

Typically, $I_{ds(off)}$ and I_{gso} are about 0.1nA at 25°C for junction FET's and double for every 11°C rise. Insulated-gate MOSFET's have higher $I_{ds(off)}$, typically 1 to 5nA at 25°C, and gate leakage in the femtoampere $(10^{-15}A)$ region, which can be neglected. For either type, 10:1 variations of leakage parameters can be expected from device to device.

Generally, leakage is a problem only when working from high source impedances, since $R_{in} \gg R_{sl} \gg R_{on}$ under these conditions. The term $(I_{gso} + I_{ds(off)})$ is usually lumped together on the multiplexer data sheet and termed "channel leakage". The above error equation can then be simplified to the form

$V_{e(CH1)} = R_{sl} \cdot$ (number of channels $- 1$) $\cdot$ (channel leakage)

For an 8-channel multiplexer with channel leakage of 2nA at 25°C with source resistance of 50kΩ, leakage error would be 0.7mV. At 50°C, this error would increase to 2.8mV.

It is manifest that if 8-channel multiplexers were paralleled to form, say, a 256-channel multiplexer, the leakage error would increase to a massive 25.5mV. Although it leads to additional complexity (and the purchase of additional multiplexers), it is usually considered good practice to cascade multiplexers in a serial pyramid fashion (or sub-multiplex), as shown in Figure 16. This greatly reduces the leakage problem and also improves the dynamic performance. Leakage error in the submultiplex connection becomes:

$$V_e = R_s \cdot (\text{Number of channels/stage} - 1)$$
$$\cdot (\text{Number of stages}) \cdot (\text{Channel leakage})$$

Multiplexing 256 channels by submultiplexing with the 8-channel multiplexers of the previous example would lead to a leakage error of 2.1mV at 25°C, better than an order-of-magnitude improvement over simple parallel connection.

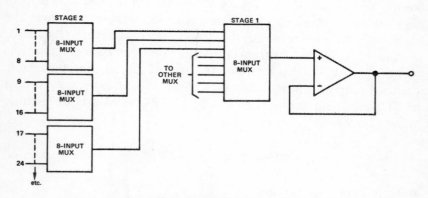

Figure 16. Use of Submultiplexers to Reduce Errors

Offset Errors and Errors Due to the Buffer Amplifier

The appreciable *on* resistance of most types of multiplexer switches calls for a high-input-impedance buffer amplifier to buffer the voltage on the output bus of the MUX. This amplifier may be provided as an integral part of the multiplexer module (but its inclusion tends to limit the versatility of the module, e.g., it is not required in every multiplexer in a subMUX connection), or it may be included as part of a sample-hold or A/D converter following the multiplexer, or it may have to be provided separately by the user. In some cases where large dynamic range is required, a programmable-gain amplifier will be needed.

In all of these situations, the offset drift and bias-current drift, and common-mode performance of the amplifier will introduce errors in addition to those already considered. Clearly, the errors introduced by the buffer amplifier should be much less (and certainly not greater) than errors associated with the multiplexer.

The need to use an amplifier with adequate open-loop gain to avoid gain-nonlinearity has already been mentioned. Calculation of voltage and current drift in non-inverting connections is covered in the chapter on operational amplifiers. Voltage drift is seldom much of a problem in high-level multiplexers operating with low-gain buffers, but current drift and offset can be very serious, since the bias current flows through the multiplexer and the source resistance. With varying values of source resistance from channel to channel, it is difficult to compensate the inverting input of the buffer so that *offset* current controls the drift; instead, the full bias-current variation with temperature controls the drift. (All of this assumes the use of the cheapest-available "general-purpose" monolithic IC's. An easy out is to use low-cost IC FET-input op amps, such as the AD540.) This sets up a static offset:

$$V_{offset} = I_{bias} \ (R_{on} + R_{source})$$

and a temperature variation:

$$\frac{\delta V_{offset}}{\delta T} = \frac{\delta I_{bias}}{\delta T} \ (R_{on} + R_{source})$$

Operating an AD741C amplifier following a multiplexer driven by a 10kΩ source would produce a static offset of up to 5mV and a temperature variation of ±1mV over the range $0 - 70°C$ due to current drift alone (neglecting R_{on}).

A common technique in large systems where a computer is available is to ground the input of one channel. This then becomes a drift-reference channel, and readings from this channel can be subtracted from those obtained from each of the other channels to give correct readings. This compensates, not only for the drift in the amplifier, but also A/D converter zero-drift and multiplexer leakage errors. It is a particularly-useful technique when measuring low-level signals (and substituting a \$5 amplifier for a 50¢ amplifier hasn't solved the problem).

Dynamic Errors

Output-Bus Settling

The output bus of a multiplexer has considerable capacitance to ground. When switched to a new channel, the output voltage cannot change instantaneously to the signal-source voltage. In the simple case where $R_s = 0$, the settling is controlled by the time constant $R_{on}C_{bus}$, where C_{bus} is the sum of C_{gs} and C_{ds} (FET capacitances), C_{in} (amplifier input capacitance, may be a function of frequency), and C_{stray} (stray bus-to-ground capacitance), as depicted in Figure 17.

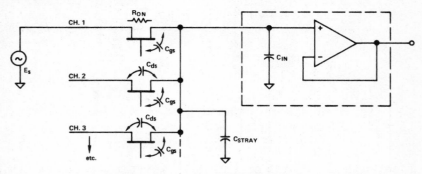

Figure 17. Factors Affecting MUX Settling Time With Negligible Source Resistance

Typically, C_{gs} and C_{ds} are 2-5pF for small-geometry FET's with *on* resistances in the 200-500Ω range; but there are wide variations depending on construction, and large-geometry low-*on*-resistance FET's have considerably higher capacitances. Stray capacitance, to a large extent a function of layout, may typically be 15pF or more. Input capacitance of the buffer amplifier will probably be about 5 to 10pF (simple buffer-amplifier designs may have considerable Miller input capacitance).

For an 8-channel multiplexer, the bus capacitance may therefore be typically in the range 36 to 65pF, which gives a time constant of 18 to 34ns with $R_{on} = 500\Omega$. The settling time to 0.01% (9.2τ) would therefore be 0.165 to $0.31\mu s$. This figure will increase in rough proportion to the number of channels working into a common bus. For large numbers of channels, this is one more good reason for submultiplexing; dynamically it will decrease the output bus capacitance and so keep the bus settling time within reasonable bounds.

In the case where R_s is appreciable, the settling time is controlled by two time constants. In general, the settling time will be longer than with $R_s = 0$, but the exact behavior depends on the relative magnitudes of the two time constants (Figure 18).

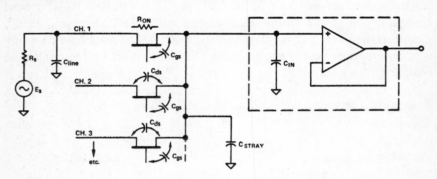

Figure 18. Factors Affecting MUX Settling Time With Appreciable Source Resistance

The settling mechanism consists of a charge transfer between C_{line} and C_{bus} through R_{on} $(\tau_1 = R_{on} \cdot C_{line} \cdot C_{bus}/(C_{line} + C_{bus}))$ and charging of C_{line} and C_{bus} through R_s by E_s (time constant $\tau_2 = R_s(C_{line} + C_{bus})$). The charge-transfer time constant τ_1 is usually the shorter, controlling the initial settling, while τ_2 controls the final settling.

In cases where $C_{line} \gg C_{bus}$, settling is controlled mainly by charge transfer and may not require much more time than with $R_s = 0$, provided that the line capacitance has adequate time to be recharged between samples. This is usually the case when an input filter is used and C_{line} becomes part of the rather large filter capacitance. Without a filter, C_{line} depends largely on the choice of input cable and is typically greater than 8pF/ft. When C_{line} is of the same order as C_{bus}, it is necessary to solve the differential equations to obtain a reasonably exact value of settling time to a given resolution. These are easily derived using the equivalent circuit of Figure 18.

Output Amplifier Settling

When the settling time of the output bus has been calculated, an output buffer amplifier should be selected; its speed of response should be such that it does not further degrade the settling time seriously. Operational-amplifier manufacturers can usually provide settling-time data for most of their products, particularly wide-band amplifiers with fast settling time that have been specifically designed for such applications as high-speed multiplexing. If settling performance is not a critical parameter and you wish to reassure yourself only as to the order of magnitude of the settling time, you can obtain a rough estimate from the slew rate and bandwidth of the operational amplifier. This technique is not recommended for situations in which accurate estimates are required, since the true settling time of an amplifier in a given circuit configuration is a function of more parameters than slew rate and bandwidth, but, as mentioned, it can prove useful for rough checks where settling data is not available.

As fast multiplexers and amplifiers carry a considerable cost premium, you should aim to design closely to your system requirements. Do not degrade a fast multiplexer with a slow amplifier, or waste a fast amplifier on a slow multiplexer; aim for a good balance of cost and performance in both components.

"Pumpback" and Charge Injection

Each time a channel is switched in any type of multiplexer, some of the switch-control signal is coupled inductively and capacitively into the analog signal path. In FET multiplexers, coupling occurs mainly via the gate-drain and gate-source capacitance of the FET switches. Each time a switch is operated, a quantity of charge,

$V_c(C_{gd} + C_{gs})$, is injected into the bus and line (V_c = gate-driving voltage). This charge has to leak away through the switch *on* resistance and the source resistance R_s. In cases where $R_s \rightarrow 0$, charge injection produces a short spike on the output bus each time a switch operates. The spike consists of an initial voltage step of approximate magnitude $V_c(C_{gs} + C_{gd})/C_{bus}$, and an exponential decay with time constant $R_{on}C_{bus}$.

If the output amplifier response to the transient remains in the linear range (i.e., the amplifier is not overloaded or driven into slewing), charge injection will only produce a slight increase in settling time: the time required for most of the injected charge to leak away and for the amplifier to recover from the (small) transient.

If R_s is large, the initial voltage step will be reduced to $V_c(C_{gs} + C_{gd})/(C_{bus} + C_{line})$, but the decay time constant will be increased to $R_s(C_{bus} + C_{line})$ while the switch remains on. The effective values of C_{gs} and C_{gd} may differ between the switch *on* and switch *off* conditions, due to nonlinear switching effects, and for this reason the line capacitance may remain charged, decaying through its own time constant R_sC_{line}. Operating the switch again will add to the charge on the line capacitance, and at high sample rates, charge can be pumped into the line capacitance more rapidly than it can leak away to zero, producing a standing offset voltage in series with the signal source. This phenomenon, known as "pumpback," can limit the sampling rate in very high-speed systems. For high sampling rates, it is therefore essential to use low-capacitance, medium *on*-resistance switches to minimize pumpback error.

Crosstalk

This is a measure of the coupling between the *off* channels and the conducting channel of a multiplexer. It is very largely a function of the cable and circuit-board layout used for the multiplexer, but it is also a function of switch *on/off* impedance. Manufacturers specify crosstalk figures for multiplexers, but these figures are liable to be enormously modified in a practical system.

Crosstalk is measured by applying a voltage of known magnitude and frequency at one or more of the *off* channels of a multiplexer and measuring the output voltage on the bus or at a source with a defined R_s (usually 1kΩ). The results will differ slightly, depending on where the output voltage is measured (bus or source), so the test configuration should be specified. Also, crosstalk varies according to which channels are used for measurement; it is customary (or at least, desirable) to give a figure for the worst-case pair. Measurement details are shown in Figure 19. Crosstalk can be measured at both dc and ac (usually 1kHz) and is strongly affected by the source resistance.

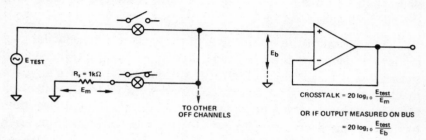

$$CROSSTALK = 20 \log_{10} \frac{E_{test}}{E_m}$$

OR IF OUTPUT MEASURED ON BUS

$$= 20 \log_{10} \frac{E_{test}}{E_b}$$

Figure 19. Measuring MUX Crosstalk

Switching Time

Besides the delays required for analog settling, there are propagation and risetime delays associated with the digital logic that drives the switching elements, and corresponding delays inherent in the operation of switches, e.g., mechanical switching time of reed relays. Turn-on and turn-off times of switches are measured on each channel with full-scale input voltage. *Turn-on* time is the delay from application of channel address to 90% output voltage appearing on the bus, and *turn-off* time is the delay from removal of channel address to 10% output voltage on the bus. In practice, to make a meaningful measurement, it is necessary to load the bus with a resistive load to make the bus time-constant short with respect to the switching time.

Switching time must be added to the total settling time to obtain the minimum delay required between channel address and conversion command of a multiplexed A/D converter.

ERRORS IN LOW-LEVEL MULTIPLEXERS

All the errors encountered in high-level multiplexers also occur in low-level multiplexers but the effects are more serious because of the small signal amplitude involved. Low-level multiplexers are always made differential or two-wire, and a data amplifier is used, so that the converter sees only the difference in the errors of two identical channels. Leakage, gain, pumpback, crosstalk, etc., can all be greatly reduced, provided that adequate matching is maintained for the channels. The *magnitudes* of settling errors are also decreased, although their *time constants* (and hence duration) remain unchanged.

The calculation of the magnitudes of these effects in each side of a differential channel is performed as for high-level multiplexers and the results subtracted to obtain the differential error. Clearly, the result would always be zero if channels were perfectly balanced, but this is never attainable in a practical system. Calculation then has to be based on some known or estimated unbalance on each side of the channel.

As channels are differential, they also have the ability to reject common-mode interference. To do so effectively requires maintenance of a high degree of balance in the channel to avoid common- to differential-mode conversion. The equivalent circuit of a channel of a differential multiplexer is shown in Figure 20.

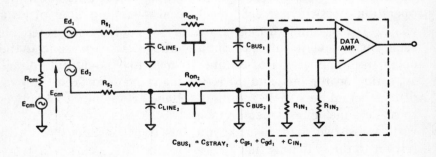

Figure 20. Equivalent Circuit of a Differential-MUX Channel.

From this equivalent circuit, in the case where $R_s \gg R_{on}$, the effective common-mode driving voltage E_{cm}' at the source is

$$E_{cm}' = \cfrac{E_{cm}}{1 + \cfrac{2R_{cm}}{R_s + \cfrac{\cfrac{1}{j\omega(C_{line} + C_{bus})} \cdot R_{in}}{\cfrac{1}{j\omega(C_{line} + C_{bus})} + R_{in}}}}$$

The differential error V_e produced by this common-mode voltage is then:

$$V_e = E_{cm}' \left[\frac{1}{1 + j\omega(C_{line_1} + C_{bus_1})R_{s_1}} - \frac{1}{1 + j\omega(C_{line_2} + C_{bus_2})R_{s_2}} \right]$$

neglecting R_{in}. Clearly, for "infinite" CMR,

$$(C_{line_1} + C_{bus_1}) \cdot R_{s_1} = (C_{line_2} + C_{bus_2}) \cdot R_{s_2}$$

The C_{line} terms are commonly matched by twisting the input lines together. A typical twisted shielded pair may have a line-to-shield capacitance of 55pF/ft and a mismatch of about $3 - 5$pF/ft. The C_{bus} terms must be matched by careful layout and the use of matched components, and R_s must be matched as closely as practical arrangements allow. If $R_s \to 0$, the CMR is controlled mainly by the match of the switch R_{on}'s.

In all these cases, the common-mode to differential conversion of the channel can be approximately calculated. A good design goal is to aim to achieve a channel CMR about an order-of-magnitude greater than the CMR of the following data amplifier. There is little point in buying a 120dB-CMR data amplifier if the channel rejection due to imbalance is only 90dB; an 80-90dB device would provide essentially identical performance at lower cost.

THE MULTIPLEXER SYSTEM IN HIGH-NOISE-LEVEL ENVIRONMENTS

When multiplexers are operated in conditions of high common-mode interference, two-wire differential and guarded or flying-capacitor multiplexers are mandatory. If, as is likely, considerable normal-mode interference also exists, further precautions will be required to make reproducible measurements. Common techniques include filtering, digital averaging, and the use of integrating converters. These are briefly outlined as follows.

Filtering

The addition of low-pass filters to the channel inputs of a multiplexer is an economical method of reducing normal-mode interference. The filter characteristics can be tailored to the requirements of the channel it serves. Filters may increase the settling time of a channel and aggravate pumpback effects, but these are usually small tradeoffs. It is also possible to place the filter after the multiplexer, but this is not recommended, since each channel will have to charge the filter, increasing the settling time enormously.

In differential systems, filters should have balanced impedance in both inputs (or be connected differentially) to preserve common-mode performance.

Integrating A/D Converter

Where passive filtering of each channel is not practicable, an integrating A/D converter can provide very high normal-mode rejection, particularly at frequencies which have periods that are integral submultiples of the integration interval. Such rejection is obtained with a conversion time that is usually much shorter than the settling time of a filter required to provide the same rejection. Rejection of normal-mode interference to the extent of 40-70dB is easily obtained with an integrating converter. Many integrating converters are also designed for floating guarded-input operation and provide the best overall common- and normal-mode performance attainable with any type of converter.

Digital Averaging

In systems where a computer or small central-processing unit and store are available, and where the converter can track the variations in input signal produced by interference (a sample-hold can assist), a software approach can be used to reduce the effects of interference. Multiple samples can be taken on each channel and the results digitally summed and averaged. The signal/noise ratio improves as the square-root of the number of samples, provided that sampling and interfering frequencies are uncorrelated.

III Sample-Hold Modules

Chapter 4

A Sample-Hold module is a device having a signal input, an output, and a control input. It has two steady-state operating modes: *Sample*, (or "Track") in which it acquires the input signal as rapidly as possible and tracks it faithfully until commanded to *Hold*, at which time it retains the last value of input signal that it had at the time the control signal called for a mode change. Sample-Holds are often more-appropriately known as "Track-Holds" if they spend the major portion of the time in *sample*, tracking the input.

Sample-Holds usually have unity gain and are non-inverting. The control inputs are operated by "standard" logic levels, and are usually TTL-compatible. Logic "1" is usually the *Sample* command and logic "0" the *Hold* command.

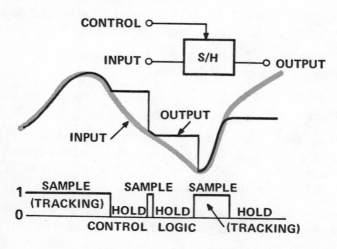

Figure 1. Typical Sample-Hold Waveforms

USES OF SAMPLE-HOLDS

In data-acquisition systems, Sample-Holds are used either to "freeze" fast-moving signals during conversion or to store multiplexer outputs while the signal is being converted and the multiplexer is seeking the next signal to be converted. In analog data-reduction, they may be used to determine peaks or valleys, establish amplitudes in resolver-to-digital conversion, and facilitate analog computations involving signals obtained at different instants of time. In data-distribution systems, Sample-holds are used for holding converted data between updates. Fast Sample-Holds may be used to acquire and measure fast pulses of arbitrary timing and width.

CHARACTERISTICS OF REAL SAMPLE-HOLDS

In the ideal Sample-Hold of Figure 1, tracking is error-free, acquisition and release occur instantaneously, settling times are zero, and hold is infinite. Commercially-available units are specified in terms of the extent to which they depart from the ideal. Here are some of the commonly-occurring deviations (See also Figures 2, 3, 4, 5) during the four states: *Sample,* transition from *sample-to-hold, hold,* and *hold-to-sample.*

During SAMPLE (Figure 2):

OFFSET: For zero input, the extent to which the output deviates from zero, a function of time and temperature.

NONLINEARITY: The amount by which the plot of output vs input deviates from a "best straight line."

SCALE FACTOR ERROR: The amount by which the output deviates from specified gain (usually unity).

SETTLING TIME: The time required for the output to attain its final value within a specified fraction of full scale when a full-scale input step is applied (0 to ±FS or −FS to +FS). See also *Acquisition time* (discussion of Fig. 5).

In this state, the unit behaves as a slow unity-gain follower. Thus one might expect to encounter other specifications typical of such devices, such as phase shift, slew rate, full-power bandwidth, small-signal bandwidth, etc.

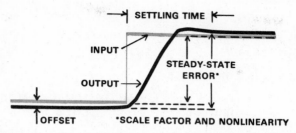

Figure 2. Tracking Errors During Sample. Magnitude Scale Here and in Figs. 3, 4, & 5 is Greatly Exaggerated.

SAMPLE to HOLD (Figure 3):

APERTURE TIME: The time elapsing between the command to *Hold* and the actual opening of the *Hold* switch. It has two components: a nominal time delay, and an uncertainty caused by jitter or variation from time-to-time or unit-to-unit. If a signal changing at a rate of 1V/μs must be resolved to within 0.1% of 10V (FS), the aperture *uncertainty* must be less than 10ns, provided that it is possible to anticipate the nominal delay and advance the command by an appropriate interval. In some sampled-date system applications, such as spectrum analyzers, auto- and cross-correlation function generators, the delay is unimportant, but the uncertainty directly affects uniformity of the sampling rate. Manufacturers — to date — have not displayed consistency in their usage of *aperture time;* hence it is a good idea to find out exactly what the specification means for a unit you may be considering.[1]

SAMPLE-TO-HOLD OFFSET: A step error occurring at the initiation of the *Hold* mode caused by "dumping" of charge into the storage capacitor via the capacitance between the control circuit and the capacitor side of the switch (e.g., the gate-to-drain capacitance of a field-effect transistor). It can be partially compensated by coupling an out-of-phase signal through a compensating capacitor, but usually only under a given set of tightly-controlled and highly-"tweaked" conditions. This offset does not occur in units having digital *Hold*.

---

[1]The inconsistency in the industry extends even to the spelling. However, there seems little question that *aperture,* which is derived from the Latin *apertura* (from *apertus,* open) is the correct spelling, preferable to *aperature,* which cannot be found in most dictionaries.

SWITCHING TRANSIENTS: Residual transients coupled from the switching gate that cannot be compensated; they remain after compensation of the *sample-to-hold offset.*

SETTLING TIME: The interval required for the output to attain its final value within a specified fraction of full scale, following the opening of the switch.

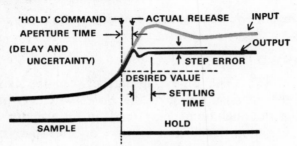

Figure 3. Sample-to-Hold Errors

<u>During HOLD (Figure 4):</u>

"DROOP:" A drift of the output at an approximately constant rate caused by the flow of current through the storage capacitor. (dV/dt = I/C). The current is the sum of the leakage across the switch, the amplifier's bias current, and leakage to the power supplies and to ground. In a well-designed unit, only the first is of any consequence. Units having digital storage have no droop. A rough figure-of-merit for analog Sample-holds is the ratio of droop time to settling time for the same percentage (FS) error. For example, a unit having settling time of 5µs to 0.01% and droop rate of 50mV/s (0.02s to 1mV), would have a figure-of-merit of 20,000/5 = 4,000.

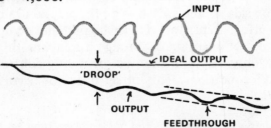

Figure 4. Errors in Hold. Droop may be either Positive or Negative

FEEDTHROUGH: The fraction of input signal that appears at the output in *Hold,* caused primarily by capacitance across the switch. Usually measured by applying a full-scale sinusoidal input at a fixed frequency (e.g., 20Vp-p at 10kHz), and observing the output.

DIELECTRIC ABSORPTION: The tendency of charges within a capacitor to redistribute themselves over a period of time, resulting in "creep" to a new level when allowed to rest after large, fast changes. Less than 0.01% for good polystyrene and teflon capacitors, as large as several percent for ceramic and mylar capacitors.

Output impedance of the Sample-Hold should be low and recovery fast to minimize transients caused by dynamic loads, such as A/D converter inputs.

HOLD to SAMPLE (Figure 5):

ACQUISITION TIME: The time duration for which an input must be applied for sampling to the desired accuracy. Essentially the same as *Settling time* for feedback types, but shorter than *Settling time* for two-stage units and for open-loop follower types in which the amplifier's settling time is appreciable compared to the capacitor's charging time.

HOLD-TO-SAMPLE TRANSIENTS: Transients (e.g. spikes) occurring between the *Sample* command and final settling. Not too

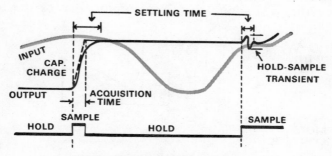

Figure 5. Hold-to-Sample Errors

important for large changes, but can be crucially important in some applications if the spikes are large compared to the actual change (e.g., at constant input). Such "glitch"-like spikes may be due to limiting and other sources of dynamic disequilibria within the Sample-Hold circuit, or to capacitive feedthrough from the control signals.

TYPICAL DESIGNS

The choice of storage element divides Sample-holds into two major classes. The more conventional, popular, and the lower in cost employs a capacitor for storage (*analog* storage): several forms of this design will be discussed here. The other technique, which uses an A/D converter and a register for storage, and reads out via a D/A converter, is somewhat more complex and costly (especially where high accuracy or fast sampling are necessary), but it has the undisputed advantage of arbitrary — and essentially "infinite" — *hold* time. Some ways of instrumenting that approach are discussed later in this chapter.

Open-Loop Follower (Figures 6, 7, 8)

The most obvious circuit to come to mind is that shown in Figure 6. When the switch is closed, the capacitor charges exponentially to the input voltage, and the amplifier's output follows the capacitor's voltage. When the switch is opened, the charge remains on the capacitor. The capacitor's *acquisition time* depends on the series resistance and the current available to charge its capacitance. Once charge is acquired, to the appropriate accuracy, the switch may be opened, even though the amplifier has not yet settled, without affecting the final output value or the settling

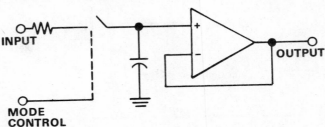

Figure 6. Simple Follower

time (assuming that the amplifier's input stage does not draw appreciable current at any time). The switch is typically a FET, and the amplifier is a FET-input type. This circuit has the disadvantage that the capacitor loads the input source, which — often enough — will either oscillate or lack sufficient current to charge the capacitor speedily. The circuit of Figure 7 includes a follower to isolate the source. The Analog Devices general-purpose SHA–IA uses this scheme. A detailed example of a Sample-Hold circuit is shown in Figure 17, at the end of this chapter, accompanied by a detailed discussion. For extremely fast charging at

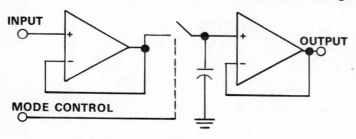

Figure 7. Same as Fig. 6 but with Isolated Input

approximately a linear slew rate, a diode bridge scheme may be used, essentially as shown in Figure 8. Here, current sources are switched on to charge the capacitor. If the bridge and current sources are appropriately balanced, current flow into the capacitor will cease when the capacitor voltage is equal to the input voltage. Figure 8 is a simplified block diagram of the SHA–II, which has an acquisition time of 200ns to 0.1%, for a 10V step.

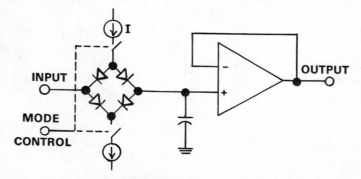

Figure 8. Switched Current Sources for Shorter Acquisition Time

Feedback Circuits (Figures 9 & 10)

The circuits of Figures 6, 7, 8 have the essential advantage of potentially fast acquisition and settling, but they are open-loop devices. If low-frequency tracking accuracy is more important than speed, the cascaded configuration of Figure 7 will be less satisfactory than a configuration which is, in effect, a single amplifier, yet provides isolation. This can be accomplished by closing the loop around a storage capacitor, and using high loop gain to enforce tracking accuracy. Figure 9 shows a configuration in which the

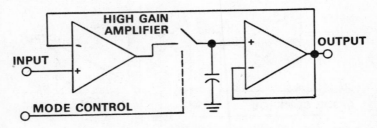

Figure 9. Track-Hold Employing Feedback

input follower of Figure 7 is replaced by a high-gain difference amplifier. Now, when the switch is closed, the output (which represents the charge on the capacitor) is forced to track the input, within the gain and common-mode errors and the current-driving ability of the input amplifier.

Common-mode and offset errors in the output follower are automatically compensated for by adjusting the charge on the capacitor. When the switch is opened, the output retains the final value.

In Figure 10 (a simplified schematic of the SHA–IIA, SHA–3 and SHA–4), an integrator is used, permitting the switch to operate at ground potential, simplifying leakage problems.

In the circuits of both Figure 9 and Figure 10, because the charge on the capacitor is controlled by the output, as well as the input, the *acquisition time* and the *settling time* are identical. If the circuit of Figure 9 is switched into *hold* before the output has settled at the input value, the sample may be in error, Also,

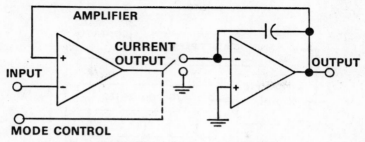

Figure 10. Feedback Track-Hold with an Integrator

because the loop is open during *hold,* it must re-acquire the input when returned to *sample,* even if the input is unchanged. As a rule, this will result in a spike, if the input amplifier has high voltage gain.

Cascaded Sample-Holds (Figure 11)

If a long period of *hold* is required, in conjunction with very fast acquisition, a fast Sample-Hold, such as SHA–II, may be cascaded with one having slower acquisition but less droop. The resulting figure-of-merit can approach the product of the two.

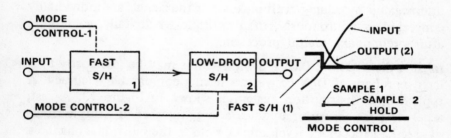

Figure 11. Use of Two Cascaded Sample-Holds for Fast Acquisition and Long Hold

APPLICATIONS

Sample-Holds are most-widely used in data acquisition systems, typically as shown in Figure 12. The Sample-Hold maintains the input to the A/D converter constant during the conversion interval; meanwhile, the multiplexer is seeking the next channel

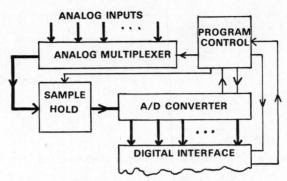

Figure 12. Typical Data-Acquisition System

to be converted, either randomly or sequentially. As soon as conversion is completed, the Sample-Hold samples the newly-established input, and the cycle is repeated. This mode of operation is known as *synchronous* sampling: the Sample-Hold operates in synchronism with the other system elements. If the input signals vary at widely disparate rates, programmed random access is necessary, to ensure that the signals with the most information are sampled most often. In another mode (viz., *asynchronous*), a large number of Sample-Holds are used, to acquire and store data at rates pertinent to each individual channel. They are then either interrogated by analog multiplexers, or the signals are individually converted asynchronously, then multiplexed digitally, sometimes after preliminary digital processing.[2]

In data distribution, 0.01% Sample-Holds may be less costly than large numbers of D/A converters having comparable accuracy. A typical data distribution system is shown in Figure 13. A fast, accurate D/A converter updates a large number of Sample-Holds at speed and accuracy levels appropriate to the individual channels. Sample-Holds may be used to "de-glitch" D/A converters, in systems that are sensitive to spikes, by sampling their outputs after they've settled.

There are many applications in analog and hybrid computing and data-reduction. A typical example is shown in Figure 14: a peak follower, using a Sample-Hold and a comparator circuit.

[2] See the discussion of an adaptive low-redundancy data-acquisition system in *Analog Dialogue,* Vol. 5, No. 1: "New Approaches to Data-Acquisition System Design."

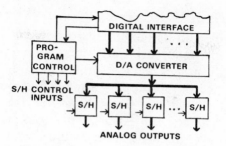

Figure 13. Data Distribution System with Analog Storage

The Sample-Hold output (or the Comparator input) is biased by a few millivolts of hysteresis to avoid ambiguity during step inputs, and minimize false triggering by noise. Here's how the circuit works: When the input is greater than the S/H output, the comparator's positive output causes the S/H to track. When the input backs away and becomes less than the S/H output, the comparator's "0" output causes the S/H to *Hold* until the input once again becomes greater than the output. To reset, the control input is arbitrarily switched into *Sample,* and the lowest level contemplated is applied at the input.

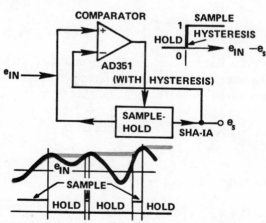

Figure 14. Peak-Follower using Sample-Hold and Comparator

The above are but a few examples of the wide applicability of these versatile modules.

SAMPLE/ARBITRARY HOLD USING A/D CONVERSION

As we have indicated earlier in this chapter, digital storage can provide the benefits of arbitrarily-long *hold* duration with no droop. Other advantages include: no sample-hold offset, no feed-through, no dielectric absorption effects, and no sample-to-hold transients or settling time, since the system is automatically in *hold* after a conversion, unless a *sample* command is applied. In addition, both analog and digital outputs are available. Disadvantages are increased cost and complexity, typically longer acquisition time, and possible need for pre-sampling, in the manner of the two-stage Sample-Hold example, Figure 15.

Figure 1 shows how this function can be achieved with a D/A Converter, an up-down counter, a comparator, a clock, and a few gates. The initial acquisition time may be quite long, since the

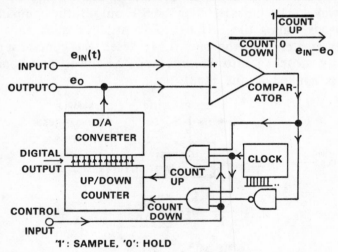

Figure 15. Tracking Sample-Hold Using Up-Down Counter

choice of clock period (τ_s) depends on the LSB settling time of the D/A converter, and the number of counts required depends on its resolution. For a full-scale step, acquisition time is approximately $(2^n - 1)\tau_s$. Smaller, slower changes, however, will be followed quite rapidly. The system can be converted into a *peak* follower by disabling the *up* count. Reset, for peaks, is to negative full scale, and for valleys to positive full scale (− 1 LSB). The range of input signal levels and polarity determine the choice of D/A-converter output specifications. If a BCD counter and BCD DAC are used, with a numeric display, one has an "all-time-peak"-reading DVM.

Figure 16 shows the generic approach, using an A/D converter and a D/A converter. Where averaging is desired, the A/D converter may be an integrating type. The overall acquisition time is approximately equal to the sum of the A/D converter's conversion time and the DAC's settling time. If the D/A output of a successive-approximations type is available, suitably scaled and buffered, a separate D/A converter is unnecessary, and acquisition time is equal to conversion time.

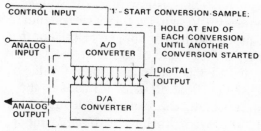

Figure 16. Sample-Hold Using A/D and D/A Converters

EXAMPLE OF SAMPLE-HOLD AMPLIFIER DESIGN

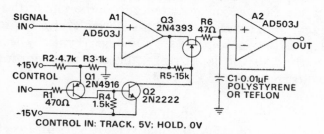

Figure 17. Sample/Hold Amplifier

The low input current and high slew rate of such FET-input op amps as the AD503J make it an excellent device for track-hold applications. The circuit of Fig. 17 will track a ±10V input signal at frequencies up to 4kHz. When the control input changes from *track* (+5V) to hold (0V), the series FET switch, Q3, opens, and the input signal voltage is retained on capacitor C1. The output amplifier, A2, provides a high input impedance to keep C1 from discharging too rapidly.

The drift rate in *hold* is determined primarily by the "off" leakage current of Q3, which tends to be greater than that of the amplifier, A2 (25pA max, 5pA typical for AD503J). For example, at 100pA leakage current, the drift rate (for $C_1 = 0.01\mu F$) is 10mV/s, and the rate doubles for every 10°C increase of temperature. Lower drift rate and higher accuracy — at the proportional expense of slower acquisition time — can be had by increasing the value of C1. The capacitor should be a type having low dielectric absorption (typically its dielectric would be polystyrene or teflon).

The switching FET, Q3, has low pinchoff voltage, and allows the circuit to handle ±10V signal voltages with standard ±15V supply. In the *track* mode, with +5V applied to the control input, Q1 and Q2 are cut off, and the gate of Q3 is at the same voltage as A1's output. Thus, the FET is zero-biased for any value of input and has a resistance less than 100Ω. Resistor R5 adds to the "on" resistance so as to better isolate the capacitive load, C1, from the input follower, A1, to prevent ringing. In the *hold* mode, both Q1 and Q2 conduct and pull the gate of Q3 toward −5V. When the gate voltage drops to about 3V below the source (about 100ns after a step change to zero control voltage), the capacitor voltage ceases to track the input. Because of capacitance from the gate to the drain of Q3, the gate swing causes the small transferred charge to produce a small step (offset in *hold*) in C1's voltage. Typically less than 10mV over the ±10 volt input range, this step is proportional to the gate voltage swing ($15V + V_{in}$).

There are also settling transients in A1 and A2, which increase the settling time to within 1mV of final value to about $2\mu s$. For a 10-volt step applied during the *track* mode, the settling time to within 1mV of final value is less than $15\mu s$ (caused by the limited charging rate of C1) and roughly proportional to C1. The dielectric absorption of C1 may account for an additional 3mV of error if the input signal is changing rapidly at the time the circuit is gated into Hold.

IV

Guide For the Troubled

It must be confessed that one of the hoped-for byproducts of this book is a more interesting life for Sales Engineers, because the technical inquiries they receive should become more challenging. This should be in addition to a saving of time and telephone expense for both customers and manufacturers.

It is accomplished by making broadly available as much as possible of the information that most commonly passes during conversations with customers; this we have sought to do in the preceding pages of this book.

To be useful, such information must also be accessible. In this Part, access is aided by relating material in the book to the typical inquiries that are received, and by listing specific, recurring points. Telephone conversations typically involve one of the following:

Requests for information
Requests for assistance when things don't seem to work right
Requests for advice
Urgent pleas for rescue

Listed below are a few of the most-frequently-occurring topics of conversation, with comments and sources of information likely to resolve the problem.

FREQUENTLY-ASKED QUESTIONS

Q. What do the codes mean? What is complementary BCD? How does offset-binary relate to 2's complement?
A. *See Part II, Chapter 1*

Q. How do converters work?
A. *See Part II, Chapter 1*

Q. How do I choose the right converter?
A. *See Part II, Chapter 4*

Q. What are the differences between voltage- and current-switching DAC's?
A. *See Part II, Chapter 1*

Q. What's a "glitch?" How is it caused? How eliminate it?
A. *See Part I, Chapters 3, 5; Part II, Chapters 1, 2, 3, 4*

Q. How does input noise affect A/D conversion? How combat it?
A. *See Part I, Chapter 2; Part II, Chapters 2, 3, 4, 5*

Q. Where can I find out about sampled-data systems?
A. *See Bibliography*

Q. What are the contributions of various components to errors?
A. *See Part II, Chapters 2, 4, 5; Part III, Chapters 1, 2, 3, 4, Product Guide*

Q. What are the timing constraints on D/A converters with registers?
A. *See individual data sheets and Product Guide*

Q. What factors affect timing of systems with sample-holds and multiplexers?
A. *See Part I, Chapters 2, 3; Part II, Chapters 4, 5; Part III, Chapters 3 & 4*

Q. What are the requirements on power supplies?
A. *See Part II Chapters 4, 5; data sheets, Product Guide*

Q. When is it desirable to use registers with DAC's?
A. *See Part I, Chapter 3*

Q. How do I connect a 10-volt device for a 10.24V full-scale range?
A. *Scale-factor adjustment will usually have insufficient range, especially in high-resolution devices. Add series feedback resistance with DAC's (the loop is usually closed externally), or use attenuation ahead of the ADC input buffer (sometimes*

series input resistance can be used with current-summing comparators). Information on 10.24V full-scale range will be found in Part II, Chapter 1: see Table 3.

Q. How is the bipolar offset circuitry connected and adjusted? How does it affect the specifications?

A. *See Part II, Chapters 1, 2, 3, 4*

Q. What are the suggested grounding techniques?

A. *See Part II, Chapters 1, 5*

Q. What are the issues in low-level multiplexing vs. instrumentation-amplifier-per-channel? How do instrumentation and isolation amplifiers differ?

A. *See Part I, Chapter 2; Part III, Chapters 2, 3*

Q. What is "Differential Nonlinearity?"

A. *See Part II, Chapters 1, 3, 4*

Q. Can I use the analog power supply as a source of constant voltage?

A. *Yes — if it is sufficiently quiet and well-regulated to provide the desired degree of stability and accuracy. Otherwise, derive a reference voltage using a Zener diode and, if necessary, an op amp (See Fig. 21a, Part II, Chapter 1.)*

FREQUENTLY-ENCOUNTERED PROBLEMS

Gross Malfunctions

Wrong digital code ("Positive true" vs. complementary)
Wrong analog polarity relationship
Grounds not interconnected
Power supply not connected, wrongly connected, or zapped
Missing or improper connections (Study the connection diagram)
Wipeouts due to applying power to devices in the wrong order (In general, power downstream units first; avoid or protect multiplexers that short in the power-off condition)
Control-logic improper (polarity, duration, timing, levels) Check logic and timing diagrams on data sheets
Uncontrolled overflow in counter configurations
Wrong diode polarity

Poor Functioning

Common-mode problems in "single-ended" system (use proper grounding or difference amplifier)

Grounding problems: no ground connection, fortuitous ground connection, wrong ground connection (common analog and logic return), shields returned to wrong ground or grounded at both ends.

Pickup due to proximity of digital ground plane to analog circuits, or proximity of analog and digital wiring, in general, or poor lead dress: Keep stray capacitance low.

Excessive load capacitance on outputs of voltage DAC's or other analog devices can in some cases cause slow response, poor settling, ringing, or oscillation ("noise")

Improper connection of built-in references (unused bipolar offset references may require grounding in unipolar applications; external use of internal Zener voltage reference generally requires buffering)

Op amp voltage offset adjustment used for zeroing anything but op amp *voltage* offsets, e.g., system offsets, can result in increased thermal drift

Logic overloading (logic outputs may also be used for internal purposes; check actual specified loading on data sheet)

Too much attenuation because "current-output" DAC's output impedance neglected

Nonlinearity because current-output DAC's specified maximum output voltage range exceeded

Noisy A/D conversion, increased differential nonlinearity, and missing codes caused by widening of quantization band due to noise on input signal, or picked up in wiring

Bent pin that didn't go into the socket (or perhaps even broke off)

Unanticipated "glitches" due to lack of filtering, inappropriate converter choice, marginal logic timing, limited logic slewing rates due to excessive capacitive load, stray capacitive coupling to analog circuitry

Gain and offset adjustments performed in wrong order in bipolar DAC's and ADC's (See Part II, Chapter 3, Figure 5)

Excessive thermal drifts due to: improper converter adjustment procedure; bias current flowing through resistances (MUX R_{on}, for example); use of op amp voltage offset adjustment to counteract bias-current or system offsets

Loss of monotonicity over small temperature ranges: possible if a converter is specified at ±1 LSB differential nonlinearity at room temperature. A conservative specification of ½LSB allows variation of an additional ½LSB with temperature

RFI or fast pulses causing rectification that produces offsets

"Long-tailed" responses due to thermal transients (some op amp or comparator circuits), or inappropriate capacitor choice (precision capacitors should always have low dielectric absorption — polystyrene, teflon, polycarbonate are among recommended materials)

Excessive drift in low-level circuitry due to differential "thermocouple" effects in input leads (e.g., copper-to-Kovar at IC inputs) Differential-input leads should always be close together and their junctions should be as-nearly-as-possible isothermal.

When all other possibilities have been eliminated, one should not discount the possibility that the device is malfunctioning or out of specification, either innately, as a result of some recent trauma, or as a result of some "early failure" mechanism. Many manufacturers subject certain of their products to "burn-in" to eliminate innate and "early failure" problems.

By no means all problems are chargeable to the user. Manufacturers of devices and components (including Analog Devices) have been known to have made available — inadvertently, and despite considerable effort —
    Data sheets with errors or insufficient data
    Devices that have failed, for no apparent reason, when first plugged in.

Though rare, these possibilities should not be discounted. The user of conversion devices — especially in quantity — should be prepared to perform at least simple tests on devices to verify their performance; Chapter 3, Part II, may be found useful in this respect. If a user finds information on a data sheet that raises questions in his mind, he will find most manufacturers quite willing to discuss them and clarify the point in question, especially as it pertains to his application.

FREQUENTLY-GIVEN ADVICE

Preventive

Nothing beats good initial analysis of the basic problem and conservative initial design, with double-checking to make sure that the best-available data has been used, the tolerances on resolution, accuracy, and timing are adequate, and the connection scheme is proper, and follows the manufacturer's suggestions — where appropriate. Perhaps breadboarding should be used to verify sticky points. The design should include features that facilitate testing and trouble-shooting.

Be sure that common-mode, normal-mode, and induced noise problems have been considered and dealt with adequately. (Differential amplifiers, filtering, lead locations and directions.)

Be sure that grounding is proper: no ground "loops" (i.e., ground current is allowed only one path); digital and analog grounds separated; high-power and low-level signal grounds separated; One main "mecca" point where all grounds meet, if feasible; heavy ground conductors, to avoid voltage drops in signal return leads.

Be sure that interconnections of devices do not produce surprises as a result of (e.g.) currents and impedance levels, transient overloads during MPX switching, etc.

After assembly, the system should be thoroughly inspected and "buzzed-out", to be sure that all connections have been made, the right elements have been plugged into the right spots, and there are no bent or broken pins.

Check the system out in small pieces and functional groupings before putting it all together. "Going for broke" often results in just that.

Measuring Devices

For monitoring performance and troubleshooting, the devices that perform dc measurements should have at least twice the resolution and accuracy of the devices they are checking; the devices that perform high-speed measurements should have faster response than the devices they are checking. An oscilloscope should always be used to avoid "flying blind." A simple multimeter may be a trap (it can't see dynamic signals or oscillations; its dc resolution may be inadequate for useful measurements on the kind of high-resolution devices usually found in data systems; and its load impedance may affect the accuracy (if not the actual character) of measurements.

Measuring and Trouble-Shooting

First, check supply and ground voltages at terminals of pluggable devices, with the devices removed.

A useful procedure is to then perform dc, manual, and low-speed checks before performing measurements at speed. This ensures that the system is at least working properly under *some* conditions.

Try to isolate the problem.

If more than one unit of a given type is in use, an apparent failure at its location can be checked by substituting another unit. If similar units of the same kind exhibit the same problem, it is likely a design or system problem. (If it's a sufficiently serious problem, involving a fault condition, the original unit and its substitute may no longer be in fit condition for further use.)

Check grounding with a simple continuity test. Use an orderly procedure. Have you localized the problem? Is it static or dynamic? Gross or subtle? Catastrophic or slightly "off?" Reproducible or intermittent? Affected by mechanical manipulation (kicking the cabinet)?

IF ALL ELSE FAILS. . .

We want to help you solve the problem, whether it involves simple advice or the return of a unit. If the problem seems to be related to one of our conversion components (either definitely or suspected),

1. Prepare a summary of the problem, and outline it to your local Analog Devices, Inc., sales office or representative, over the telephone. He may suggest some useful diagnostic procedures or that the unit be returned.

2. If the unit is to be returned within the United States,* send it to our Norwood location, marked to the attention of "Returns Department". If you are outside the United States, our local sales office or representative will give you appropriate instructions. (We maintain a complete repair depot at our Karlsruhe office, and limited repair facilities in England and Japan.)

3. Be sure to include with any returned units
   A. The name(s) and telephone number(s) of the person(s) with whom we can discuss technical (and business) aspects of the problem.
   B. Complete information on the (suspected) malfunction, and the application in which it occurred.

4. If you are in a critical "bind," wire or phone the nearest sales office or our Internal Sales Department at the factory directly. Our factory address is

> Analog Devices, Inc.
> Route 1 Industrial Park
> Norwood, Mass. USA 02062

Telephone:	(617)–329–4700†
Telex:	924491
TWX	(710)-394-6577
Cable	ANALOG NORWOODMASS

---

*See the *Analog Devices, Inc. Product Guide* for complete information on returns and warranty service.

†Note in the margin the phone number of your nearest sales representative, or office.

APPENDIX

BIBLIOGRAPHY

The references listed here have appeared in the form of books, manuals, brochures, or articles in technical publications. Individual items have been selected because of their general or specific interest, or because of an excellent list of reference sources.

It should be noted, however, that much of the most-advanced, relevant, and useful material available in this rapidly-growing and changing field is that published by manufacturers of products in the course of the ordinary business of trying to sell their products. Such publications as the Analog Devices *Product Guide* and technical data sheets, as well as those of our competitors, may well have the most current and useful information available relating to a given product area.

Certainly, every designer should be sure that his suppliers keep him up to date on new products, applications ideas, and techniques. (Analog Devices uses *Analog Dialogue* as a vehicle to accomplish this objective.) Our readers are invited to request any material of interest mentioned above, that is published by Analog Devices, as well as to subscribe to *Analog Dialogue.*

It is important for the reader to note that *material in this Bibliography is NOT available from us unless preceded by an asterisk (*),* which indicates that it is an Analog Devices publication or reprint that is currently in print.

CONVERTERS

Digital-to-Analog Converter Handbook. Hybrid Systems Corporation, 1970.

Hoeschele, David F., Jr. *Analog-to-Digital, Digital-to-Analog Conversion Techniques.* John Wiley & Sons, Inc., 1968.

Schmid, Hermann. *Electronic Analog/Digital Conversions.* Van Nostrand Reinhold, 1970.

Stephenson, Barbera W. *Analog-Digital Conversion Handbook.* Digital Equipment Company, 1964.

Aniebona, E. N. and R. T. Brathwaite. "A Review of Analog-to-Digital Conversion," *Computer Design,* December 1969.

*Brown, Cy. "The Multiplying D/A Converter," *Electronic Products,* June 21, 1971.

"Digital-to-Analog Converters: Trading off bits and bucks," *Electronics,* March 13, 1972.

Gordon, B. M. "Bernard Gordon . . . on What's Wrong With Converter Specs," *EEE Magazine*, February 1969.

Lindheimer, Michael. "Guidelines for Digital-to-Analog Converter Applications," *EEE Magazine*, September 1970.

Moore, R. D., and J. J. Pastoriza. "Low-Power a-d converter is a battery lifesaver," *Electronics*, March 29, 1971.

Neidich, Michael I. "Multiplying Digital-to-Analog Converters," *EEE Magazine*, September 1970.

*Spofford, W. R., Jr. "Putting D/A Converters to Work," *Electronics*, October 26, 1970.

*Thiel, H. "Converters for the Ruggednova Computer," *Analog Dialogue*, volume 5, no. 5 (1971).

DATA ACQUISITION AND DISTRIBUTION

*Anderson, T. O. "New Approaches to Data-Acquisition System Design," *Analog Dialogue*, volume 5, no. 1 (1970).

Baumann, Wallace, & Brenden. "Interfacing Chromatographs to the Computer," Varian Aerograph, Walnut Creek, California.

"Digitally Controlled Voltage Sources," Technical Data 6129. Hewlett-Packard, September 1971.

DiRocco, J. V. "Signal-Conditioning for Analog-to-Digital Conversion in Instrumentation Systems," *Electronic Instrument Digest*, Kiver Publications, May 1970.

Johnson, Melvin D. and Dale C. Gunderson. "An Associative Data Acquisition System," Honeywell, Inc. Systems & Research Div., St. Paul, Minn. 55113.

Melton, Ben S. "Digital Recording of Extended Range Signals," *IEEE Transactions on Geoscience Electronics*, May 1968.

Mitra, Sanjit K. "Synthesizing Active Filters" (with extensive bibliography), *IEEE Spectrum*, January 1969.

*Sheingold, D. "Selecting the Optimum Multi-Path Digital-to-Analog Configuration," *Electronic Instrument Digest*, July 1970.

HYBRID COMPUTING AND CIRCUITS

Kuo, J. F. and J. F. Kaiser. *Systems Analysis by Digital Computer*. John Wiley & Sons, Inc., 1966.

Breikss, Ivars. "Digital IC's + VOR = simpler navigation," *Electronics*, March 15, 1971.

Karplus, W. J. and R. A. Russell. "Increasing Digital Computer Efficiency with the Aid of Error-Correcting Analog Subroutines," *IEEE Transactions on Computers*, volume C20, no. 8 (August 1971).

Katz, A. I. and A. H. Moreno. "Analog/Hybrid Computers in Physiological Research," *Journal for the Advancement of Medical Instrumentation,* volume 5/3 (June 1971), 178-183.

TESTING

Bailliet, John V. "Automatic Testing Provides Economic Leverage," *Solid State Technology,* March 1970.

"Closed-Loop Production Testing," application note 135-4. Hewlett-Packard, April 1971.

Computer-Controlled Test and Monitoring Systems, Boston Section IEEE Lecture Series course notes, Spring 1971.

"Computerized Data Acquisition Aids Final Testing," application note 135-1. Hewlett-Packard, February 1971.

Lyons, Pambookian, Krawiec, and Curran. "Computerized Micromechanical Testing," *Instruments and Control Systems,* March 1971.

McAleer, Harold T. "A Look at Automatic Testing," *IEEE Spectrum,* May 1971.

Sorensen, Carl. "Angle-to-Digital Converters for Synchro and Resolver Testing," *Singer Instrumentation Review,* Bridgeport, Connecticut, volume 1, no. 2 (August 1969).

Theory and Applications of Peak Electrical Measurements, Micro Instrument Co., Hawthorne, California, March 1970.

Van Veen, Frederick. "An Introduction to IC Testing," *IEEE Spectrum,* December 1971.

SIGNAL ANALYSIS AND COMMUNICATIONS

A Pictorial Digital Atlas (1966 Edition). Bendix: United Geophysical Corp. Presented at 36th SEG Meeting November 1966.

"An Introduction to Correlation," Federal Scientific Corp., New York, Monograph no. 1 (January 1, 1972 review).

Brochure and Application Notes on the MW-10 Correlator-Convolver: Processing Example, Phase Relationship Determination, System Transfer Function, Detection of Signals in Noise, Seismic Data Analysis, System Characterization, System Emulation. Real Time Geophysics, Inc., Norwood, Massachusetts.

Domizi, D. B. and R. H. Earle. "On-Line Pulmonary Function Analysis: Program Design," Digital Equipment Corp. "DECUS", Maynard, Mass.

Flynn, George. "A Special Report on Signal Averagers," *Electronic Products,* February 1969.

Langenthal, Ira M. "Analyzing Signals for Information," *Instruments and Control Systems,* I: December 1970, and II: January 1971.

Langenthal, Ira M. "Correlation and Probability Analysis," Signal Analysis Industries Corp., Hauppage, New York, TB14 (April 1970).

"Real Time Signal Processing in the Frequency Domain," Federal Scientific Corp., New York, Monograph no. 3 (June 1, 1971).

Rothchild, Richard S. "Real Time Signal Analysis," *Medical Electronics & Data,* March-April 1971.

Sound and Vibration, General Radio, Concord, Mass. publishers.

"610B Transient Recorder," Biomation, Palo Alto, California, June 15, 1971·

DISPLAYS

Stadtfield, Nick. *Information Display Concepts.* Tektronix, Inc., 1968.

Brackett, John (M.I.T.) and Van Dam, Andries (Brown University). "Bibliography" on Computer Graphics. Private Communication, 1970.

Bryden, Joseph E. "Design Considerations for Computer Driven CRT Displays," *Computer Design.* March 1969.

Bryden, Joseph E. "Visual Displays for Computers," *Computer Design.* October 1971.

Bryden, Joseph E. "Visual Display Systems," *Electronic Progress,* Raytheon, Bedford, Mass., volume XIII, no. 3 (fall 1971).

"Computer-Driven Printers," *Digital Design.* April 1972.

Korn, Simons, Steinbach, and Wiatrowski. "A New Graphic Display/Plotter for Small Digital Computers," Spring Joint Computer Conference, 849-858, 1969.

Lyman, Jerome. "Digital Printers," *Electronic Products.* April 17, 1972.

INDUSTRIAL APPLICATIONS

Fink, L. H. "Concerning Power System Control Structures," *Advances in Instrumentation* (ISA), volume 26, part 1 (1971). Includes a brief but interesting discussion of aliasing at ½Hz sampling rates.

Grodsky, Harry R. "Process Control Information on a Continuous Basis," *Advances in Instrumentation* (ISA).

Ibanez, Miller, Matthiesen, and Smith. "Experimental Vibration Tests at Nuclear Power Plants," *Advances in Instrumentation* (ISA), volume 26, part 2.

Johnson, Bert. "Hybrid Computing Considerations Applied to On-Line Control," *Advances in Instrumentation* (ISA).

Lathrop, Dr. J. W. and James W. Jones. "Improved Electronics for Water Quality Monitoring," *Advances in Instrumentation* (ISA).

Lauher, Verlin A. "A Control Room on a CRT," *Advances in Instrumentation* (ISA).

"Publications on Process Instrumentation" (catalog of publications), The Foxboro Company, August 1970.

Zepf, Paul A. "Remote Supervisory Control System Using a Voice-Grade Line," *Advances in Instrumentation* (ISA).

COMPONENTS

Krabbe, H. and F. Molinari. "A Monolithic Multiplying D/A Converter Circuit," Digest of Technical Papers 1971 International Solid-State Circuits Conference.

Pastoriza, James. "Technical Background Facts on the μDAC Monolithic IC D/A Converter," *Orbit*. October 1971.

Rudin, Erdi, Walker, and Ricks. "Application of the μA722 10-Bit Current Source," application note. Fairchild Semiconductor, 1968.

*"The Many Scale Factors of the AD855 R-2R Ladder Network," application brief, *Analog Dialogue*, volume 5, no. 4 (1971).

OPERATIONAL AMPLIFIERS

Applications Manual for Operational Amplifiers. Teledyne Philbrick, 1968.

Smith, John I. *Modern Operational Circuit Design*. Wiley-Interscience, 1971.

Stata, Ray. *Operational Amplifiers, Parts 1, 2, and 4*. Analog Devices, Inc.

Tobey, Graeme, and Huelsman. *Operational Amplifiers - Design and Applications*. McGraw-Hill Book Co., 1971.

Birman, Paul. "Operational Power Supply Technology," Kepco, Inc., Flushing, New York, 1968.

Borlase, W. H. and M. A. Maidique. "Applying the Precision IC Operational Amplifier," Analog Devices, Inc., 1972.

*Borlase, Walter. "An Introduction to Operational Amplifiers," Analog Devices, Inc., 1968.

Sheingold, D. "Select the Right Op Amp for the Job," *Electronic Design*, June 21, 1970. (monolithic, hybrid or discrete?)

SIGNAL CONDITIONING AND CIRCUIT PRACTICE

*Brown, Cy. "Applications for Instrumentation Amplifiers," *Electronic Products*, May 17, 1971.

Condon, C. P. "Baluns cut ground noise," *Electronic Design*, July 22, 1971.

Hickey, Jack. "Powering Your IC's," *The Electronic Engineer*, April 1971.

Hueckel, John H. "Input Connection Practices for Differential Amplifiers," Neff Instrument Corp.

Multiplexing, *Electronic Products,* May 1969. 4 Parts: 1. "Multiplex System," by M. English; 2. "Digital Multiplexing" by R. Burlingame; 3. "Multiplexing with Junction FET's" by R. Schuttenhelm; 4. "Multiplexing in the Jumbo Jets" by H. Evander.

"Signal Conditioning," Gould, Inc., Brush Instruments Div., Cleveland, Ohio, November 1969.

Strassberg, Daniel D. "Multiplexing and Grounding in Analog-Digital Data-Acquisition Systems," *Advances in Instrumentation* (ISA), volume 26, part 4 (1971).

Tobey, Gene. "Programmable Data Amplifiers," *Advances in Instrumentation* (ISA), volume 26, part 4 (1971).

Zicko, C. Peter. "New Applications Open up for the Versatile Isolation Amplifier," *Electronics,* March 27, 1972.

SAMPLING AND SAMPLE–HOLDS

Abernathy, J. D. W. "Boxcar Detectors," *Research/Development,* June 1971.

Gordon, B. M. "Digital Sampling and Recovery of Analog Signals," *EEE Magazine,* May 1970.

Sanchez, A. "Understanding Sample-Hold Modules," *Analog Dialogue,* volume 5, no. 4 (1971).

INDEX

Accuracy, absolute, II-135
Accuracy, relative, II-144
Acquisition time, II-135, III-74-78, 80, 81, 85, 86
Adjustment, automatic, I-75, 76, 79-83, 105, 106, 111-113
automatic set point, I-75, 76, 105, 106
Amplifier, instrumentation, I-4, 20, 21, 23, 27, 32, 34, 35, 82, 88, 105-106, II-158, 165-168, III-31-42, 55, 56, 68, 69
Amplifier, isolation, I-4, 15, 82, III-31, 32, 40-42
Amplifiers, operational, I-3
applications, I-23-25, 33, 37, 44, 48, 55, 59-61, 63, 82, 105, II-34-39, 41-44, 49, 57, 58, 60, 65, 67-71, 80, 106, 107, 109, 112, 113, 115, 123, 160, III-1-30, 32-34, 52-56, 58-65, 67, 78-81, 85, 86
choosing, III-14-21, 29, 30
circuits, basic, III-2-11
classifications, III-15-21
definitions of specs, III-21-29
principles, III-1-14
Anomalous errors, I-102, 103, II-32, 33, 127
Averaging, Digital, I-40, 87, 88, III-71

Binary code (fractional), II-3, 4, 5
base-10 to, I-58
Bipolar conversion, II-17-28, 41-44, 48, 49, 51, 63, 68-71, 73, 76, 98-101, 110, 111, 132, 143, 146
Bus lines, I-5, 6, 107, 108, III-50-51, 63-65
Buffering, digital from analog, in DAC's, II-58-61

Cathode-ray tube (CRT) displays
(see Displays)
Checklists for conversion system design, I-16, 17, 41, 42, 54, 55, 111-113, II-23, 29, 131-135, III-29, 30, 39, 40, IV-1-8
Classifications
amplifiers, III-15-20, 38
converters, II-148, 149
sample-holds, II-150
Code conversion, II-13, 14, 23

Codes, digital, II-2,3
binary, II-3, 4, 5
binary-coded decimal (BCD) 8-4-2-1, II-10
BCD 2*-4-2-1, II-12
Gray code, II-13-16
complementary, II-16, 17, 24, 25
bipolar, II-17-25
sign-magnitude, II-18, 19, 20, 24
offset binary, II-18, 19, 21
two's complement, II-18, 19, 22
one's complement, II-18, 19, 22, 24
Common-mode errors and rejection, I-20, 21, 31, 32, 105, 106, II-135, 136, 166-168, III-9, 10, 21, 22, 24, 31-42, 53, 55-56, 68-70
Common-mode range, II-135, 136, III-22, 24, 25, 38, 40-42
Common-mode voltage, I-4, II-136
Communications, digital, I-84-92, 106-108
Comparators, I-9, 73-76, II-46-54, 80-87, 116-119, 127, III-3, 82-84
Components, analog vs. digital, I-1, 2, 24, 53, 54, 63-65, 82-84, 92, 95, 96,
Compression
data, see Data compression
logarithmic, see Data compression
time, I-89, 90
Conversion, applications, I-1-113, III-81-85
industrial, partial listing, I-111-113
Conversion relationships, II-5-10, 14-23, 25-28
Conversion time, I-14, 18-23, 27, 29, II-138, III-74, 81, 82
Converters, A/D, I-7, 13-36, 63-65, 70-76, 82, 84-92, 104-110, II-7-12, 20, 29, 30, 32
applying, I-2, II-155-166
choosing, II-132, 133, 137, 149
circuits, II-45-53
designing, II-80-87
testing, II-92-94, 122-130
Converters, A/D, counter types, I-73, 74, II-51, 52, III-84, 85
Converters, A/D, dual-slope, I-18, 19, II-48-50, 139, III-70-71
Converters, A/D, parallel, II-52, 53
Converter (A/D)-per-channel, I-26, 27, 28, 29

Converters, A/D, successive-approximations, I-19, II-46, 47, 48, 80-87
errors, I-19, 20, 22, 23, II-3, 4, 5
Converters, D/A, I-7, 8, 41-52, 55-76, 82, 84-92, 95-108, II-5, 6, 7, 16, 19, 27, 28, 29, 30, 32, 33
circuits, II-34-45
designing, II-56-80
testing, II-89-92, 95-122
choosing, II-131, 132, 136, 148
current-source, I-59-61, II-32-36, 38-44, 56-80
multiplying, I-7, 61-64, 66-71, 90-91, 100-102, II-27, 28, 29, 132, 142, 143, 148
Converter, frequency-to-voltage, I-72
Correlation, I-70, 90
Counters, up, down, up-down, I-8, 9, 34, 51, 52, 65, 68-70, 97, 108, II-48-52, 107, 109, 114, III-84
Crosstalk, I-32, II-138, III-66, 67, 68
Current, bias and difference, III-3, 12-17, 19, 20, 23, 24, 27, 29, 62, 77
Current sources (see also converters, D/A), III-11, 15, 21
digitally-controlled, I-59, 60, 61
floating load, I-60, III-36, 37
buffered load, I-60, III-36
grounded load, I-61, III-36, 37

Data acquisition, I-13-40, 81, 104-113, II-150-153, 155-168, III-31, 32, 34, 35, 37, 39-42, 43-71
vs. distribution, I-48, 49
Data compression,
log devices in, I-24, 35-38, II-158, 159
Data distribution, I-41-52, III-82
Definitions of specifications
amplifiers, III-21-29, 37
converters, II-135-146
multiplexers, III-57, 69
sample-holds, III-74-78
Deglitcher (see Glitches)
Delay lines, analog, I-70, 71, 72, 85-92, 99, 100
tapped, I-71, 91, 92
Digital servo techniques, I-50-52, 75, 76, 105, 106, III-84, 85
Displays, CRT, I-93-103
rasters, I-95, 96
dot-matrix, I-96-98
graphic, I-98-103
vectors and segments, I-100-102
Displays, digital, I-11

Dither, use of in testing, II-113-115, 124-127
Division, Signal
ratiometric conversion, I-33, 34, 63, 64, II-27, 28, 48, 50, 133
using ratio module, I-24, 26
Dot-matrix displays (see Displays), I-96-98
Droop (sample-hold), I-6, 29, 42, 43, 49, 73, II-139, III-77, 81, 84, 85
Dynamic-crossplot ADC test, II-124-127
Dynamic range, extended, I-34, 35, 36, 37, 38, II-158, 159
Electron-beam recording, I-93, 94, 96
Encoder
Gray-code, II-14, 15, 16
thumbwheel-switch, I-56
toggle-switch register, I-57, 58, II-93, 94, 96, 113, 114, 115, 123, 128
Environment, I-15, 16, II-131, 132, III-29, 30
Error budgets, I-17, II-76, 77, 131-135, 151-153, 162, 163, III-39, 40

Feedthrough, II-132, 139, 143, III-45, 57, 65-67, 77
Filters, active, I-9, 24, 49, 50, 91, 92, II-47, 70, 133, 159, 160, III-11, 15, 19, 70
digital, I-91, 92
recursive (digital), I-92
Force measurement, I-3, 105, 106
Four-quadrant, I-61-67, 69, 70 II-27, 28, 132, 140
Functional relationships, I-64, 65, 66, 84-92
and function generators, I-64, 68, 69, 70
time functions, I-70-76, 84-92
Function modules, I-4, 5, 23, 24, 26, 35-38, 82

"Gain" in converters, I-20, 21, 23, 33-38, 50-52, 61-64, II-5, 27, 28, 29, 32-34, 41, 43, 63, 65-77, 94-101, 107-111, 124-126, 131-133, 140, 153, 157, 158
Glitches, I-42, 49, 50, 102, 103, II-45, 79, 89, 113, 120, 121, 132, 138, 140, III-82
Graphic displays (see Displays)

Grounding, grounds, I-15, 27, 52, II-29, 30, 77-80, 84, 86, 87, 163-168, III-2, 32-37, 40-42

High-resolution ADC's and DAC's, I-34, 35, 51, 52, 55, 63, 64, 82, 94, 96, 98, II-4, 9, 11, 56, 64, 148, 149
Hysteresis, I-75, II-127, III-82, 83
in peak-follower, I-75, III-83

Integrator, I-23, 99, 100, III-11, 15, 19
in dual-slope conversion, II-48, 49, 50
delay-line, I-99, 100
Interquad divider, I-59, II-36, 37, 40, 41, 65, 66, 71, 72
Layout considerations, II-77-80, 163-168, III-45, 63
Leakage, switch, III-55, 59-61
Least-significant bit (LSB), II-3-11, 140
Linearity, I-91, 93, 96, 102, II-5-8, 71-74, 90-97, 100-113, 122-128, 141, 142, III-3, 39, 40, 59, 74
in displays, I-93, 96, 102
Linearizing nonlinear data, I-23, 25, III-11
Logarithmic amplifier, I-35, 36, 37, 38, II-158, 159
Log conformity, I-35, 36

Major carry
glitch, I-42, 49, 50, II-21, 113, 121, 122, 140
linearity, II-15, 21, 102, 104, 120, 121, 138
testing, II-106-111, 113, 114, 120-122, 124-126
Memory, read-only (ROM), I-65, 66, 70
delay-line, I-70, 71, 72, 84-92
recirculating, I-86-92
Meters, DVM, DPM, I-10, 17, 78, II-96
Monitoring, I-96
power rectifiers, I-108-110
Monotonicity, II-5-8, 102-105, 125, 142
Most-significant bit (MSB), I-34, II-3-8, 10, 11, 17-25, 43, 44, 46, 142
Multiplexers, analog, I-5, 29-33, 47, 48, 107-110, II-133, 134, 154, 156-163, III-43-50, 52-71
high level, III-52-54
errors in, III-57-67
high noise environments, I-24-28,

III-70, 71
in music distribution, I-107, 108
low-level, I-31-33, III-55, 56
errors in, III-68, 69
Multiplexers, digital, I-5, 26, 27, 28, 42, 43, 45, 46, III-43-45, 50-51
Multipliers, analog, I-24, 25
high-precision, using con-version, I-63, 64
Multiplying DAC (see Converters, D/A, multiplying)
Music-distribution, I-107, 108

Noise, I-38, 39, 40, 84, 87, 88, 106, 107, II-104, 105, 122, 125, 133, 143, 157, 159, III-8, 9, 15, 25, 38, 70, 71
Nonlinearity, differential, I-102, II-5-8, 89, 100-104, 111-113, 123-126, 138, 157
temperature coefficient, II-137, 138, 157

Offset (in bipolar converters), II-18, 21-22, 25-27, 41-44, 48, 49, 51, 62, 63, 70, 71, 73, 92, 98-100, 143

Peak follower, I-75, III-82, 83
Polarity of converters, (analog), II-17-28, IV-3
Power supplies, I-9, 10, II-30
sensitivity to, II-136, 137, 143-144, III-22, 38
precision, I-55, 56, II-94-96
Preamplification, I-3, 20, 21, 82, 105, 106, II-158, 165-168, III-31-42, 55, 56, 68, 69
Pumpback, III-65, 66, 75, 76

Quantizing uncertainty, II-7, 94, 104, 105, 122-124, 128, 144

Raster displays (see Displays), I-95, 96
Ratiometric conversion, I-33, 34, 63, 64, 87, 88, II-27, 28, 33
Ratios (see Division)
Reference input, I-33, 34, 56, 61-64, 66-68, 70-72, 88, 91, 100, 101, II-27-30, 33, 41, 42, 67-71
data amplifier, III-32-37
Reference loop, II-39-43, 66-71
Registers, shift, I-8, 70, 71, 72, 85-92, 106-108, II-47, 81, 82
Registers, storage, I-8, 35, 43, 44, 71, 72, 105, II-29, 44, 45, 81, 104, 123, 128

Register, toggle-switch, I-57, 58, II-93, 94, 96, 113, 114, 115, 123, 128

Resistance networks, I-35-40, II-61-66, 71-76

Resolution, I-16, 24, 34-40, 42, 48, 49, 106, 108, II-5, 17, 18, 49, 56, 71, 131, 133, 144, 151, 157

Response, full power, II-136, 145, III-22, 23, 26, 27, 38, 65, 74

Sample-Holds, I-6, 21-23, 27, 29-31, 44, 48, 49, 87-91, 106-108, III-73-86
    characteristics, III-73-76
    digital (peak-follower), I-75, III-83-85
    digital (pulse-stretcher), I-74, III-81, 83-85
    digital (tracking), I-73, III-84, 85

Sawtooth generator, I-68, 95, 96

Scale factors (see also Gain)
    digitally-controlled, I-34, 35, 61, 62, 63, 100, 101 (see also Converters, D/A, multiplying)
    direct, I-62
    inverse, I-63

Sensors, I-2, 3, III-32, 42

Sequencer, in A/D converters, II-46, 47, 81-83

Serial data, I-27, 28, 41, 47, 72, 106-108, II-2, 32, 81, III-51

Settling time, I-41, 49, 52, 102, 103, II-45, 47, 116-122, 132, 144, 153, 157, 161, 162, III-15, 19, 26, 27, 38, 44, 45, 46, 54, 63-66, 70, 74. 75

Shafts, position-sensing, I-3, II-14, 15

Shift register (see Register, Shift)

Signal analysis, I-84-92

Signal-conditioning, I-17, 23, 24, 25, 26, 33-38, II-133, 158-160, 166-168, III-11, 12, 15, 19, 20, 31, 32, 34-37, 40-42

Sinusoidal functions
    input-output, I-65, 66, 67
    function generation, I-69, 70

Slew(ing) rate, I-73, 75, II-69, 145, III-16, 17, 22, 23, 27. 74

Stability, converter, II-66, 145

"Status" line, I-5, 6, 8, 11, 15, 18-24, 71, 72, 75, 76, II-29, 30, 32, 46-48, 80-83, 123, 128

Strobe, I-43-48, 51, 52, 71, 72, 85-92, 105, II-29, 30, 32, 44, 45, 123, 128, III-81-83

Sweeps, digital, I-68
    in displays, I-95-98

Switches, I-34, 44, 48, III-46-50
    converter, II-35-39, 41
    mechanical, I-48, 56-58, III-46
    monolithic, II-42, 57-65, III-49, 50
    multiplexer, I-32, 48, III-43-71
    sample-hold, I-44, III-78-81, 85, 86

Switching time, II-145, III-46, 51, 67, 75-78
    aperture: III-75, 76

Tables
    BCD, 2-4-2-1, II-12
    BCD code, II-11
    BCD coding, toggle-switch register, I-57
    BCD vs. binary resolution, II-11
    Binary equivalents of decimal fractions, I-58
    Binary resolution (to 20 bits), II-4
    Binary vs. Gray Code, II-13
    Bipolar code conversion, II-23
    Bipolar codes, II-18
    Bipolar codes, modified & complementary, II-25
    Complementary unipolar codes, II-16
    Code transitions in differential linearity test, II-111
    Converter interface connections, II-29
    Fractional binary code, II-3
    Industrial applications, a small sampling, I-111-113
    LSB and FS-LSB for 10 & 10.24V (to 20 bits), II-9
    Peak-to-peak vs. rms, for Gaussian noise, I-39
    Specifications
        A/D converter, II-137, 149
        D/A converter, II-136, 148
        Instrumentation amplifiers, III-38
        Operational amplifiers, III-16, 17
        Sample-holds, II-150
    Temperature coefficient, II-62, 63, 67, 73-76, 100-102, 109-11, 131-135, 145, 146, 157, 162, III-16, 17, 19, 20, 27, 28, 37-40, 60-63, 74, 86

Temperature measurement, I-3

Testing,
    automatic, I-79-83

converter, II-89-128
dynamic programming, II-106-111
Time delay (see delay lines)
Time functions (see functional relation-
    ships)
Tolerances, component, II-60-76
Transducers, I-3
Transient storage and recording, I-84-86
Triangular-wave generator, I-68, 69,
    II-126
Trigonometric functions
    digital phase shifter, I-66
    digital/resolver converter, I-67
    resolver (digital) control trans-
        former, I-67
Trimming converters, II-71-76

Update, simultaneous, I-29, 30

Vector generation (see Displays)
Voltage source, digitally-controlled, I-55,
    56, 82

Waveform averaging, I-87, 88
Weighing, automatic
    scale zeroing (tare-weight nulling),
        I-104-106
Weighted current sources (see Current
    sources)

NOTES

MC 1408 — 8 bit D/A conv. 300 nsec. switching time
needs external ref. voltage
and needs output op. amp.

AD 7520 — 10 bit D/A conv. 500 nsec. ...
(CMOS)

AD 7522 — 12 bit D/A conv. 500 nsec. .. "
(CMOS)

Intersil 6202 — 16 bit ADC 33 msec. ...

National
semi.
8 chip   mm 5357 — 8 bit ADC 80 μsec
needs ref. volt.

AD 7550 — 13 bits quad slope 40 msec
AD 7570 — 10 (needs comparator) 20 μsec approx.

Teledyne   8700 — 8 bit ⎫ charged 1.8 msec
1 — 10 " ⎬ balancing 6 msec.
2 — 12 " 24 msec.